POWERING THROUGH

FROM FRAGILE INFRASTRUCTURES TO COMMUNITY RESILIENCE

An Action Guide
By the Electromagnetic Pulse Special Interest Group of InfraGard
(Version 1.0)

This Action Guide (Version 1.0) is a voluntary collaborative of the Electromagnetic Pulse Special Interest Group of the InfraGard National Members Alliance ("InfraGard")

InfraGard is an association of persons who represent businesses, academic institutions, state and local law enforcement agencies, and other participants dedicated to sharing information and intelligence to prevent hostile acts against the U.S. Each InfraGard Members Alliance (IMA) is geographically linked with an FBI Field Office, providing all stakeholders immediate access to experts from law enforcement, industry, academic institutions and other federal, state, and local government agencies. By utilizing the talents and expertise of the InfraGard network, information is shared to mitigate threats to our nation's critical infrastructures and key resources.

The Federal Bureau of Investigation did not prepare materials for, nor does it endorse the contents of this Action Guide.

InfraGard National Members Alliance, Inc. ("INMA" or "InfraGard") is a non-profit 501(c) (3) Delaware Corporation. The INMA is comprised of 84 separate 501(c) (3) InfraGard Member Alliances (IMAs) with a membership of more than 43,000 Subject Matter Experts, representing our Nation's critical infrastructures.

**Electromagnetic Pulse (EMP) Special Interest Group (SIG)
MISSION STATEMENT**

The EMP SIG™ Mission is to inform communities how to mitigate the high-impact threat of long-term power and communications failure (greater than 30 days) which could lead to catastrophic, cascading losses of life-sustaining infrastructures and resources for recovery. Our purpose is to foster communications and coordination that will address and mitigate the threat of a simultaneous nationwide or regional collapse of infrastructure from any hazard such as man-made EMP, or other intentional or naturally occurring hazard.

ISBN: 978-0-9983844-0-5 (HC)
ISBN: 978-0-9983844-1-2 (EB)

The InfraGard EMP SIG™ is providing this Action Guide

and seeks to continually improve it.

We view this as Version 1.0.

Please send any proposed updates, lessons learned, and insights gleaned from using this

Guide to the InfraGard National EMP SIG™ at EMPcenter.org

Thank you!

EDITORS

Mary Lasky
William Harris
Stephen Volandt

Endorsements for "Powering Through"

"Those of us concerned about our nation's ability to survive and ultimately recover from a sustained and massive loss of electric power are agnostic about the cause. I'm still inclined to believe that a cyber-attack represents the likeliest danger, but whatever the cause—electromagnetic pulse, solar flare, or physical attack—recovery remains the greatest single challenge; and, as things now stand, the federal government has no plan to deal with what surely ranks as one of the worst threats to our national security. This collaboration—*Powering Through*—is a gigantic step in the right direction. While its proposals may be helpful to individual communities, its most immediate value is as a potential blueprint to the federal government and to individual states. This is a sober, detailed analysis of the problems, linked to smart and thoughtful proposals for confronting those problems. Now, if we can only find a way to get our policy makers to read it."

—Ted Koppel, author of *Lights Out: A Cyberattack, A Nation Unprepared, Surviving the Aftermath*

"Timely and compelling. This guide accomplishes a first by combining under one cover an orientation to the hazards to our electric grid, our water supplies, and cascading vulnerabilities to civilization's infrastructures. This book is a call to action—to mobilize whole communities, to prepare, to respond, and to overcome both natural disaster and willful adversaries."

—Ambassador R. James Woolsey, former Director of Central Intelligence

"This is a comprehensive guide to thinking through the challenge of losing power for an extended period of time, and developing state, local, and federal strategies for protecting and preparing ourselves to cope with it and with the sudden loss of related critical infrastructure systems upon which modern society depends. It identifies specific actions states and localities can take on their own, and in tandem with each other and with infrastructure owners and managers, as and to tie in with the "all community" federal initiatives. It directs attention to the roles of bodies that cross governmental lines, such as the National Guard and emergency management agencies. It provides a layered look at preparedness that allows for both separate and cooperative steps to take place, essentially describing a catastrophic challenge in manageable terms. I think it will be embraced with relief and enthusiasm by those who seek to engage in helping preserve our great civilization. Accolades to all the revered national leaders who contributed to this landmark tome."

—Rep. Andrea Boland, sponsor of enacted Maine law (2013) to protect electric grids

"Today, few live 'off the electric power grid' and everyone depends on the grid for important aspects of life: transportation, food, communications, and other essentials. But the grid is fragile, and it takes a major effort to keep it running even in normal circumstances. Nevertheless, it does still fail from time to time even in relativity benign environments. These failures have been geographically limited, but grid failures are possible that extend much more widely, and even cover whole continents. This book reviews what has been done in recent years to decrease the fragility of the power grid to several large-scale threats, and unlike current federal efforts, does not make the mistake of addressing what can be done for one threat while ignoring others. Only an integrated approach to strengthening the grid against all large-scale threats can provide the protection we need."

"*Powering Through* is a 'must read' for local and state leaders—and the public. Our nation's very survival will depend upon fortifying our infrastructures and whole of community response if we experience an indefinite blackout of the electric power grid from an EMP attack—or from a massive solar storm that will one day envelop the Earth. The only question is *when*. We not only should prepare for such events, but urgently demand that our political and federal leaders provide effective defenses against these existential threats, as they are sworn to do. Informed citizens urgently need to take initiative to assure their and America's survival."

"An attack on our nation's vulnerable electric grid presents an existential threat to our civilization. As our politicians and bureaucrats dither over the details and price tags, belligerent and unpredictable nations and stateless terrorist organizations make plans to assault our undefended grid; from cyber-attacks to physical assaults on our power stations to delivering a nuclear device to high orbit above the continental U.S., our enemies know of this vulnerability and seek to exploit it. Consequently, this work is at once timely and important. While providing actionable advice for families, communities, and local governments, it is even more important for compellingly identifying the threats and providing policy solutions for the states and federal government. If I knew every member of Congress and every bureaucrat in the Departments of Energy and Defense read this book, I would sleep much more soundly at night."

"Energy is everything and everything starts with energy. We all intuitively know this. We got it when Einstein taught us that $E=MC^2$. E is all the energy of physical universe in two forms knotted up and congealed as (M) matter or as radiance or light in many forms (C2). The great news is that America has delivered energy to every one of us relatively flawlessly. Now, for the first time in our history our energy is vulnerable and subject to attacks of several kinds. This book clearly communicates the problem/opportunity and the challenge to create resident communities with decisiveness, alacrity, and quietly effective finesses. As world's best-selling author and now an alternative energy company leader and owner, I believe and declare that we need these solutions implemented with urgency and effectiveness now."

"The *Powering Through: From Fragile Infrastructures to Community Resilience: Version 1.0* planning guide is a one of a kind resource that comprehensively examines the potential actions that could be taken now to be more resilient in the event electrical power is not available nation-wide or over extended service regions for weeks or months or even a year. This guide has been uniquely tailored to address and plan for the consequences of a severe solar storm event, high-altitude nuclear electromagnetic pulse, cyber-attack, deployment of a non-nuclear radio frequency weapon, or physical attack on the nation's electric grid. I applaud and strongly support the InfraGard EMP Special Interest Group's foresight to develop a planning guide specifically designed to better prepare the whole of community to be more resilient when electricity is unavailable for an extended period of time. I highly recommend this guide to government officials, first responders, the general public, and all other entities that share a responsibility in preparing for these threats."

—Texas State Senator Bob Hall

"During my tenure as the Deputy Director of the President's Critical Infrastructure Assurance Office (CIAO), the White House published the National Plan for Information Systems Protection. This was the first attempt by any national government to design a strategy to protect its cyberspace and the underlying power grid on which it depended. The Plan also announced the idea of the Public-Private partnership framework to protect our nation's critical infrastructure assets. Although similar government plans have been published in the intervening years, none, I repeat none, have set out with any clarity on what the private sector can and must do in the event of a catastrophic power failure. *Powering Through* fills that void. As the former Director of Global Cyber Security Management, Department of Homeland Security, the single most worrisome issue was what would and could our government do in the event of a digital disaster impacting our power grid? What if the disruption were caused by a physical attack or distributed denial of service attack similar to the rehearsals we have witnessed of late? Damaged generators would take months to replace since they would need to be procured primarily from overseas manufacturers. The challenges of resilience and reconstitution pale in comparison to the cascading consequences across society should the inevitable occur. *Powering Through* is more than an educational and fascinating read; indeed, it is a call to action. A call to action by all of us!"

—Richard H. L. Marshall, former Deputy Director
President's Critical Infrastructure Assurance Office

The following statement by a senior federal official responsible for critical infrastructure protection planning is not an endorsement of the book *Powering Through*. It is a commentary on the significance of viable critical infrastructures. Comments on the likelihood of electromagnetic pulse attack (assessed as "a low probability") may be compared with the EMP SIG commentary on pages 4-5 of this book, which lacks confidence in any particular assessments of threat likelihood that is independent of the state of EMP infrastructure protection in the United States and abroad.

Think About How Critical Infrastructure Touches Your Life

Critical infrastructure not only enables and enriches our daily experience, but also underpins our national security and prosperity. Infrastructure keeps the economy moving, spurs innovation, and bolsters our national competitiveness. Building in resilience when we create or replace critical infrastructure and ensuring security against all hazards not only keeps our country strong for future generations, but it also makes good business sense.

The Nation's infrastructure includes the physical facilities that supply our communities with goods and services like water, transportation, fuel and communication, as well as the cyber technology that connects people and supports our critical infrastructure. These systems ensure that you can get cash from the bank, map out the best route to your destination, get gas for your car, and heat and cool your home depending on the season. And I suspect often times that we tend to take these benefits for granted … until something goes wrong.

Among the many risks we face are the impacts of an electromagnetic pulse, which while a low probability, would impact the electric grid. The electric sector follows a multi-layered risk management approach to grid resilience, including protecting the most critical grid components against likely threats and hazards; coordinating preparation and response efforts with the government; and developing contingency plans for response and recovery when grid operations are impacted, no matter what the cause.

As a Nation, it is vital that we remain aware of the vast, interconnected network of systems, products, and services that we all depend on to keep our infrastructure highly functional. Ensuring the security and resilience of these systems is a shared responsibility that involves a strong private-public partnership committed to sustaining and improving these essential assets.

Just as we all rely on critical infrastructure, we all play a role in keeping it strong, secure, and resilient. Those running and safeguarding critical infrastructure on the front lines can be powerful force multipliers for awareness and action. It takes communities, business and industry, governments at all levels, and millions of men and women working day in and day out across the Nation to "keep the lights on" in all the sectors that provide food, roads, health care, emergency response, communication, and much more, to make sure these essential services are there when we need them.

I urge businesses and organizations of all kinds to review and revise organizational plans, processes, and protective measures to ensure strong, resilient infrastructure that can withstand and recover from all hazards. We can all help manage risk to critical infrastructure by being vigilant and proactive.

Caitlin Durkovich
Assistant Secretary
Department of Homeland Security
National Protection and Programs Directorate
Office of Infrastructure Protection

Preface

Purpose: As citizens of the United States, we are dependent on secure and reliable electrical power for our current way of life. If electric power is not available for weeks, months, or even a year, then cascading impacts would degrade multiple critical infrastructures: water supply and wastewater treatments; telecommunications and the internet; food production and delivery; fuel extraction, refining, and distribution; financial systems; transportation and traffic controls; emergency services; hospitals and healthcare; supply chains; and other critical societal processes. Loss of life could be catastrophic. Life itself would change.

The purpose of the *Powering Through: From Fragile Infrastructures to Community Resilience, an Action Guide* (hereafter, the "Guide") is to examine actions that could be taken now to be more resilient, protect life and property during grid outages, and prepare for expedited recovery. This Guide emphasizes critical actions to be taken during extended grid outages to mitigate devastating effects.

InfraGard EMP SIG: In July 2011, the InfraGard National Member Alliance (INMA) Board and the Federal Bureau of Investigation (FBI) approved the formation of the InfraGard National Electromagnetic Pulse Special Interest Group (EMP SIG) for the purpose of examining and sharing information about catastrophic, long-lasting threats to the nation's critical infrastructure and encouraging local communities to become more resilient. The threats specifically include man-made EMP, cyber-attacks, coordinated physical attacks, pandemics, and extreme space weather.

In October 2011, the National Defense University and the EMP SIG co-sponsored a workshop and exercise on extreme space weather examining nationwide impacts. In December 2011, the EMP SIG reported the findings of the October exercise at the DuPont Summit hosted by the Policy Studies Organization in Washington, D.C. In 2012, 2013, 2014, and 2015, the EMP SIG held meetings at the DuPont Summit.

In October 2015, the InfraGard National EMP SIG published the *Triple Threat Power Grid Exercise: High-Impact Threats Workshop and Tabletop Exercises Examining Extreme Space Weather, EMP and Cyber Attacks*, which includes three separate scenarios and potential causes of grid failure affecting local and regional communities; and the review process illuminates benefits of preparedness efforts. The *Triple Threat Power Grid Exercise* book may be obtained through Westphalia Press or Amazon (see Appendix 9, References) or on the InfraGardmembers.org site. This Guide was based on a workshop held the day before the December 2014 DuPont Summit at the headquarters of the National Guard Association of the United States (NGAUS) in Washington, D.C.

In December 2015, the EMP SIG convened another workshop at NGAUS to develop a framework for planning including: goals for states, the National Guard operating under state or federal command, local governments, and volunteer/neighborhood communities for a long-term outage of critical infrastructures. The potential challenges for communications, energy/fuel, water/wastewater, medical, food, commerce/contracts, civil order, and other components of critical infrastructure were examined to set a foundation for the Guide. Thereafter, for much of year 2016, volunteers within the EMP SIG participated in weekly conference calls to develop the material for and vet the Guide. Facing gaps in preparedness programs or identifiable plans for consequence management, the EMP SIG reached out to national experts, who provided both planning suggestions and reference materials. The authors who contributed content to the Guide are listed below with their bios in Appendix 10.

Some caveats are appropriate. First, institutional affiliations are provided for identification only; none of the institutions named is a sponsor of nor responsible for the contents of the Guide. Second, individual authors may not concur in aspects of the Guide for which they were not the authors responsible. Third, neither the authors nor the InfraGard National Members Alliance provides any express or implied warranty that actions or preparations proposed for consideration will succeed in preventing an electric grid blackout or mitigating the consequences of such an event.

Throughout the late 20th century and early 21st century, no post-industrial society has experienced a widespread and prolonged electric blackout. Nations that develop resiliency and recovery plans are in uncharted territory. While there may be unforeseeable points of failure, cascading effects, and barriers to recovery, plans can still be made for prevention, mitigation, adaptation, and recovery. Imperfect plans, thoughtfully developed, are far better than no plan at all.

Readers should take into account both unknowns and unknowables, and exercise their own judgment and care when considering preparations or emergency actions by individuals, households, communities, or businesses. This Guide considers a wide range of hazards to critical infrastructure; uncharted cross-dependencies that are beyond full visibility; and uncertain outcomes for any and all pre-crisis mitigation and recovery initiatives.

Neither InfraGard nor its Electromagnetic Pulse Special Interest Group, nor any of the individual authors makes any representation or any express or implied warranty of merchantability or fitness of use for a particular purpose. Neither the authors nor the publisher shall be held liable or responsible for any loss or for incidental or consequential damages caused or alleged to have been caused by the information, programs, or institutions identified herein.

Editors: Mary Lasky, William Harris, and Stephen Volandt

Contributing Authors

Dr. George Baker
Professor Emeritus, James Madison University

Steve Bieber
Washington Metropolitan Council of Government

Torry Crass
SPX Corporation

John Contestabile
Johns Hopkins Applied Physics Laboratory

William (Bill) Harris
Foundation for Resilient Societies

David Hunt
Homeland Security Consulting

John Jackson
Fusion Risk Management Inc.

John Juhasz
Telepath Systems Inc.

William (Bill) Kaewert
Stored Energy Systems LLC

Frank Koza
PJM Interconnection LLC

Mary Lasky
Johns Hopkins Applied Physics Laboratory and Vice Chair, EMP SIG, and Coordinating Manager for this Guide

Stephanie A. Lokmer
Lokmer International LLC

Charles (Chuck) Manto
Instant Access Networks LLC Chairman, EMP SIG

Curry Mayer
CA Dept. of Food and Agriculture

Robert McCreight
Professor and Advisor

General Robert Newman
Sera-Brynn

Philip J. Palin
CNA and Rutgers University Graduate School

Steve Pappas
Consultant

Thomas (Tom) Popik
Foundation for Resilient Societies

Fred M. Rosa, Jr.
Johns Hopkins Applied Physics Laboratory

John Rosica
NVIS Communications

Janet Thomas
Federal Bureau of Investigation

Dr. James (Jim) Terbush
Innovative Health Systems

Stephen Volandt
Auroros Inc. Administration Officer, EMP SIG

Mark Walker
BCT

Special thanks to Mary Lasky; without her leadership this publication would not have succeeded. Chuck Manto's, chairman of the EMP SIG, support and encouragement is appreciated. Thanks also to Bill Harris and Steve Volandt who were instrumental in preparing and editing the Guide for review and publication, to Fred Rosa for supplemental review, to Terry Boston for grid-related and EMP-related corrections, and to Catherine Feinman for final editorial review and copy editing. We also thank Thomas V. Pruitt of Duke Energy Carolinas, LLC, for facilitating access to the pertinent technical and regulatory literature on grid generation and transmission system restoration.

John Coyle, of coylestudios.com provided the cover photography, and Stephen Volandt augmented the cover image to include wind turbines, symbolic of resiliency through diversity.

Contributors to discussions that helped to identify research issues or to locate expert resources included: Catherine Belfi, Hank Cooper, John Dew, Tom Drake, Frederick Ferrer, Robin Frazier, Brad Gair, Gary Gardner, Michael Lambert, Jim LeBlanc, Peggy Littleton, Chuck Nettleship, Chuck Sathrum, John H. Strothman, Steve Sutton, and Kelly Woods-Vaughn.

A special "thank you" to Tonia Simon and Geoffrey Sheldon for donating their digital marketing expertise.

Execut...

If there ...   ...i-month power failure, neither the federal
governm...   ...rritorial government—acting alone or in
concert—...   ...esponse by day four or maybe even by day
forty-fou...   ...households, communities, businesses, and
governme...

The purpe...   ...ons that could be taken *now* to enhance
resilience...   ...wide or over extended service regions for
weeks, mo...   ...e Guide discusses actions intended to:
mitigate pr...   ...manage the consequences; and prevent
or mitigate...

Chapter I p...   ...e purpose and intended audience, which
is the whol...   ...nation." The first chapter also discusses
the power g...   ...that could cause a widespread and long-
term failure...

Chapter II ex...   ...nd the most significant threats in detail.
Of particular...   ...nd others helped refine an important
matrix of im_____ ...... live threats to the grid and other key infrastructures (see the
"Stoplight" figure (in color) on the inside front cover of the Guide, also available as Table 2
in Chapter II. Threats evaluated include: (1) coordinated physical attacks; (2) cyber-attacks
against industrial control systems and/or other cyber-enabled technology; (3) an
electromagnetic pulse (EMP) generated by detonation of a nuclear warhead in the upper
atmosphere over the United States; (4) an EMP caused by a coordinated attack using radio
frequency weapons; and (5) a severe solar storm caused by an earth-directed coronal mass
ejection (CME). Some man-made threats might utilize a natural disaster to mask and extend
infrastructure damage.

The White House National Science and Technology Council in October 2015 issued the
National Space Weather Strategy and the National Space Weather Action Plan, calling for
the "whole of community" to plan for a severe solar storm[1] and noting that other threats
could cause similar effects. The Guide directly addresses that call. In 2016, the Department
of Energy and the Electric Power Research Institute (EPRI) issued a Joint Electromagnetic
Pulse Resilience Strategy for the national electric power grid.[2] Also in 2016, the Defense
Threat Reduction Agency (DTRA) recognized the operational importance of grid
survivability in the event of an EMP, and requested proposals to strengthen the private

---

[1] White House National Science & Technology Council, 2015 National Space Weather Strategy,
www.dhs.gov/national-space-weather-strategy
[2] Joint Electromagnetic Pulse Resilience Strategy, DOE/EPRI, July 2016

sector and military critical infrastructure upon which defense missions depend.[3] Finally, the Department of Homeland Security Office of Infrastructure Protection (IP) specifically noted the EMP threat to the telecommunications industry in a 2016 report prepared for the Regional Resiliency Assessment Program (RRAP).[4] The foregoing documentary findings validate the threat and underscore the urgent need for infrastructure planning and protection.

The Guide focuses extensively on the planning required to enhance the capability of the entire nation to prevent, mitigate, and recover. Interdependencies are also discussed with a major emphasis on water and wastewater.

Chapter III provides background information on the overall statutory and policy framework for disaster preparedness and response that the federal government has been leading. An overarching principle at the core of this national framework is the urgency of "whole of community" involvement in "all hazards" preparedness and resilience efforts. The Guide responds to that imperative with respect to major power grid contingencies.

Chapters IV, V, and VI all focus on preparedness actions. Chapter IV concentrates on protection of the nationwide grid, followed by Chapter V devoted to protective actions for selected critical infrastructures. In particular, Chapter V discusses society's reliance on the water and wastewater infrastructure and the wide-ranging consequences of their long-term loss: essentially, all other sectors are significantly degraded even if on-site electrical power is available, but water is not. Chapter VI presents a promising concept for building resilience through resilient community islands and networks of these islands.

Chapter VII identifies key actors in the "whole of nation" grid preparedness. The discussion appropriately begins by encouraging citizen preparedness. If individuals, families, and households are prepared, then it is more likely these persons will be able to support their neighborhoods and communities. After discussing both urban and rural communities, the chapter continues with: suggestions for non-governmental organizations, including volunteer and faith-based entities; businesses with supply chain challenges; and then governments—federal, state, local, tribal, and territorial—including emergency management, the National Guard, and DoD. Chapter VIII provides recommended approaches and specific actions that could be taken to help recover and re-emerge as a strong nation. In this regard, the Constitution provides a roadmap that can ensure democracy flourishes even in desperate circumstances.

---

[3] Press Release by Defense Threat Reduction Agency (DoD), "Accelerating Society-wide EMP Protection of Critical Infrastructure and Microgrids." June 24, 2016.

[4] Resiliency Assessment, Ashburn, Virginia, PSCDOperations@hq.dhs.gov

Chapter IX echoes and reinforces the national call to action. Readers are strongly encouraged to take these challenges seriously, to start planning, and to take action now to build resiliency initiatives through the months and years ahead. Chapter IX also outlines initial thinking about a 2nd Edition of the Guide.

A regional, relatively short-duration blackout (i.e., the Northeast Blackout of 14 August 2003; see Figure 1) impacted parts of Canada, New England, New York, and the Midwest. About 10 million people in Ontario Province and about 45 million people in eight U.S. states lost power. Water systems were impaired and sewage treatment system failures caused contamination of surface water. One important lesson was that mutual assistance obtainable in short-duration regional blackouts may be much less available in larger-area, long-duration blackouts for which the Guide is designed.

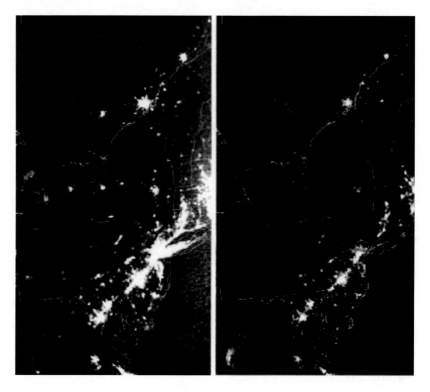

Figure 1: Before and After Images of the Northeast Blackout of 2003

Left image: The New England, New York, and Mid-Atlantic region 20 hours before the Northeast Blackout of 14 August 2003, commencing at 4:10 p.m. EDT on 13 August 2003. Right image: The New England, New York, and Mid-Atlantic region seven hours after the start of the Northeast Blackout on 14 August 2003. Images from Defense Meteorological Satellite Program Mission F15, processed by the U.S. Air Force Weather Agency, publicly available on the NOAA website.

Source: NOAA Magazine http://www.noaanews.noaa.gov/stories/s2015.htm

Contents

List of Figures and Tables:

Chapter I: Introduction

Purpose

Citizens of the United States depend on secure and reliable electric power for their current way of life. If electric power is not available for weeks, months, or even a year, then cascading impacts would degrade multiple critical infrastructures: water supply and wastewater treatment; telecommunications and the internet; food production and delivery; fuel extraction, refining, and distribution; financial systems; transportation and traffic control; government including public works, law enforcement, and emergency services; hospitals and healthcare; business supply chains; and other critical societal processes. Loss of life could be catastrophic.

The purpose of this Guide is to examine actions that could be taken now to be more resilient, protect life and property, and prepare for expedited recovery. This emphasizes critical actions to be taken during extended grid outages to mitigate devastating effects.

On its Ready.gov website, the U.S. Department of Homeland Security advises the American public to store food and water for at least three days. As useful as that is for a starting point, high-impact events must also be considered. Many who assume that the government will provide support as soon as day four may think that they do not need to plan for extended emergencies at all.

However, in the event that a widespread failure of electrical power, which takes down critical infrastructures for a much longer duration, sufficient relief, whether from government and/or other sources, probably will not be available.[5] Depending on the duration of the infrastructure failure, consequences for unprepared citizens could go well beyond economic loss to include sickness and death from dehydration, disease, pollution, exposure, starvation, fire, and civil unrest. Consequences for the nation could include a breakdown of coherent central government (local, state, and federal) leading to possible loss, at least temporarily, of effective sovereignty: the full right and power of governing bodies to govern themselves without outside interference. There could also be unacceptable delays in recovery, resulting in extensive loss of life and property. All of these are unacceptable risks.

---

[5] Restoring the commercial grid from the still functioning regions may not be possible or could take weeks or months. See "Island-mode Enhancement Strategies and Methodologies for Defense Critical Infrastructure: Defense Threat Reduction Agency (DTRA) 2015.2—Topic DTRA152-006." For a worst case that is instructive for planning, see the October 2015 National Space Weather Strategy: https://www.whitehouse.gov/sites/default/files/microsites/ostp/finalnationalspaceweatherstrategy_20151 028.pdf

The United States needs to augment the planning and investments that are essential to cope with extended duration catastrophes. Whole community participation in both planning and recovery must be the new norm, and this vital process needs to start now and continue. The fundamental criterion for success should be prepared individuals and communities capable of surviving long-term infrastructure failure, while at the same preserving families, assisting others in their communities, and defending the nation.[6]

If there is a nationwide grid failure, response and recovery will be a process of managing the consequences. FEMA, drawing on lessons learned from such disasters as the attacks on the World Trade Center and Pentagon on September 11, 2001, consistently emphasizes that consequence management is critical in all such major events.[7]

High-Impact Risks to the Electric Grid and Other Critical Infrastructures

What are the hazards that the Guide addresses, and what is the likelihood of their occurrence?

The Guide considers two types of hazard: *naturally occurring events*, such as a solar geomagnetic storm, a pandemic, or other random events, and *acts of human volition*, such as a man-made electromagnetic pulse (EMP) attack, a coordinated cyber-attack, or a coordinated set of physical attacks on critical grid equipment or related critical infrastructures.

The likelihood of natural event hazards is generally independent of efforts to prevent, mitigate, or recover from such events.[8] Solar storms cannot be deterred, though the consequences can be mitigated. In contrast, the likelihood of volitional acts may be affected by both preventive measures and by the deterrent effects of initiatives to mitigate and recover.

Severe solar geomagnetic storms have been recorded over recent millennia, but their impact on electrical systems has been measured with increasing accuracy only since the August-September 1859 Carrington event. Various models in the past decade estimate the probability of severe solar geomagnetic storms—of the magnitude of the Carrington event

---

[6] As of August 2016, the government of the Federal Republic of Germany is evaluating a mandate that each German household stockpile a minimum of five days of water and ten days of food. See BBC report, Aug. 22, 2016.

[7] Managing the Emergency Consequences of Terrorist Incidents, FEMA, July 2002

[8] Vaccination programs and stockpiling affect both likelihood and consequences of pandemics. See M. T. Osterholm, "Preparing for the Next Pandemic," *N. Eng. J. Med.* (2005); 352: 1839-1842, and Matthew Biggerstaff, et al. "Estimating the Potential Effect of a Vaccine Program Against an Emerging Influenza Pandemic—United States," *Clin. Infect. Dis.* (2015); 60: S20-S29.

or the May 1921 New York Central Railroad storm—as approximately 8% to 12% per decade.[9]

William Murtagh, at NOAA's Space Weather Prediction Center, and more recently a co-director of the National Space Weather Strategy Action Plan and related implementation initiatives of the White House Office of Science and Technology Policy, estimated that, if the probability of a severe solar geomagnetic storm striking the earth is about 10 percent per decade, only about half of these solar storms would impact the "kill zone" of the electric grid.[10]

Hence, with estimates of severe geomagnetic storms impacting the Earth about 8% to 12% per decade, the likelihood of a solar storm configured to cause significant damage in the "kill zone" of the North American electric grid is approximately 4% to 6% per decade. This is sufficient risk to initiate protective programs for the North American electric grid, and to develop consequence management strategies for the contingency of an extended and widespread electric blackout.[11]

In an Executive Order, "Coordinating Efforts to Prepare the Nation for Space Weather Events," released on October 13, 2016, President Barack Obama indicated that space weather events could impact:

> "The Global Positioning System (GPS), satellite operations and communication, aviation, and the electrical power grid. Extreme space

---

[9] For the period 1992 through 2010, a period without severe space weather, approximately 4% of disturbances to the U.S. power grid are attributable to "strong geomagnetic activity and associated geomagnetic induced current." C. J. Schriejver and S. D. Mitchell, "Disturbances in the U.S. electric grid associated with geomagnetic activity" *J. Space Weather Space Clim.* (2013); 3: A19. Sudden commencement (SC) solar storms can cause grid outages or transformer damage below the level of severe GMD events. See Tohru Araki, "Historically largest geomagnetic sudden commencement (SC) since 1868," *Earth, Planets and Space* (2014); 66:164, and J. G. Kappenman, "Great geomagnetic storms and extreme impulsive geomagnetic field disturbance events," *Adv. Space Res.* (2006); 38: 188-199. Estimates of frequency of severe geomagnetic storms impacting planet earth include: K. K. Tsubouchi and Y. Omura, "Long-term occurrence probabilities of intense geomagnetic storm events" *Space Weather* (2007) 5; A. Ruzmaikin, et al., "Distribution and clustering of fast coronal mass ejections," *J. Geophys. Res.*(2011); AWP Thomson, et al., "Quantifying extreme behavior in geomagnetic activity," *Space Weather* (2011); P. Riley, "On the probability of occurrence of extreme space weather events," *Space Weather* (2012); JJ Love, "*Credible occurrence probabilities for extreme geophysical events: Earthquakes, volcanic eruptions, magnetic storms*," *Geophys. Res. Let.*(2012); R. Kataoka, "Probability of occurrence of extreme magnetic storms," *Space Weather* (2013); 11:214-218; D. Roodman, "The risk of geomagnetic storms to the grid," GiveWell Foundation, June 2015; D. Roodman, "Geomagnetic storms: History's surprising, if tentative, reassurance," GiveWell Foundation, July 2015; D. Roodman, "Geomagnetic storms: Using extreme value theory to gauge the risk," GiveWell Foundation, July 2015; D. Roodman, "Coming Down to Earth: What if a big geomagnetic storm does hit?," GiveWell Foundation, Aug. 2015.

[10] Presentation, Space Weather Conference, Broomfield, Colorado, April 27, 2016.

[11] On September 22, 2016 the Federal Energy Regulatory Commission issued a reliability standard mandating electric utility assessments, and enabling cost-recovery for implementing "corrective action plans" for space weather hazards including hardware protections in Order No. 830, Reliability Standard for Transmission System Planned Performance for Geomagnetic Disturbance Events, 156 FERC ¶ 61,215.

weather events—those that could significantly degrade critical infrastructure—could disable large portions of the electrical power grid, resulting in cascading failures that would affect key services such as water supply, healthcare, and transportation. Space weather has the potential to simultaneously affect and disrupt health and safety across entire continents. Successfully preparing for space weather events is an all-of-nation endeavor that requires partnerships across governments, emergency managers, academia, the media, the insurance industry, non-profits, and the private sector.[12]

What is the probability of a high-altitude electromagnetic pulse (or HEMP) attack optimized to destroy critical infrastructure?[13] At the outset, it is important to note that, whatever range of probability is assigned, the likelihood increases as effective protection decreases and decreases as the society becomes more protected or resilient.

In more than seven decades since nuclear weapons were employed in World War II, a HEMP attack has not occurred. EMP-optimized atmospheric testing occurred before a Limited Test Ban Treaty, a ban on testing in outer space, the atmosphere, or underwater, took effect in 1963. Deterrence of nuclear weapon use has been successful to date. But is the past also prologue?

The government of the United States and those of other nuclear powers maintain robust detection systems and nuclear forensic capabilities to identify the unique sources of *special nuclear materials* and other unique indicators of weapons fabrication and potential weapons employment sponsorship.[14]

---

[12] Executive Order No. 13744, "Coordinating Efforts to Prepare the Nation for Space Weather Events," October 13, 2016, Section 1.

[13] On vulnerabilities of critical infrastructure to HEMP attack, see Report of the Commission to Assess the Threat to the United States from Electromagnetic Pulse (EMP) Attack: Critical National Infrastructures, April 2008.

[14] See U.S. Army, *Measurement and Signals Intelligence* Field Manual 2-0, 17 May 2004, ch. 9, "Measurement and Signature Intelligence"; Jonathan Medalia, Detection of Nuclear Weapons and Materials: Science, Technologies, Observations, Congressional Research Service, June 4, 2010; and Jeffrey T. Richelson, *Spying on the Bomb: American nuclear intelligence from Nazi Germany to Iran and North Korea*, New York: Norton, 2006. A recent Defense Science Board Task Force addressed the special challenges of monitoring illicit nuclear activities of both state and non-state actors. The Task Force recommended implementation of a more comprehensive and responsive "monitoring architecture for nuclear weapons activities worldwide." See DoD Defense Science Board Task Force Report: Assessment of Nuclear Monitoring and Verification Technologies, January 2014, esp. ch. 3, "Unilateral Measures: Transforming the Monitoring Framework," pp. 32-37, Radioactive debris from HEMP events may be sampled by high-altitude aircraft and/or balloon, even though some of the debris rises to altitudes of several hundred kilometers, and other debris moves along magnetic field lines to large debris patches. See Herman Hoerlin, United States High-Altitude Test Experiences, Los Alamos Scientific Laboratory Report LA-6405, October 1976. Augmented EMP sensors are deployed on all GPS-III space satellites launched since year 2015. See E. E. Fenimore, "50 years of Science from Space," Los Alamos LA-UR-13-27622 (Rev. 1, 2015), viewgraphs 15, 18, 53-54.

Employment of HEMP devices optimized to destroy critical infrastructures would be an act of war, justifying responsive measures under Chapter VII of the United National Charter. Per Article 51, "Nothing in the present Charter shall impair the inherent right of individual or collective self-defense." Moreover, the Convention on the Prohibition of Military or any Hostile Use of Environmental Modification Techniques effectively prohibits HEMP attack. This so-called "ENMOD" Convention, entered into force on October 5, 1978, prohibits hostile use of environmental modification techniques having widespread, long-lasting, or severe effects as the means of destruction, damage, or injury to any other state party.

Even if most nation states are deterred, will *all* nation states (including failed states) and *all* subnational groups be deterred if EMP vulnerabilities are not addressed and diminished? There is no credible way to assign a probability to HEMP attack or to ground-based or cruise missile radiofrequency weapons employment that may not violate the ENMOD Convention. However, it is reason for concern that approval for asymmetrical warfare, including HEMP attack, is found in foreign military literature.

What is the probability of cyber-attack designed to cripple critical infrastructures? Ted Koppel's book, *Lights Out: A Cyberattack, A Nation Unprepared, Surviving the Aftermath*[15] argues that cyber-attack is not entirely deterrable. Admiral Michael S. Rogers, Director of the National Security Agency and Commander, U.S. Cyber Command, openly testified in November 2014 that foreign nations have emplaced cyber-malware inside both the U.S. electric grid and in water and wastewater systems. Admiral Rogers stated that it was not a question of "if" but of "when" a significant cyber-attack would target the United States.[16]

Even assuming that, in times of relative peace, all-out cyber-warfare against critical infrastructures will not occur, is it prudent for any nation state to place the survival of its people, its property, and its means of recovery in the hands of foreign nations or subnational adversaries?

With these diverse hazards in mind, it is essential to recognize that government entities at the federal and state levels cannot protect critical infrastructures by themselves. Public-private partnerships will be necessary, and this Guide provides planning concepts and suggestions for broader audiences extending beyond government.

Audience

The Guide examines actions that can be taken by every person and every organization. The audience includes those in both the public and private sectors, specifically: government (federal, state, local, tribal, and territorial), the National Guard, DoD, NORTHCOM, critical

---

[15] New York: Crown Publishers, October 2015.
[16] Hearing of the House Permanent Select Committee on Intelligence: Cybersecurity Threats: The Way Forward, Nov. 20, 2014.

infrastructure owners, non-government organizations (NGOs), volunteer organizations, and citizens. Using this Guide, groups and citizens of the "whole-of-community" can begin to work with others to become more resilient and to anticipate their actions in the event of a high-impact disaster.

The Guide seeks to encourage actions by every individual and organization. The 2016 National Conference of State Legislatures (NCSL) featured speakers Ted Koppel and Jeanine Pirro covering threats to power grids, a reflection of the growing interest of state legislators in resilience to high-impact threats. Hopefully, governors will work with their state legislators to enact laws (with some exemplars outlined in this Guide in Appendix 8) to provide essential resources and incentives for resilience.[17] In addition, it would be excellent if every county and community learned what can be done better to prepare for and to respond to such catastrophes. Critical infrastructure (CI) owners, whether in the public or private sector (by far the majority) should prioritize preparedness and recovery initiatives. There is also an important role for volunteer organizations, universities, schools, businesses, and citizens at large in enhancing national resilience. All of these key actors are addressed in this Guide.

Table 1 identifies the most relevant chapters for many of those in the intended audience. The second column lists the chapters focused on preparedness actions in advance of a high-impact event, while the third column lists the chapters on response and recovery.

About This Guide

Chapter II examines the national power grid and the threats that could cause a failure. The U.S. grid is part of a larger North American grid. This larger grid, which is subject to reliability standards initiated by the North American Electric Reliability Corporation (NERC), utilizes regional balancing authorities that maintain the balance of supply and demand. NERC registered entities operate the "bulk electric system" through eight regional entities.

---

[17] http://www.ncsl.org/meetings-training/legislative-summit-16.aspx

Audience Member	Preparedness	Response/Recovery Consequence Management
Federal Government	Chapter VII	Chapter VIII
Northern Command (NORTHCOM)	Chapter VII	Chapter VIII
Department of Defense (DoD)	Chapter VII	Chapter VIII
State Government	Chapter VII	Chapter VIII
National Guard	Chapter VII	Chapter VIII
State Emergency Management Agency	Chapter VII	Chapter VIII
Local Government	Chapter VII	Chapter VIII
1st Responders	Chapter VII	Chapter VIII
Critical Infrastructure (CI)	Chapters IV and V	Chapter VIII
CI – Communications	Chapter V	Chapter VIII
CI – Water and Wastewater	Chapter V	Chapter VIII
CI – Agriculture and Food	Chapter V	
CI – Transportation	Chapter V	Chapter VIII
CI – Medical	Chapter V	Chapter VIII
Businesses	Chapter VII	Chapter VIII
Supply Chain	Chapter VII	Chapter VIII
Non-government organizations – volunteer organizations; e.g., Red Cross, VOAD	Chapter VII	Chapter VIII
Faith-based organizations	Chapter VII	Chapter VIII
Communities – Urban	Chapter VII	Chapter VIII
Communities – Rural	Chapter VII	Chapter VIII
Citizens	Chapter VII	Chapter VIII

Table 1: Chapter Guide for Diverse Audiences.

Three of the eight regional entities (Western Electricity Coordinating Council, Midwest Reliability Organization, and Northeast Power Coordinating Council) manage transmission systems in both the United States and Canada. Alaska and Hawaii operate their own electric grids due to geographic isolation. Within the North American electric grid, there are four interconnections: the Eastern Interconnection, which includes part of Canada; the Western Interconnection, which also includes part of Canada and Baja California; the Electric Reliability Council of Texas (ERCOT) Interconnection, which includes about 90% of the Texas grid; and the Québec Interconnection, entirely in northeastern Canada.

A cyber-attack taking down any one of these four interconnections could have a profound effect on the other three, raising immediate concern about whether and, if so, when they could be attacked. A severe solar storm might take out major portions of the Eastern, Western, and the Québec Interconnection and could even be so severe as to disable the Texas Grid.

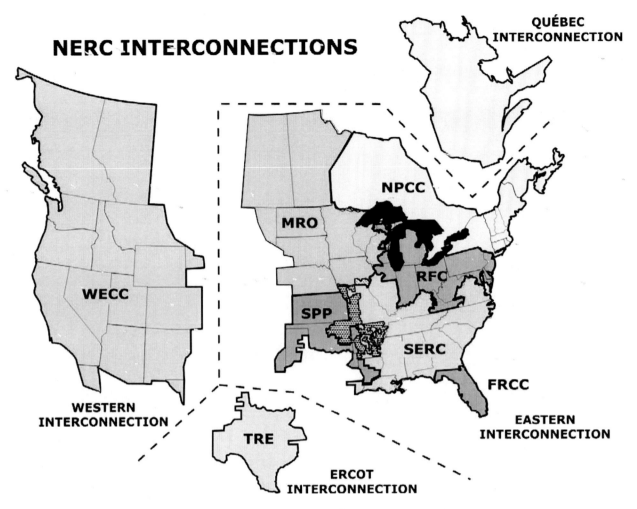

Figure 2: North American Regional Interconnections. Source: North American Electric Reliability Corporation, July 2012.

A nuclear warhead fired in a space satellite or a missile payload detonated over the United States could cause the collapse of widespread regions of the North American electric grid. Losses could include a large share of transmission and distribution transformers, generation stations, and grid control centers. Taking into account both the enhancement of EMP effects in weapons designed after the cessation of atmospheric testing in 1962 and the replacement of electro-mechanical switches with digital switches and modern electronic controls, some experts anticipate the potential collapse in its entirety of one or more of the four North American interconnection regions following HEMP attack (see Figure 2). Recovery challenges will be different from the aftermath of hurricanes because of sparcity of unaffected areas, impaired communications, and more intensive diagnostics required to identify and repair or replace damaged electronic components and the "cranking paths" needed to implement power restoration plans. A multi-weapon attack could increase both the geographic range and the proportion of damaged or destroyed critical grid equipment.[18]

Many other electronic devices unconnected to the electric grid but essential for other critical infrastructures would fail in a high-altitude EMP attack. Chapter II briefly discusses a range of scenarios that acknowledge that event aftermaths would be different depending on both the type of hazard and the scope of impacted equipment, systems, and the area. Interdependencies are also discussed with a primary focus on water and wastewater.

Chapter III provides an overview of the national policy framework for preparedness and resilience, with particular emphasis on critical infrastructure. Understanding at least the broad outlines of the framework is important for those seeking to enhance readiness for extended grid failures.

Chapter IV arrays protection options against the threats discussed in Chapter II.

Chapter V examines select critical infrastructure elements concentrating on possible preparedness actions. The elements addressed include: communications; water and wastewater; food; transportation; medical; financial; public health; public safety; and security.

Chapter VI presents promising related concepts for building resilience—specifically, "resilient community islanding" and "networks of those islands"—that would promote individual survival and societal stability.

Chapter VII identifies key actors in "whole of nation" grid preparedness with their diverse roles and contributions. The chapter begins with citizens, simply because if individuals and families are prepared, then it is more likely they will be able to turn to helping their neighborhoods and communities. This chapter differentiates preparedness for urban and rural communities because their concerns are very different. Non-government organizations, faith-based organizations, businesses, supply chains, and government at all levels are also discussed. Other key actors addressed include emergency management officials, the National Guard (whether under command of the governor or federalized), and DoD, including NORTHCOM.

Chapter VIII provides recommended approaches and specific actions that could be taken to help reemerge as a strong nation. Here it is important to note that the Constitution provides a roadmap that will help to ensure that democracy endures and flourishes.

Chapter IX is essentially a call to action, written in the hope that the message of this Guide is taken seriously and that individuals and the many other key actors start now and

---

[18] See Chapters II, IV, and Appendix 5 for grid vulnerabilities and system restoration challenges.

continue preparedness initiatives in the months and years to come. Next steps following publication of this Guide are also discussed. Preparing for a major grid failure, in part by leveraging modern "green" technology, would entail many advantages: a stronger, better protected grid; other more resilient infrastructure, increasingly capable of using alternative energy sources when needed; and government and citizens with concrete plans for major long-term disasters.

Various Appendices have been provided that explore certain topics in more detail.

Appendix 1 provides a table of acronyms and a glossary of terms.

Appendix 2 includes a crosswalk of three significant planning systems: Incident Command System (ICS), Center Management System (CMS), and Multi-Agency Coordination (MAC) Group. Business Continuity Planning is also included to help businesses that have not addressed this issue yet. Finally, the FEMA National Incident Management System (NIMS) is included because it will be a major part of the command and control system used by the government and could be used by businesses during a grid failure.

Appendix 3 presents a Preparedness Maturity Model that can be used for a self-evaluation of organizational or regional preparedness, and also provides a framework to map progress in becoming resilient.

Appendix 4 concentrates on cyber-security and Industrial Control/SCADA Systems. If the grid fails, it will be vital to restart it as quickly as possible.

The process of restarting the grid from a complete blackout is called "Blackstarting." A suggested approach to this process is presented in Appendix 5.

A special look at how the many and diverse supply chains could be resilient is provided in Appendix 6.

If the grid fails nationwide, then the United States may definitely need help from other nations. Having reciprocal agreements with trading partners would be beneficial, so how international assistance may operate is the focus of Appendix 7.

Work has been progressing nationally and in several states on protecting the grid. The status of state resiliency legislation on GMD and EMP is presented in Appendix 8.

Appendix 9 provides reference materials, many with hyperlinks to the full text available online.

Finally, Appendix 10 contains brief biographies of contributing authors.

Chapter II: Power Grids and Interdependencies

The North American Power Grid

As noted earlier, the North American bulk electric system operates through eight regional entities, three of which operate jointly in the United States and Canada. Both Canada and the United States operate under common "reliability standards" that are approved in the United States by the Federal Energy Regulatory Commission (FERC) or for nuclear power plants by the Nuclear Regulatory Commission (NRC).

There are 16 NERC Balancing Authorities, with their jurisdictions shown on the NERC map of North America, as of October 2015 (Figure 3).

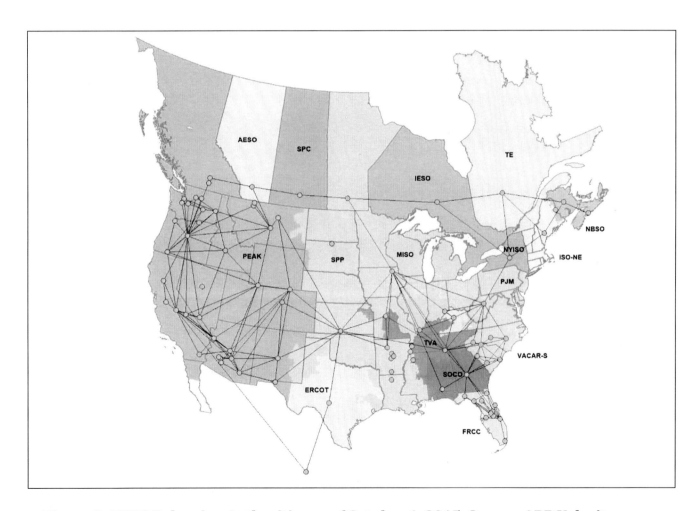

Figure 3: NERC Balancing Authorities as of October 1, 2015. Source: ABB Velocity Suite, September 2016.[19]

---

[19] See List of Acronyms specifying "Balancing Authorities" in Appendix 1.

The U.S. Electric Utilities Also Operate a Subset of NERC Assessment Areas

Within the bulk electric system for North America, there are separate NERC assessment areas (see Figure 4) that may encourage coordinated assessments, for example, whether their large power transformers or generators would benefit from installing current blockers or other equipment to protect high-voltage generators during solar storms, man-made EMP, or both.

For voluntary reliability assessments, the NERC assessment areas are important. For cost recovery authority, the two federal regulators (FERC and NRC) are essential decision-makers to whom electric utilities may apply for reliability-enhancing cost recovery. For mandatory reliability upgrades for the intrastate electric transmission and distribution systems, the state public utility (or public service) commissions have authority over rates of return, safety, reliability, and adequacy of service. So there are overlapping jurisdictions and many decision-makers in both the public and private sectors.

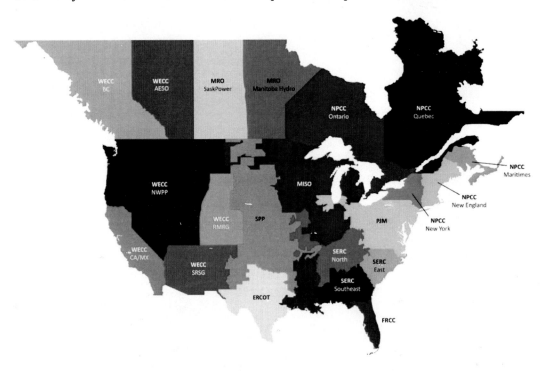

Figure 4: NERC Regional Assessment Areas in 2016. Source: NERC 2016 Summer Reliability Assessment.[20]

The bulk power system (or "national grid") in the United States is a loose confederation of over 1,400 independent and semi-independent entities, under the oversight of two independent regulatory bodies, the Federal Energy Regulatory Commission (FERC) and Nuclear Regulatory Commission (NRC), as well as the 50 state public utility commissions mentioned earlier. The industry's primary guidance on cyber-security comes from the

---

[20] See list of Acronyms specifying Regional Assessment Areas in Appendix 1. Source can be found at http://www.nerc.com/pa/RAPA/ra/Reliability%20Assessments%20DL/2016%20SRA%20Report_Final.pdf

federal authorities. By law, FERC's authority on standards is limited to approval or disapproval of industry-developed standards by the industry–sponsored not-for-profit North American Electric Reliability Corporation (NERC) functioning under the Federal Power Act as the Electric Reliability Organization (ERO). Further, those standards are not allowed to impinge on the state authorities for distribution assets and therefore apply to generation and interstate transmission assets only.

For decisions to protect critical grid equipment from solar geomagnetic (GMD) storms or from man-made electromagnetic pulse (EMP), there is concurrent federal and state jurisdiction. However, given that certain assessments and models of the EMP threat contain federally classified information, the states are at a disadvantage in designing and costing alternative protective programs. Federal agencies have an opportunity to assist states seeking to protect from combined EMP and GMD threats to their electric transmission and distribution systems. There is classified information available (e.g., testing information from the Idaho National Laboratories) and more can be learned.

Grid Threats

Supervisory Control and Data Acquisition (SCADA) systems and other industrial controls are real-time industrial process control systems used to centrally monitor and control remote or local industrial equipment, such as generators, valves, pumps, relays, circuit breakers, etc. SCADA is used to control chemical plant processes, oil and gas pipelines, electrical generation, transmission and distribution equipment, manufacturing facilities, water purification and distribution infrastructure, etc. SCADA originally was designed for managing a single location's processes, but cost and managerial benefits soon led to SCADA systems monitoring and controlling off-site, remote facilities. Industrial plant-scale SCADA is often referred to as a distributed control system (DCS). Common computer security was not built into many of these devices, and thus they are vulnerable.[21] The internet is used extensively as the conduit for SCADA operation, making it possible for hackers to control essential grid functions.

Intense solar activity, particularly large solar flares and associated coronal mass ejections, can create disturbances in the Earth's magnetic field when this "space weather" is directed toward Earth. These disturbances are referred to as geomagnetic storms and can produce rapid changes in the geomagnetic field over wide geographic regions, which, in turn, induce currents (referred to as geomagnetic induced currents, or GIC) in the bulk power system. During a major geomagnetic storm, the disturbances caused by space weather are so great that they generate electrical ground currents large enough to disrupt or physically damage electrical grid components. Geomagnetic storms can affect technological systems based in space (e.g., satellites) and on the ground (e.g., power grids and communication lines) by

---

[21] *Triple Threat Power Grid Exercise*, InfraGard National EMP SIG, 2015, p. 20.

interrupting their normal electronic and magnetic components. A geomagnetic storm takes anywhere from 16 to 18 hours up to several days to *significantly* impact Earth, with the more significant impacts generally driven by storms with the fastest arrivals. These storms typically last 6 to 24 hours but, during periods of very high solar activity, geomagnetic storms can persist for days.[22]

An Electromagnetic Pulse (EMP) is a burst of nonionizing electromagnetic radiation[23] caused by nuclear detonations or high-power electromagnetic weapons (also referred to as radio frequency weapons, or RFWs). Because of its continental-scale coverage, the risks associated with EMP generated by high-altitude nuclear explosions far outstrip those from RFWs (see Table 2). The high-amplitude electromagnetic fields produced couple large voltages and currents onto electrical and electronic equipment conductors resulting in equipment upset and damage. High-altitude burst EMP (referred to as HEMP) field environments include three temporal waveform components. More specifically, an EMP may contain some or all of the following components.

The Fast Pulse, E1 component (which occurs in nanoseconds) induces transient currents and voltages in systems sufficient to damage semiconductor electronic chips and initiate arcs in heavy-duty electrical equipment such as transformers, motors, and generators that damage electrical winding insulation. The E2 component is an "intermediate time" pulse that can last from about 1 microsecond to several milliseconds after the beginning of the EMP. E2 has similarities to pulses caused by nearby lightning strikes. Widely deployed lightning surge protectors in some cases may suffice to arrest E2 effects.

The E3 "slow pulse" component is different from the other two major components found in a nuclear EMP. The E3 component of the pulse lasts tens to hundreds of seconds and results from distortion of the Earth's magnetic field by the expanding nuclear fireball and heaving of ionized layers of the stratosphere. The E3 component amplitude and large Earth area coverage are similar to solar super storm GMD effects. Both nuclear E3 and solar GMDs couple efficiently only to long conductors (greater than a few kilometers) and are a concern for long power lines, long-haul communication lines, and pipelines. They are known to directly damage transformers and long-haul communication line repeater amplifiers. They also can damage "uninterruptable" power systems (UPS) by causing reactive power harmonics in the electric power grid.[24]

---

[22] *Triple Threat Power Grid Exercise*, InfraGard National EMP SIG, 2015, p. 22.
[23] https://en.wikipedia.org/wiki/Non-ionizing_radiation
[24] *Triple Threat Power Grid Exercise*, InfraGard National EMP SIG, 2015, p 26-27.

Equipment at Risk	EMP (Nuclear)	Solar Storm	Cyber	Physical Attack	Radio Frequency Weapons
Transformers	R	R	R – Y	R	R
Generator Stations	R	G	R	R	R
SCADA/Industrial Controls	R	R	R	R	R
Utility Control Centers	R	R	R	R	R
Telecommunications including cell phones	R	R	R	Y	Y
Radio Emergency Communications	R	P	Y	Y	Y
Emergency SATCOM Communications	R	P	Y	Y	Y
Internet	R	R	R	Y	Y
GPS	R	P	Y	Y	Y
Transportation	R	Y	Y	Y	Y
Water	R	Y	R – Y	Y	Y

Legend: Red = direct permanent effects. Yellow = Cascading effects if no backup power. Pink = temporary effect (.5-36 hours) assuming backup power. Gray = direct effects uncertain. Red-Yellow = potential permanent effects plus cascading effects.

Table 2: Potential Impacts on Critical Infrastructure of Five Threats to the Electric Grid.

(See inside front cover for a color version.)

The U.S. House of Representatives has passed several bills that address U.S. electric power grid vulnerabilities. FERC sponsored research at Oak Ridge National Laboratories to characterize EMP effects on the national power grid. There are several indications that these threats are being taken seriously by federal officials. The White House National Science and Technology Council's National Space Weather Strategy and Action Plan are certainly strong indicators.[25] In addition, the Defense Threat Reduction Agency (DTRA) has

[25] White House National Science & Technology Council, 2015 National Space Weather Strategy, www.dhs.gov/national-space-weather-strategy

recognized the EMP effects on the national electric power grid in a request to strengthen the critical civil infrastructure on which military facilities in the United States depend for at least 98% of their electricity.[26] A Joint Electromagnetic Pulse Resilience Strategy was issued by DOE and EPRI in July 2016.[27] The EMP threat to the cyber industry was explicitly noted by the Department of Homeland Security Office of Infrastructure Protection (IP) in the public and more detailed "For Official Use Only" (FOUO) reports issued in 2016 by the Regional Resiliency Assessment Program (RRAP).[28] All of the foregoing initiatives validate the threat.

Comments on Equipment at Risk

Transformers—Transformers are vulnerable to EMP, solar GMD, or physical attacks. Because unprotected relays supporting transformers can be rapidly opened and closed, transformers may be damaged or destroyed via remote manipulation.[29] Radio frequency weapons can be used to disable substation controls, but are unlikely to affect the transformers themselves directly unless targeted substation SCADA systems cause secondary damage. If these are attacked and disabled, then the time to replace high-voltage and ultra-high-voltage transformers is likely to be lengthy, and often dependent on overseas manufacturers. There are smaller transformers, designed to serve the residential and small business consumer, that are generally less vulnerable, more easily transportable, and manufactured in the United States; hence, these transformers might be replaced relatively quickly.

Generator Stations—Unless protected, grid generators at electrical power stations may be disabled by an EMP. Generator control electronics are highly susceptible to EMP. If there is a severe solar storm, there is evidence that the generators themselves could be harmed.[30] Cyber, physical, or radio frequency weapon attackers may target grid generator stations.

SCADA/Industrial Control Systems (ICS)—These are industrial control devices that regulate the operation of machinery, breakers, and transformers. SCADA systems are vulnerable to EMP and RFWs. Solar GMD could debilitate SCADA operations if SCADA

---

[26] Press Release by DTRA (DoD), "Accelerating Society-wide EMP Protection of Critical Infrastructure and Microgrids." June 24, 2016.

[27] Electromagnetic Pulse Resilience Strategy, Department of Energy and EPRI, July 2016.

[28] See Michael Thompson, Key Findings of the 2015 Ashburn, VA Data Center Resilience Project, Argonne National Laboratory, June 2016.

[29] See Solveig Ward, Jim O'Brien, et al., "Cyber Security Issues for Protective Relays," Power System Relay Committee. Power Engineering Soc. Gen. Mtg. 2007; Vladimir Gurevich, "Problems in Testing Digital Protective Relays for Immunity to Intentional Destructive Electromagnetic Impacts," Global J. Advanced Research (2014) 1: 159-173.

[30] A. Rezaei-Zare and Luis Marti of Ontario One, "Generator Thermal Stress During a Geomagnetic Disturbance," IEEE Power and Energy Society Conference, Vancouver, B.C. 21-25 July 2013, 5 pp., reports evidence of generator tolerance exceedance and generator rotor damage when geomagnetic disturbances cause Generator Step Up transformers to experience GIC currents in excess of 50 amps per phase.

electronics are connected to long landlines. Since they are accessible from the internet, they may be targeted in cyber-attacks. They also may be targets of physical and RFW attacks.

Grid Control Centers—Control facilities vary in size and are the hubs for grid communication and SCADA networks. They provide important situational awareness for directing both normal grid operation and grid reconstitution following a blackout. Because of their long-line interfaces, they are highly susceptible to EMP and GMD effects. If communications lines going into or out of the center were disabled, SCADA functions would be disabled. A cyber-attack could target the SCADA devices used in the control center. The facilities could be targets for physical and RFW attacks.

Cell Phones—Although many individual cell phones may be unharmed, the phones depend on cell towers interconnected with the local and long-haul telecommunications networks, which are vulnerable to EMP, GMD, RFW, cyber-attacks, and physical attack.

Radio Emergency Communications—Some of the emergency radio systems, such as FEMA National Radio System (FNARS) continue to work if they are hardened. However, in an EMP, public radio stations and their power sources may not be hardened and may fail. In a solar storm, this communication may be temporarily disabled by atmospheric conditions, but could return in hours to days. The other threats would not affect radio systems if the attack were focused on the grid.

SATCOM—The military's MILSTAR system is EMP protected and will continue to operate. Some additional military portable UHF SATCOM radios that link through high-orbit geo-stationary satellites may also continue to function. Unhardened ground stations may fail in an EMP environment. Commercial satellite phones rely on satellite and ground stations that are likely to fail under EMP stress.

Internet—An EMP would disable the internet and users' IT equipment. A cyber-attack on the grid taking out the generators, SCADA devices, and control centers would also have a cascading effect on internet data centers depending on the capacity and longevity of their back-up power resources. A solar storm can damage long-haul internet interconnects including both metallic and fiber optic links (the latter due to the vulnerability of optical fiber regeneration equipment). Physical or RFW attacks targeting grid assets would disable local internet equipment within Endpoint Group data centers and substation control facilities, but leave the larger internet intact.

Transportation—Railroad signals and highway traffic signals could be directly damaged by an EMP and cause significant delays. Controls and communications elements that use rails for transmitting communications signals are in great jeopardy if not protected and tested. A solar storm should not disable these transportation items if backup power is available for the duration of the grid failure. Likewise, a cyber-attack or RFW attack on the grid would not disable transportation systems if backup power is available. In a widespread grid blackout, standard operating procedures to close ports safely could result in delays in prioritized reopening of U.S. ports that are essential for throughput of disaster relief supplies. Chemicals or liquefied natural gas facilities within ports could benefit from backup power capabilities that prevent hazardous chemical releases due to loss of external power. In turn, preventing these chemical releases could avert extended port shutdowns after regional grid blackouts and help to re-establish priority supply chains and accelerate lifesaving and recovery operations.

Water—Because water purification and wastewater purification plants are controlled by SCADA devices, these could be disabled by EMP. Backup emergency diesel generators (EDGs) and solar panels are also vulnerable to E1 pulses unless the generators and the solar panel inverters and controllers are EMP-protected. A cyber-attack or RFW attack on the grid would not directly disable the water/wastewater systems if protected backup power were available. Nevertheless, if electric substations continue to be exempt from cyber-protection standards for "high-impact" grid assets, adversary takeover of substation controls could disable aqueduct pumps and locks, as well as other water and wastewater pumps and motors that provide essential water pressure and that process and manage wastewater products.[31]

Assumptions and Scenarios

Based on the situations above, this Guide proposes a set of scenarios ranging from moderate to severe. The following *assumptions* are used in developing the scenarios:

1. A high-altitude electromagnetic pulse (HEMP) is man-made and could be delivered by a satellite, missile, or other method capable of delivering a 10+ kiloton weapon between 10 and 300 miles above Earth's surface. The height of the nuclear explosion would determine the area covered and peak EMP fields on the ground from a multi-state area or a major part of the North American continent.

2. Cyber-attacks could be designed to damage or destroy key generators so as to disable large portions of the U.S. grid (as demonstrated by the Idaho National Laboratories' 2007 Aurora experiment). Cyber-attacks could also damage or destroy transformers through rapid switching of relay circuits or through manipulation of overvoltage protection relays on which transformers depend.[32] Remote cyber

---

[31] Order No. 822 of the Federal Energy Regulatory Commission (issued January 21, 2016) excludes about 45,000 U.S. electric substations from encryption requirements now applicable to "high-impact" grid assets within the bulk electric system. For potential vulnerabilities of water and wastewater systems if electric substation control systems are cyber-unprotected, see Viewgraphs of Joseph M. Weiss, Applied Control Solutions January 28, 2016, filed in FERC Docket RM15-14-000. Electric substations operated by intrastate electric distribution entities are also excluded from mandatory encryption duties. See also CIPAC Water Sector Strategic Priorities Workgroup, <u>CIPAC Final Report & Recommendations (Cyber)</u>. April 2015, 15 pp.

[32] See Vladimir Gurevich, *Cyber and Electromagnetic Threats in Modern Relay Protection*, CRC Press, 2015, pp. 107-110, addressing targeting and vulnerability of relay circuits that protect transformers.

operators could, as has been demonstrated, merely open breakers without damaging equipment, thus allowing the grid operators to achieve system restoration more quickly.[33]

3. Physical attacks, such as the Metcalf station attack in California in 2013, on a relatively small number of selected substations could shut down large portions of the U.S. grid for months.

4. Coordinated attacks using RFWs on regional grid control facilities could also cause large-scale disruption of grid operations and impair situational awareness needed for recovery.

5. Nuclear EMP would have the most ubiquitous effects from a single weapon, disabling generator stations, SCADA devices, computer equipment, and telecommunications networks.

EMP, Severe—A nuclear attack with one or more high-altitude detonations blanket the entire continental United States. This attack damages strategic equipment, which would need to be replaced and could not be repaired. Unprotected high-voltage generators and their control systems could be damaged. Data centers that are not protected stop working. Vehicles, for the most part, still operate. All use of electrical power stops: rail lines signals, traffic signals, and the internet. Refineries are not working to supply additional fuel. FEMA's FNARS and DoD/National Guard communications systems continue to function. Since the entire country is affected, there is no region of the country to reliably provide mutual assistance to severely impacted regions. It is vital to restart the grid, a process known as *blackstart*, as quickly as possible. Expeditious replacement of major transformers is a high priority. Initially, the grid blackstart occurs within isolated "grid islands." Once the grid islands are functional, neighboring grid islands are reconnected to restore the larger grid. People who can be part of a grid island that has protected generators or microgrids are able to work together to survive. There are almost no suitable places to relocate if people try to evacuate.

EMP, Less Severe—The nuclear explosion is over one region of the country. Therefore, some areas of the country come to the aid of the affected region. The electric utility industry has contingency plans for remote communication centers and inter-region mutual assistance. FEMA's and DoD's communications systems could be working. Radio transmissions work well for emergency messages. The power is blackstarted in grid islands, and those grid islands are reconnected more quickly (weeks versus months) than

---

[33] The Russian takedown of three electric utility distribution companies in Western Ukraine on December 23, 2015 did not cause permanent damage to grid equipment, despite remote opening of circuits and disruption of electric power to about 230,000 customers. Since most of the power was restored in six to eight hours, it is apparent that the purpose was to "teach" Ukrainians about their persistent vulnerability to Russian cyber-attack, including the future potential for resumed remote management of Ukrainian grid control centers. There was no evidence of a plan to cause long-lasting damage to essential grid equipment.

in the severe scenario. Those within functioning grid islands or who have operational local generators or microgrids work together and survive with minimal hardships. Populace migration from blackout regions to powered regions complicate the restoration process.

Solar Storm, Severe—Only 30 minutes of warning or even less time is available for grid shutdown. Unprotected high-voltage transformers are at risk of permanent damage despite widespread voltage collapse within the bulk electric system.[34] The storm is of sufficient intensity and scope to affect facilities throughout North America. Local restoration must occur without any, or with only selective, outside assistance. Major grid components are damaged resulting in a national-scale blackout. Internet connectivity is disrupted due to long-line equipment failures. Water and wastewater systems may continue to function until they run out of diesel fuel or natural gas for emergency generators. The functionality of solar photovoltaic (PV) systems may depend on presence or absence of connectivity to long-line systems within electric grids since long-line connectivity increases vulnerability to E3 pulses. Many PV systems are only functional when tied to a working grid. Others have transfer switches that allow them to feed power directly into local loads or batteries. However, these localized systems also need protection from the same threats, such as EMP that impacts large grids. If most large transformers are still operational, then there is much less delay in restarting the grid. GPS and HF radio transmission are out for 1-2 days due to atmospheric effects, but will then revert to normal operation.

Solar Storm, Less Severe—Warning times are the same as for the severe storm case. It is more likely that northerly areas and facilities near high-salinity coastal waters of the country are affected. The Texas grid may be fully operational. There are parts of the western and eastern grids working from California across to Virginia that are operational. Consequently, the grid can be restored in weeks, not months.

Cyber-Attack, Severe—A coordinated Aurora-type attack against the generation stations in key locations damages generators across the nation.[35] There is a denial of service along

---

[34] In a February 2012 Interim Report of the North American Electric Reliability Corporation, "Effects of Geomagnetic Disturbances on the Bulk Power System," NERC claimed that voltage collapse due to inadequate reactive power could result in extended blackouts without permanent damage to large power transformers. However, the historic evidence of solar storms in 1989, 1991, 1998 and 2003 indicates transformers remained operational for sufficient time to cause overheating and permanent transformer damage at Salem-1 (March 1989), Maine Yankee (March 1989 and April 1991), Seabrook Unit 1 (Nov. 1998), and seven transformers in South Africa (Oct. 2003). Capacitors, generators, and other grid equipment are also at risk of loss in severe solar storms.

[35] Rotating equipment utilizing alternating current is vulnerable to out of phase opening and closing of relay circuits. Idaho National Laboratory demonstrated the vulnerability of power generators to out-of-phase relay closures in experiments conducted in year 2007 within *Project Aurora.* While protective equipment is commercially available to prevent the "Aurora" effect, a small cyber-security firm recently demonstrated that the control system for one of the "Aurora" protection devices, SEL751-A, was itself vulnerable to remote hacking and adversary takeover. See Joseph M. Weiss, "Unfettered Blog: The use of protective relays as an attack vector—the cyber vulnerability of the electric grid," July 22, 2016.

with the power grid attack so that the internet and telecommunications are not working. The capability to take control of cyber-unprotected electric substations can result in targeting of rotating equipment in other critical infrastructures (beyond the electric grid) that are served by alternating current (AC) power. Overvoltage relay circuits and other safety relays that protect transformers are also at risk of cyber-attack that places transformers at risk of loss, even though transformers themselves have no rotating parts.[36] Without power, traffic signals and rail signals are not working. Backup generators are working and, depending on fuel supplies, can operate for days to weeks. Because the entire country is affected, local communities must recover without extensive inter-regional mutual assistance. Pockets of resiliency may be associated with regions served by microgrids.

Cyber-Attack, Less Severe—Generation stations in one or more major cities are debilitated. Assistance from other parts of the nation is available. Recovery is dependent on the transportation and connection of large backup generators.

Physical Attack, Severe—Coordinated attacks on key substations damage hundreds of large high-voltage transformers. Nationwide power outages last for up to 18 months. Recovery is delayed due to lengthy procurement, transportation, and installation of new high-voltage transformers.

Physical Attack, Less Severe—Coordinated attacks on key substations damage large high-voltage transformers in substations feeding one or several major cities. Assistance from other parts of the nation is available. Recovery is dependent on the transportation, compatibility, and installation of spare high-voltage transformers.

RFW Attack, Severe—Coordinated attacks on multiple regional control centers and large generation stations could cause shut down of grid communications and SCADA systems. Top-level situational awareness and load balancing are affected. Load imbalances cause some portions of the grid to collapse, but without damage to grid generation, transmission, and distribution systems. System diagnostics and replacement/resynchronization of damaged digital communication and SCADA electronics delay recovery for several weeks.

RFW Attack, Less Severe—Coordinated attacks on control centers and generation stations shut down grid communications and SCADA systems in one or several major cities. Local situational awareness and control is affected. Load imbalances cause local grids to collapse, but likely without damage to grid generation, transmission, or distribution systems. System diagnostics and replacement/resynchronization of damaged digital communication and SCADA electronics delay recovery for 2 to 3 weeks.

---

[36] See Vladimir Gurevich, *Cyber and Electromagnetic Threats in Modern Relay Protection*, CRC Press, 2015, ch. 4, for cyber-attack targeting of relay circuits.

Frequently Asked Questions

The authors have encountered frequently asked questions, some of which are listed in Table 3 for reference.

Table 3: Frequently Asked Questions About EMP.

EMP FAQs	Answers
Will anyone have electrical power in an EMP?	There is evidence from the period of atmospheric nuclear testing in the early 1960s that electric generation capabilities and electric transmission capabilities will be impacted differently depending on many variables. All will not be impacted to the same degree, but enough capabilities would be impacted (unless protected) in such a way as to cause long-term regional electric outages. The (unclassified) April 2008 EMP Commission report highlighted vulnerabilities of high-voltage transformers to the E3 pulses from long transmission lines. A substantially larger class of electronic systems will be inoperable, some unrepairable, due to E1 (fast) pulses. Due to the concurrent loss of potentially thousands of high-voltage transformers with extended replacement times and logistical challenges to delivery and installation, much of the "bulk electric system" may be inoperable for extended periods of time. Depending on the penetration of cabling systems and their shielding or lack thereof, there may also be impairment of control centers, SCADA systems, and many electric generation facilities. An unclassified assessment of Watts Bar 1, a nuclear power plant proximate to the Tennessee River, demonstrated significant signal attenuation inside the containment system. This included shield attenuation of the fast E1 pulses. However, the study revealed variability of signal attenuation indicating a lack of systematic modeling and protection. The study did not address EMP conducted to internal equipment on lines penetrating the shield or effects on control room electronics. Some generation facilities may have inherent resilience against HEMP attack, but others lack that resilience. Some assessments of nuclear power plants remain classified.
Will cars work?	According to conversations at the EMP SIG DuPont Summit 2013 with the late Bronius ("Bron") Cikotas, formerly on the EMP Commission Staff, a relatively small sample of automobiles from model years 2002 and earlier were tested for EMP vulnerability in year 2007. Automobiles that were running during the EMP simulation generally were inoperable after the testing. Some automobiles when restarted were able to operate. Generally speaking, vehicles that were not in operation during the test were able to operate post-test. In the roughly 15 years since the manufacture of the vehicles tested in EMP simulators, there has been a substantial increase in vehicle dependence on microelectronics. It would be prudent to test modern-era automobiles to consider whether a higher percentage of vehicles would be inoperable after a HEMP event. Moreover, changes in vehicle antennae systems can impact post-EMP operability.
Will there be	Systems with survivable backup power will continue to function for a period of

no electricity, no water, no sewer systems, no natural gas, and no retail operations?	time depending on their fuel reserves. Otherwise, these systems' ability to operate through an attack is unlikely. Some of these systems may be repairable, especially if spare backup equipment is on hand.
Will there be any telephone, cell service, or internet?	The long-haul network systems necessary for land line, cell phone, and internet service will likely be disabled by EMP.
Will there be any transportation system other than people-powered ones?	Most commercial aircraft and many maritime vessels will likely remain operable. Transportation control systems will likely be out of service, including the air traffic control system, municipal traffic control systems, railroad signal control system, and truck dispatching systems. There may be considerable uncertainty about railroad locomotives that are not in operation at the time of a HEMP event. Many vehicles will operate, but interstate highways may take extensive time to "clear" for emergency operations.
Will there be radio or TV, other than possibly HAM radio?	Many radios and TVs will be inoperable due to the fast E-1 pulses. Other radios may be operable, but unable to communicate during ionospheric disturbances, and then work normally. The FirstNet system designed for emergency responders was considered for EMP protection, but the initial bid specs in the spring of 2016, now in the first phase of contracting, did not include EMP protection and post-HEMP operability requirements. Certain military systems may be mobilized to provide post-HEMP emergency communications to the general public. Moreover, FEMA will deploy emergency telecommunications systems—specifics of which are not publicly detailed. See Chapter V: Communications.
How bad will the EMP be?	Infrastructure exposed during the atmospheric nuclear tests of the major nuclear weapon states was limited and dated. The largest set of systems effects data accrues from the Soviet high-altitude nuclear tests, where severe effects on long-line power and communication networks were observed. However, in the more than one-half century since implementation of the Limited Nuclear Test Ban of 1963, many of the core critical infrastructures have become more vulnerable to E-1 and E-3 nuclear effects due to advances in electronics miniaturization and digitization. The GPS satellite system is a contemporary example of a vulnerable system on which much critical infrastructure relies. Lack of atmospheric testing since 1962 results in a broad range of uncertainty about survivability and operability of various critical infrastructures. At present there are at least six sets of "modeling" initiatives underway: 1. The Electric Power Research Institute (EPRI) launched a $6 million program in April 2016 to assess EMP vulnerabilities and resiliency initiatives impacting the electric grid. 2. The U.S. Department of Energy has initiated a $15 million Grid Modernization Program to assess a broader range of EMP vulnerabilities (including both EMP and GMD) and resiliency initiatives for FY2017, mainly through the DOE national laboratories. 3. The U.S. Department of Homeland Security has re-initiated modeling of EMP impacts and infrastructure resiliency.

	4. The reconstituted EMP Commission is due to commence an independent assessment, with a current deadline to report to the U.S. Congress in June 2017.
	5. For European and other critical infrastructure facilities, an IEC standard is being modeled. This standard may be substantially lower than the U.S. military standards in Mil-STD 188-125.
	6. The Defense Threat Reduction Agency (DTRA) has a small business set-aside research program to incubate EMP resiliency for energy systems supporting defense facilities and the civilian critical infrastructure on which they depend.
	7. The Israel Electric Corporation is in a phased implementation of EMP protection of the Israeli electric grid. The supervising state agency, the Ministry of Energy and Water, may also proceed to further harden the water and wastewater systems in Israel. At some point, the Israeli EMP protection initiatives, which reportedly are assessing cost-reduction technologies, may help the United States reduce its own protection costs.
	8. Samsung Electronics, in South Korea, may also develop EMP protective technologies to be applied first in the Republic of Korea, which has been bombarded with North Korean propaganda about vulnerability to EMP attack. Samsung Electronics has an extensive track record of bringing down costs of electronic system innovation.
	The best unclassified overview of functionality, by type of critical infrastructure, is contained in the "Stoplight" charts of Dr. George H. Baker (see Table 2).
Would all seem irrelevant after a few days?	With preplanning and community coordination, there is good reason to believe that communities can recover. Some widely read books are based on worst-case scenarios. Stockpiling food and water, coupled with having emergency power available along with the necessary fuel supply, is a useful first step. A more important recommendation is to petition local, state, and national public officials to protect the grid to prevent long-term outages. This Guide outlines actions that can be taken to be prepared and to help recover.

Interdependencies

When thinking of grid failure, the consequences can be a complex catastrophe. The complexity stems from the way in which all critical infrastructures are essentially an interconnected web of dependencies and interdependencies. Figure 5 shows some of the interdependencies. The power grid and communications are the foundation, which supports four life-essential pillars: food, water, transportation, and emergency services.

However, the figure does not show all of the critical infrastructure elements or all of the interdependencies. For example, the water sector is particularly dependent on the chemical industry and reliable electric power, including emergency backup power. Emergency backup power is dependent on fuel. Loss of water sector services for a prolonged period of time represents a national security risk, especially considering the critical interdependencies for many core functions, such as food production, fire suppression, military bases, hospitals, data centers, commercial real estate, electric production, and more. Providing a minimum amount of water during long-term emergencies is essential for national security; dams, critical manufacturing, and commercial facilities all depend on power. The nuclear reactors are considered part of the power grid for this Guide.

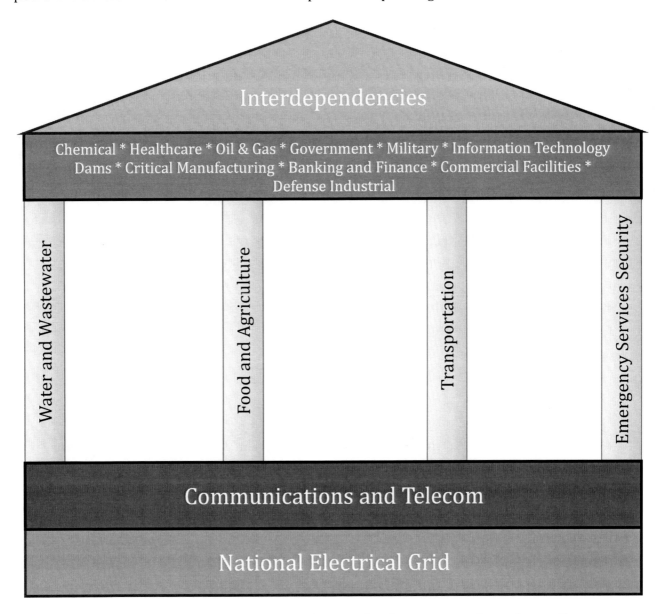

Figure 5: The Foundation and Pillars of Critical Infrastructure Interdependence.

Source: John Jackson, Fusion Risk Management Inc.

Power failures could have simultaneous direct impact on the power grid and communications infrastructures themselves. The immediate impact of the loss of communications to the power grid and the loss of power to communications will cause cascading outages in other critical infrastructures.

The *Electric Infrastructure Protection (EPRO) Handbook II Volume 1—Fuel* points out that "deepening interdependencies between natural gas and electric utilities are creating new challenges… Gas is rapidly replacing coal as the primary fuel for power generation in many regions of the United States. At the same time, key components of gas pipeline systems, including the compressors and industrial control systems that keep gas flowing to power generators and other users, are increasingly reliant on electric power. These growing interdependencies create risks of cascading, mutually-reinforcing failures."[37]

The dependencies and interdependencies of the healthcare and public health (HPH) sector are another example. Due to the increasingly interconnected nature of the sector's physical and cyber components, even a single point of failure within the HPH sector can cause cascading impacts throughout. By way of illustration, the 2009 H1N1 pandemic highlighted the importance of the medical supply chain in providing the drugs, vaccines, medical devices, electronic records, and personal protective equipment needed for workforce protection. The HPH sector is closely integrated with other sectors, which creates dependencies and interdependencies that can cause disruptions in one sector to very quickly and profoundly impact operations in another. Local disasters can cascade to multiple jurisdictions and interdependent sectors, triggering disruption across larger geographic areas. Limited awareness of the risks related to sector dependencies and interdependencies may subject an organization to "hidden risks"—meaning those risks that it assumes another entity can adequately manage.[38]

In addition, for the water sector, and others too, the rise of the "megacity" and the trend toward more and more people living in mega-city regions could pose a challenge. Strategies for cities/regions with 10 million+ people might be very different from those with substantially fewer residents. Consider the following written by Professor Michael Batty and taken from the Summer 2009 edition of "palette," University College London's journal of sustainable cities: www.ucl.ac.uk/sustainable-cities

> "It is well known that by the end of this century the proportion of the world's population living in cities will have increased from 45% now to some 80%. The world's biggest city at any point in the last 100 years has grown inexorably: in 1900 it was London with 6.4 million; in 1950 it was New York with 12.4 million; in 2000 it was Tokyo with 34.1 million; and the forecasts for the next 100 years show that the cities of the developing world will overtake those of the developed. New technologies will determine how big cities can grow as well as how high they will grow in terms of skyscrapers. In 1900, the highest building in the world was in Philadelphia some 167 meters in height; in 1950, it was 381 meters in New York City; and in 2000, it was 452 meters in Kuala Lumpur."

[37] See EIS Council, Electric Infrastructure Protection (EPRO) Handbook II Volume 1\Fuel p. 45
[38] Healthcare and Public Health Sector Specific Plan May 2016, p. 12

Water Closely Follows Energy in Importance

For the water sector, lack of water for coolant can impair the energy sector, and the controls for aqueducts are vulnerable to cyber-attack via electric substation communications. Which critical infrastructures will suffer rapidly degraded performance if a loss of electric grid power degrades utility water service, wastewater treatment, or both? Figure 6, released in the July 2016 National Infrastructure Advisory Council (NIAC) Report on Water Sector Resilience, shows rapid degradation of other critical infrastructures within 2 to 8 hours of water service outages.

Figure 6 provides an excellent illustration of how tightly coupled modern civilization is to modern water delivery systems. It clearly illustrates that every category of water user surveyed will experience significantly degraded capabilities after 8 hours without water. Thus, even if they have emergency generators that can provide on-site power for an extended period, they are degraded nonetheless by a lack of water.

A typical water utility using water towers may store approximately 24 hours of normal supply in their tower system, relying on refilling them each night. Much of the public is trained to fill their bathtub and other containers with water during a power outage caused by a natural disaster, such as a hurricane, expecting the power to return within three days. This action of draining the towers to provide on-site water storage depletes the system and may reduce its capacity to approximately 12 hours, after which there is little to no water pressure to provide water for drinking, industrial uses, or firefighting.

Thus, there is a maximum of one day of water pressure in most municipal systems that rely on gravity pressure. Systems that rely on pumps to maintain pressure, to include those with on-site wells, will lose pressure immediately. Those properties with wells typically maintain very little on-site water storage, if any. Without power, the majority of sites with wells will be unable to retrieve water from their well casings due to lack of manual equipment.

Additionally, should the water utilities have power, they maintain a limited quantity of treatment chemicals on site. These chemicals are necessary to produce potable water and require routine re-supply. Timely re-supply is unlikely in the scenarios discussed in this Guide.

Catastrophic loss of potable water has many consequences to include degrading or eliminating much of healthcare capacity and hospital use. The NIAC Report on the Water Sector indicates that hospital capabilities may be degraded by 67% to 99% within just two hours of loss of water services. Emergency replacement of healthcare facilities relies on nearby facilities being operable. This is not a feasible planning consideration in the event of a regional or larger-scale loss of electrical power and corresponding loss of water and wastewater utilities.

The July 2016 NIAC Water Sector Resilience Final Report also provided findings of common resilience themes:

- The energy-water nexus and its potentially adverse impacts on water utilities during a disruption is the most common theme across both man-made and natural disasters.
- Elevating the priority status of the water sector is a common after-action need, particularly as it relates to the energy-water nexus.
- Water utilities depend on the energy, transportation, and communications sectors for disruption response and recovery. The public health sector experiences the greatest downstream impacts from water disruptions.
- Major disruptions were beyond the capacity of the water utility to exclusively resolve and as such, water utilities relied on external resources and coordination with other water utilities, sectors, and emergency management. Across all disruptions, it was evident that additional pre-event relationship-building, exercising, and understanding roles/responsibilities would have improved disruption management.
- Timely, accurate information sharing to the public, media, and emergency management liaisons is critical to ensure public health and safety, mitigate panic, and facilitate response. Risk communication is essential.
- Utilities will experience major impacts if their infrastructure is not built to withstand impacts from a low-probability, high-impact event (e.g., major flooding).
- Water facility access issues significantly complicated recovery operations. These include: access control and credentialing for water utility personnel; security infrastructure losing power; and transportation issues.

Personnel represent a potential point of failure in response and recovery, as they can also be significantly impacted by major disruptions and unable to reach the facility. Once at a facility, they must be assured of personal safety along with food and drinking water.

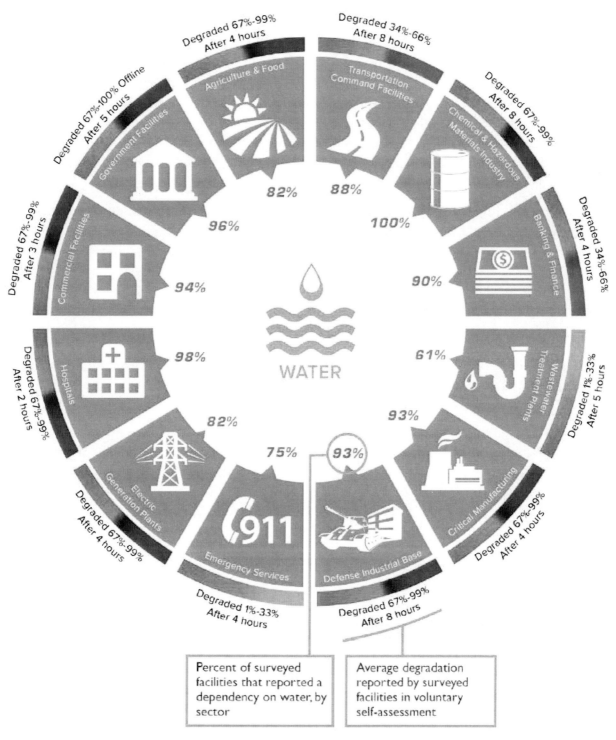

Degraded 67%-99% After 4 hours

Degraded 34%-66% After 8 hours

Degraded 67%-100% Offline After 5 hours

Degraded 67%-99% After 8 hours

Degraded 67%-99% After 3 hours

Degraded 34%-66% After 4 hours

Degraded 1%-33% After 5 hours

Degraded 67%-99% After 2 hours

Degraded 67%-99% After 4 hours

Degraded 67%-99% After 4 hours

Degraded 1%-33% After 4 hours

Degraded 67%-99% After 8 hours

Agriculture & Food — 82%

Transportation Command Facilities — 88%

Government Facilities — 96%

Chemical & Hazardous Materials Industry — 100%

Commercial Facilities — 94%

Banking & Finance — 90%

Hospitals — 98%

Wastewater Treatment Plants — 61%

Electric Generation Plants — 82%

Critical Manufacturing — 93%

Emergency Services — 75%

Defense Industrial Base — 93%

WATER

Percent of surveyed facilities that reported a dependency on water, by sector

Average degradation reported by surveyed facilities in voluntary self-assessment

Figure 6: NIAC Critical Infrastructure Dependence on Water and Potential Function Degradation Following Loss of Water Services.[39]

---

[39] *Source:* National Infrastructure Advisory Council (NIAC), *Water Sector Resilience: Final Report and Recommendations*, July 2016, Figure ES-1, p. 2.

Another factor to consider is the loss of power to the wastewater utility. These utilities rely on electricity to treat the wastewater and pump the wastewater to the treatment station via lift stations. Lift stations are located in low-lying areas and may be expected to overflow with raw sewage within a few days or sooner, depending on their design. This unpumped wastewater will also backup into lower lying buildings and homes in an uncontrollable manner. Depending on the design of the wastewater transport system, the suspended solids may settle after three to four days and render the pumps and portions of the piping permanently unusable. The consequences of untreated sewage overflowing into low-lying areas include their entry into the very surface water that will be turned to as a replacement source of drinking water, rendering it a potent vector of diarrhea-causing micro-organisms with tremendous potential to infect the local population. This type of disease caused more casualties than actual combat in the wars waged prior to modern medicine.

Raw sewage backing up into medical facilities and hospitals will trigger facility shutdown protocols. With widespread loss of clean water pressure and wastewater treatment, the provision of professional healthcare services will be degraded and possibly eliminated.

Industrial manufacturing facilities, refineries, and chemical and food processing plants will become inoperable. Sudden unexpected loss of electrical power will create catastrophic damage to any rapidly rotating, highly pressurized, high-temperature, or extreme low-temperature manufacturing and chemical processing equipment. Such finely tuned and computer-managed equipment can be expected to rupture and release uncontrollable discharges of hazardous materials into the atmosphere and nearby surface water. Industrial facilities are typically located adjacent to the same bodies of surface water that water utilities also rely on so they can draw feed water and discharge treated industrial wastewater. Such releases from facilities that process large quantities of chemicals or petroleum products will heavily contaminate the surface water sources used by water utilities.

Water utility systems are designed to process raw water based on a normal operating range of typical water contaminants and suspended solids. This normal range will be exceeded in most water intake zones by the introduction of both untreated sewage and catastrophic upstream chemical releases. Many if not most remaining operable water treatment systems are not designed for and will not anticipate the introduction of such contaminants and may not be able to produce potable water even if they have electrical power.

Appendix C of the NIAC Water Sector Resilience Final Report provides a disruption scenario case study. This case study concluded that water utilities should be a "Tier 1" priority for power restoration after a disruption.

It should be noted that, if there is water and wastewater management in the cities, plus restoration of emergency food stockpiles, then people could be encouraged to stay in their homes (to "shelter in place") and not to evacuate except for compounding separate events (e.g., flooding, fire, or hurricane).

Uncoordinated and unplanned self-evacuations are contraindicated. The Three Mile Island (TMI) Nuclear Incident of March 1979 showed that self-evacuation was not beneficial and caused prolonged congestion of transportation systems and fuel shortages. Between March 28 and April 4, an estimated 144,000 regional residents self-evacuated from the region of the power plant.[40] Within the 20-mile radius of TMI, the residential population was about 600,000; so roughly one-quarter of the population evacuated, mainly before official instructions were broadcast.[41] Since that incident, the Nuclear Regulatory Commission has mandated installation and monitoring of radiological sensors within designated evacuation zones of licensed nuclear power plants, in part to avert rumor-based evacuations that congest and undermine recovery capabilities.

Overall, a strategy to protect and rapidly restore lifeline sectors—including water, electricity, food, medical and emergency services, and telecommunications—offers the potential to maximize "shelter in place" capabilities and minimize uncoordinated evacuations. Uncoordinated evacuations have the potential to escalate threats to public safety, protection of supply chains, and equitable distribution of life-essential goods and services.

Ted Koppel explored the real or potential contradictions among federal policies to prepare for and to recover from a long-term grid blackout in his book, *Lights Out* (2015), "In the case of a power grid going down urging people to stay in their homes may be exactly the right thing to do … leaving routes open for resupply convoys."[42]

For a long-term electric grid outage, relying on "shelter in place" as the preferred policy to the maximum extent feasible has multiple advantages, including conservation of scarce fuel, prioritizing uses of transportation routes, preserving law and order, and benefitting from community networking by those in their own neighborhoods. Others share this

---

[40] See Robert A. Stallings, "Evacuation Behavior at Three Mile Island," *Int'l J, Mass Emergencies and Disasters* (1984), pp. 11-26. Since the TMI events, the Nuclear Regulatory Commission has mandated installation of radiological sensors in spatially distributed rings around all licensed nuclear power plants, and mandates that nuclear power licensees and communities in potential evacuation zones participate in graded evacuation drills every two years. The Post-Katrina Emergency Management Reform Act of 2006 authorizes federal funding for states to develop catastrophic mass evacuation plans. For policy considerations, see FEMA's Mass Evacuation Incident Annex to the National Response Framework, June 2008.

[41] William W. Chenault, Gary D. Hilbert, and Seth D. Reichlin, *Evacuation Planning in the TMI Accident*, Human Sciences Research, Sep. 1979, DTIC Report 80128032.

[42] Ted Koppel, *Lights Out: A Cyberattack, A Nation Unprepared, Surviving the Aftermath*, New York: Crown Publishers, 2015, p. 115.

preference for "shelter in place" outcomes.[43] A preferential policy to "shelter in place" depends on the resiliency of "lifeline services" such as prepositioned food, restoration of water and wastewater services, essential transportation, and communications. The Administrator of the Federal Emergency Management Administration, Craig Fugate, expressed concern about the advisability of mass evacuations for long-duration disasters. The government, he noted, "Can't move 'em fast enough." And as Ted Koppel replied, "anyway where are you going to move them?"[44]

The following chapters explore governmental processes for protection, mitigation, and recovery, as well as capability gaps that undermine the current feasibility of "shelter in place" outcomes.[45]

---

[43] The Electric Infrastructure Security (EIS) Council supports "enabling the largest possible numbers of people to 'shelter in place' during that multi-week or longer restoration [of the power grid]," EPRO Black Sky Systems Engineering Process, 2016, p. 15.

[44] Koppel, *Lights Out*, p. 116.

[45] See, for example, indications of reduced emergency food stocks for civilians since years 2008-2010, at pp. 71-72.

Chapter III: U.S. National Framework for Disaster Preparedness

Ongoing efforts across the country to improve readiness for extended grid failures take place in the broader context of the current national campaign to enhance preparedness for all threats and hazards. Understanding the basic outlines of this larger context is important for those seeking further progress with respect to extended grid failures.

With its early origins grounded in a strong American tradition of individual and community self-reliance, the nation's overall approach to homeland security has evolved in significant ways over more than two centuries. Four key drivers have been among the most important factors in shaping the current approach: governance principles enshrined in the Constitution; many legislative and executive branch initiatives at all levels of government; and the dynamic and increasingly daunting threat environment.

Evolution of National Approach to Preparedness

As is well articulated in the White House report *The Federal Response to Hurricane Katrina: Lessons Learned* (February 2006), enduring constitutional principles of limited government and dispersed powers are central to an understanding of how the nation is organized to prepare for, respond to, and recover from disasters in the homeland. The Tenth Amendment specifies that, "powers not delegated to the United States by the Constitution, nor prohibited by it to the states, are reserved to the states respectively, or to the people." This provision essentially assigns to the states—and, by extension, tribal, territorial, and local governments—those authorities and responsibilities that are viewed as neither practical nor appropriate for the federal government to undertake. Consistent with this provision, the United States prepares for and responds to domestic disasters through a fully-inclusive national system that begins with and builds up from the lowest possible jurisdictional level, with higher-level jurisdictions involved only to the extent necessary.

Today, it is generally accepted that the federal government: (1) is usually not the appropriate first responder; (2) does not in any case have the resources required to undertake this role for all disasters; and (3) should therefore defer to non-federal government entities, as well as private sector actors and community organizations, to handle the large majority of disasters that are of low to moderate severity. In keeping with the "provide for common defense" clause in Article I of the Constitution, this construct for the most part reserves the federal government for the larger-scale disasters involving major, if not catastrophic, impacts.

Legislation has also been a key driver in shaping the 21st century national approach to preparedness. While state, local, tribal and territorial (SLTT) legislative initiatives frame much of the homeland security context, the most significant laws—particularly in the years since World War II—have been enacted by Congress. Moreover, especially in recent decades, SLTT governments have been incentivized by federal emergency preparedness grant programs to adopt certain standard strategies and organizational models that have contributed to greater overall uniformity.

A detailed history of key federal preparedness and related disaster assistance laws is beyond the scope of this Guide. Three landmark initiatives, however, not only serve to illustrate the pivotal role of Congress, but also have particular relevance with respect to energy sector preparedness. These initiatives include: the Robert T. Stafford Relief and Emergency Assistance Act (1988); the Homeland Security Act (2002); and the Cybersecurity Information Sharing Act (2015).

The Stafford Act established the current system for providing federal disaster assistance for SLTT governments to support their efforts to aid citizens impacted by disasters. The Act is noteworthy not only because of the financial assistance and other disaster response resources made available, but also because its implementation reflects decades of practice in allocating government responsibility for disasters. In brief, disaster response generally takes place first at the local level; then, if necessary, escalates to the state, tribal, or territorial level; and, finally, *only* if even more assistance is required, ultimately escalates further to the federal level.

Turning to the Homeland Security Act, this landmark legislation established the new Department of Homeland Security (DHS) that stood up in early 2003. The Act brought 22 agencies with homeland security responsibilities into one new department in the most sweeping federal government reorganization since the Department of Defense was created after World War II. Beyond signaling the strong post-9/11 U.S. resolve to safeguard the homeland, the Act designated DHS as the lead federal department for orchestrating the entire "whole of nation" homeland security mission.

The third landmark initiative was the Cybersecurity Information Sharing Act of 2015. Its fundamental purpose was to improve cyber-security throughout the country by promoting increased information sharing about cyber-security threats and countermeasures between and among federal government entities and technology and manufacturing companies. Much of the impetus for this legislation stemmed from acute awareness of increasing cyber-threats to vulnerable critical infrastructure, including the national power grid. In fact, more than a third of recent cyber-attacks involving critical infrastructure have targeted the energy sector.

Similar to the case with legislation, although executive preparedness initiatives below the federal level have always been important for their respective jurisdictions, comparatively recent White House directives have been the single most significant driver in shaping the current overall national approach to homeland security readiness. Both post-9/11 administrations have been very proactive in this arena. The leading relevant initiatives on President Bush's watch included the following:

- The first-ever comprehensive *National Strategy for Homeland Security* (July 2002) issued less than a year after the unprecedented terror attacks;
- Homeland Security Presidential Directive (HSPD) 5 entitled *"Management of Domestic Incidents"* (February 2003) directing DHS to develop: (1) a National Management Incident System (NIMS) to provide a consistent national approach to disasters regardless of cause, size or complexity; and (2) a National Response Plan for federal support to SLTT governments;
- Homeland Security Presidential Directive (HSPD) 7 entitled *"Critical Infrastructure Identification, Prioritization, and Protection"* (December 2003) setting forth national policy requiring federal departments and agencies to enhance ongoing efforts to protect critical infrastructure; and
- Homeland Security Presidential Directive (HSPD) 8, entitled *"National Preparedness"* (December 2003) establishing the first-ever comprehensive framework for an integrated national initiative to enhance preparedness.

President Obama has essentially ratified the solid policy foundation laid by his predecessor, focusing primarily on refining and expanding the scope of Bush Administration directives. Three Obama Administration initiatives are arguably the most significant in terms of understanding the current overall national approach: Presidential Policy Directive (PPD) 8, entitled "National Preparedness" (March 2011); the National Preparedness Goal (September 2015); and the most recent set of National Planning Frameworks (June 2016).

PPD-8 not only underscored the importance the Obama Administration placed on enhancing preparedness, but also detailed a road map for establishing a "National Preparedness System" to promote more rapid progress. In so doing, the White House directive emphasized that preparedness is the "shared responsibility of all levels of government, the private and nonprofit sectors, and individual citizens" and called for "an integrated, all-of-nation, capabilities-based approach to preparedness."

The first task mandated by PPD-8 was development of a National Preparedness Goal to define and focus relevant efforts. The current goal, issued in late 2015 as a revision to the initial Obama Administration articulation in 2011, reads as follows: "A secure and resilient nation with the capabilities required across the whole community to prevent, protect against, mitigate, respond to, and recover from the threats and hazards that pose the greatest risk."

After the National Preparedness Goal was initially promulgated, PPD-8 implementation efforts turned to launching the National Preparedness System. Arguably the most fundamental component of this system is the library of National Planning Frameworks intended to organize and facilitate progress in five distinct preparedness mission areas. These frameworks—all of which apply to each of the current 16 designated critical infrastructure sectors—are as follows:

- *National Prevention Framework*, 2nd Edition, June 2016;
- *National Protection Framework*, 2nd Edition, June 2016;
- *National Mitigation Framework*, 2nd Edition, June 2016;
- *National Response Framework*, 3rd Edition, June 2016; and
- *National Disaster Recovery Framework*, 2nd Edition, June 2016.

Figure 7 provides an overview of the key policy cornerstones for the current National Security Strategy and Current National Preparedness System.

Turning to the threat landscape, from the early days of the republic until at least the mid-20th century—apart from the early wars fought on American soil—the most common security threats in the homeland were famine, disease, and violent crime. For the most part, the responsibility to prepare for and respond to such threats remained primarily at the individual and community level, with increasing involvement over time by local and state governments. With a few notable exceptions, the role of the federal government was quite limited, except in those few instances when there was a significant "external" dimension to the threat.

Fast-forwarding to the Cold War era and the years beyond, the threat picture has changed dramatically owing to the emergence and complex interaction of myriad political, economic, societal, technological, and environmental developments. Today's threats in the homeland are—and are increasingly perceived as—more numerous, more harmful, and more directly menacing than ever before. As a result, the American people—especially post-9/11—have come to expect "more security" from government at all levels, and particularly from the federal level given the high-profile role Washington now plays with respect to the full range of governance challenges.

There are many extant threat assessments focused in whole or in part on homeland security. One of the most comprehensive is the World-Wide Threat Assessment of the U.S. Intelligence Community, typically published early each year by the Office of the Director of National Intelligence. The most recent assessment, issued in February 2016, identifies "systemic and persistent vulnerabilities in key infrastructure sectors" including energy.

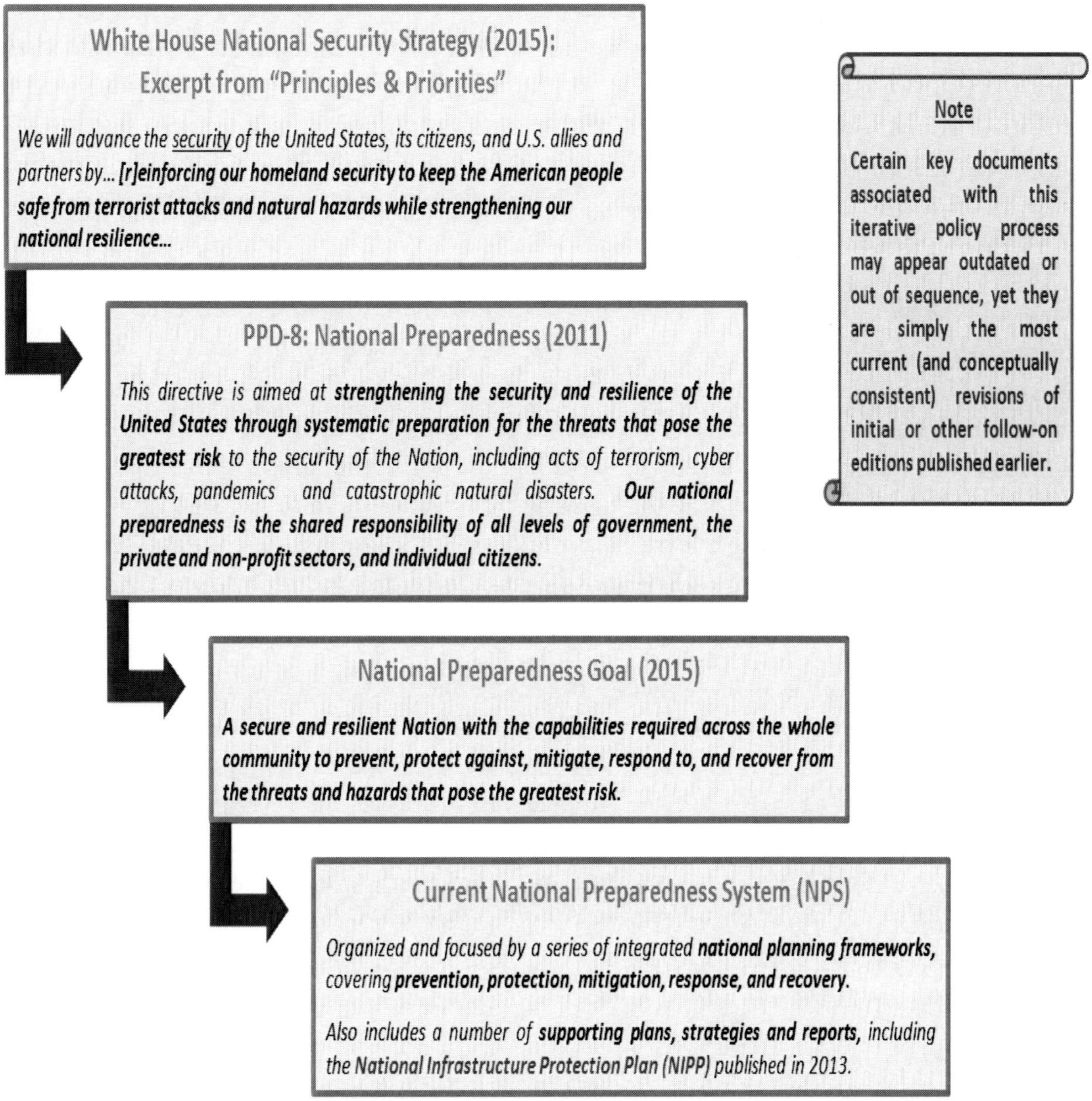

White House National Security Strategy (2015):
Excerpt from "Principles & Priorities"

We will advance the security of the United States, its citizens, and U.S. allies and partners by... [r]einforcing our homeland security to keep the American people safe from terrorist attacks and natural hazards while strengthening our national resilience...

PPD-8: National Preparedness (2011)

*This directive is aimed at **strengthening the security and resilience of the United States through systematic preparation for the threats that pose the greatest risk** to the security of the Nation, including acts of terrorism, cyber attacks, pandemics and catastrophic natural disasters. **Our national preparedness is the shared responsibility of all levels of government, the private and non-profit sectors, and individual citizens.***

National Preparedness Goal (2015)

A secure and resilient Nation with the capabilities required across the whole community to prevent, protect against, mitigate, respond to, and recover from the threats and hazards that pose the greatest risk.

Current National Preparedness System (NPS)

*Organized and focused by a series of integrated **national planning frameworks**, covering **prevention, protection, mitigation, response, and recovery**.*

*Also includes a number of **supporting plans, strategies and reports**, including the National Infrastructure Protection Plan (NIPP) published in 2013.*

Note

Certain key documents associated with this iterative policy process may appear outdated or out of sequence, yet they are simply the most current (and conceptually consistent) revisions of initial or other follow-on editions published earlier.

Figure 7: Policy Basis for Current National Approach to Preparedness Resilience.

Source: Fred M. Rosa Jr., Johns Hopkins Applied Physics Laboratory

Overview of the Current National Approach

Shaped in large part by the various factors highlighted above, the national approach to preparedness has indeed evolved tremendously across the span of U.S. history. Today's approach is much more prominent, deliberate, comprehensive, and better resourced than ever before. It is also definitely a national, *not* federal, system at its very core.

The expression "all disasters are local" is appropriate to cite in describing the current national approach. In most instances, disasters of whatever nature and magnitude are experienced, recognized, and responded to first right where they happen. Local government and non-government resources, with state, tribal, and territorial assistance as necessary, are expected to handle those of low to moderate severity at their level and are able to do so more often than not. Local governments—together with their respective state, tribal, and territorial governments—know the unique circumstances and requirements of their areas of responsibility, and they are most directly accountable to their citizens for securing public safety and welfare.

As noted earlier, if local resources prove inadequate, the next recourse is typically assistance from other neighboring or nearby local jurisdictions pursuant to mutual aid or other similar agreements. Should the additional resources from these sources still prove inadequate, the next option is assistance from the state, tribal, or territorial level. The final recourse, if necessary, is a request from the pertinent state, tribal, or territorial government for federal assistance to augment, not replace, resources already committed to the disaster. Through the Stafford Act and other programs, the federal government provides substantial financial support for disaster response and recovery efforts, as well as certain unique assets and capabilities that exist only at the federal level.

The above allocation and sequencing of government responsibility for response and recovery—proceeding in phases from the local, to the state, territorial, or tribal level, and then ultimately to the federal level—also applies to preparedness planning and related efforts in advance of actual disasters. All levels of government are expected to prepare as necessary to optimize both their use of organic response resources and their ability to integrate their efforts with those of other jurisdictions, the private sector, and community organizations.

With respect to preparedness efforts in advance of disasters, the federal government has a particularly important function in view of its unique status as the overarching "common denominator" jurisdiction. That role is to promote effectiveness and efficiency by providing not only a comprehensive planning framework, but also common doctrine and a national set of standards for terminology, communications, information sharing, equipment, etc. As the primary agency responsible for this critical function, the Federal Emergency Management Agency (FEMA) has facilitated substantial progress in enhancing coordination and interoperability between and among all levels of government, as well as key non-government actors.

Critical Infrastructure
Given the vital importance of critical infrastructure to national and economic security, PPD-8 and the many linked policy documents assign a high priority to—and provide a particularly detailed framework for—related preparedness and resilience efforts. Four

Obama Administration directives are particularly significant with respect to all critical infrastructures, including the energy sector's power grid:

- Presidential Policy Directive (PPD) 21, entitled "Critical Infrastructure Protection and Resilience" (February 2013);
- Executive Order 13636, entitled "Improving Critical Infrastructure Cybersecurity" (February 2013);
- The "National Infrastructure Protection Plan" (NIPP), published by DHS (December 2013); and
- The "Energy Sector-Specific Plan," published jointly by the Department of Energy (DOE) and DHS (December 2015) as an annex to the NIPP.

The first directive, PPD-21, designated a Sector-Specific Agency (SSA) for all 16 critical infrastructure sectors to lead a collaborative process for enhancing preparedness and resilience across each sector. DHS is the lead or co-lead for 10 of the 16 sectors. PPD-21 also mandated development and implementation of a Sector-Specific Plan (SSP), the purpose of which is to apply NIPP concepts to the unique circumstances of that sector. It is also significant to note that the directive designated the energy sector as uniquely critical owing to the essential dependency of all other sectors on its outputs.

Executive Order 13636, "Improving Critical Infrastructure Cybersecurity," directed federal agencies to coordinate with critical infrastructure owners and operators to improve information sharing and to collaboratively develop and implement risk-based approaches to cyber-security. The directive was consistent with the increasing emphasis on integrating physical and cyber-security measures, and outlined approaches to managing risks across all five national preparedness mission areas.

The third directive, NIPP 2013, is organized by the 16 domestic critical infrastructure sectors, including the energy sector that encompasses the electric grid. Of particular importance, the directive establishes a hierarchy of consulting and coordinating groups, including both government entities and private sector stakeholders. The purpose of these groups is straightforward: enhance the preparedness and resilience of their respective sectors with respect to all threats and hazards. While there are many examples of promoting progress outside these sector-coordinating mechanisms, the frameworks have proven an important catalyst and enabling tool.

The fundamental NIPP scheme strongly reflects current critical infrastructure realities. The vast majority of all such infrastructure is owned and operated by private entities, and the private sector is largely responsible for the security of this infrastructure. Moreover, statutory and regulatory authority remains minimal with respect to most of this infrastructure, and much of the authority that does exist is below the federal level.

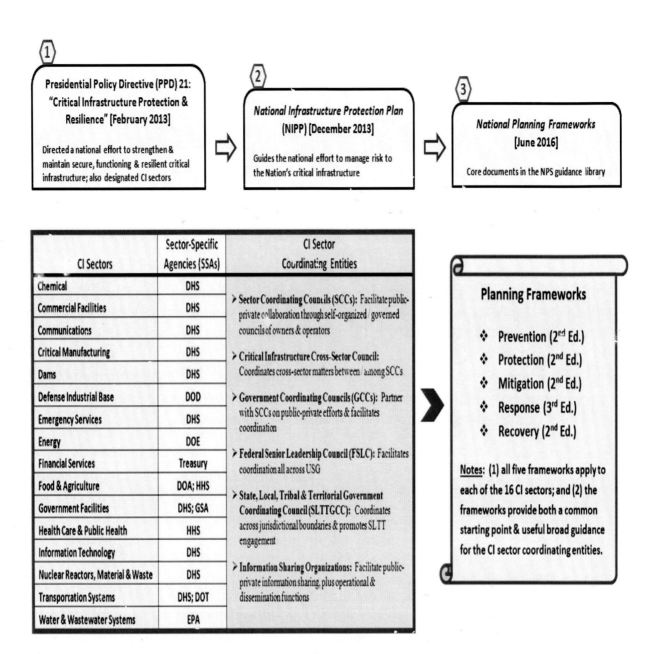

Figure 8: National Preparedness System (NPS)—Application to Critical Infrastructure.

Source: Fred M. Rosa Jr., Johns Hopkins Applied Physics Laboratory

Finally, as the SSA for the energy sector, DOE led numerous government and private sector partners, primarily through the various Energy Sector Coordinating Councils (SCCs) and the Energy Government Coordinating Council (GCC), to develop the Energy Sector-Specific Plan (SSP). The SSP provides an overview of strategic-level activities intended to advance national critical infrastructure security and resilience goals. SSP highlights relate generally to four key topics: risk management; interdependency and coordination; information sharing and communication; and resilience and preparedness.

Section 4.2 of the Energy Sector Specific Plan highlights the complex interdependencies between and among all critical infrastructure sectors. Of particular note, energy, communications, transportation, and water, are identified as "critical sectors" that provide "lifeline functions" to all other critical infrastructure sectors." Figure 8 depicts the way in which the National Preparedness System sets forth broad guidance that applies to all critical infrastructures, including the national grid and other energy sector components.

Chapter IV: Enhancing Nationwide Grid Preparedness

Steps to enhance nationwide grid preparedness can be divided into two categories: first, steps to prevent wide-area grid outages; and, second, steps to ensure quick recovery should such a blackout occur. Preventive steps should correspond to major electric grid threats:

- Physical attack
- Cyber-attack
- Solar storms
- Man-made electromagnetic pulse (EMP)

Steps to ensure quick recovery may apply to multiple initiating events. Recovery steps could include:

- Adoption of a "grid islanding" architecture and a priority ranking within an inventory of "grid islands" including key power plants to be restarted following a major grid blackout[46];
- Special attention to protecting power to ensure nuclear power plant cooling systems continue to operate to avoid Fukushima-type disasters;
- Installation of equipment to "blackstart" the grid from total outage and enhanced operator training to practice for "black sky" events[47];
- Backup diesel generators and sufficient fuel to operate critical equipment necessary for grid restoration[48];
- Stocking and pre-positioning of spare equipment, especially hard-to-replace extra high-voltage transformers[49];
- Voluntary agreements for mutual assistance[50];

---

[46] See the discussion on "Resilient Microgrids" at pp. 55-58, *infra*, and associated Appendix 5, "Blackstarting the Electric Power Grid." A top priority should be assigned to assuring that nuclear power plants remain safe after a major grid shutdown; and to the extent feasible that nuclear power plants can be restarted to provide energy to accelerate and sustain grid restoration.

[47] See Electric Infrastructure Security Council, Handbook, released in December 2014, edited by Paul Stockton, Chris Beck, and Avi Schnurr. It includes a class of "black sky" hazards for which critical infrastructures should be protected. See also the EIS Council pamphlet, Black Sky/ Black Start Protection Initiative, 2016, available online.

[48] The Nuclear Energy Institute has initiated a program, adopted by the U.S. Nuclear Regulatory Commission (NRC) in Order EA-12-049 of March 2012, known as the SAFER Program. This authorized a set of regional warehouses, the *FLEX program*, to provide emergency communications, spare transformers, emergency diesel generators and other spares to assure protection of commercial nuclear reactors and cooling of spent fuel pools, and to facilitate reoperation of nuclear power plants. In Feb. 2016 the Foundation for Resilient Societies urged the NRC to validate that emergency equipment stored in the FLEX program is protected against both GMD and EMP hazards. See NRC ADAMS database Doc. ML-16043A431.

[49] In addition to the FLEX program for nuclear power plants, now operational, a consortium of electric utilities jointly pools investments in loanable transformers spares and other equipment managed by the recently incorporated Grid Assurance LLC.

- Establishment of microgrids for communities and critical facilities[51]; and
- Cyber-operational responses by grid asset owners, aided by federal coordination and technical assistance.[52]

Both preventive and recovery steps must be realizable and cost-effective. It makes little sense to propose expensive actions that will never be implemented. The regulatory authorities play an important role in setting reliability and safety standards for grid preparedness. Public awareness is also vital. If the public is aware and concerned, they will be supportive of the costs incurred by utilities as they put protective measures in place.

Protections for Major Electric Grid Threats

Protections for Physical Attack

Components of electric grids exposed to physical attack include generation plants, transmission lines, transformer substations, utility-owned communications systems, and control facilities. Most generation plants are manned facilities, generally with defined defensive perimeters such as chain-link fences. Transmission lines are inherently difficult to defend; redundancy may be the best protective strategy. Redundant telecommunications and data links can enhance resilience. Among the remaining components, high-voltage transformer substations and control facilities should receive the most attention for protection against physical attack because these critical facilities can be cost-effectively defended.

Protection of Transformer Substations

Although substations are nearly always above ground and therefore exposed to physical attack, there are steps that should be considered to enhance their protection. Chief among the hardening steps are the installation of anti-ballistic walls or shelters to protect the transformers and control buildings. In the consideration of new substations, space-compacting technologies such as Geographic Information Systems (GIS) should be assessed to minimize the substation footprint and make the protection investment more reasonable. Certainly, there is no physical protection strategy short of placing the substation underground that would completely protect the substation. Selective protection of critical

---

[50] Edison Electric Institute, a consortium of investor-owned electric utilities, has supported seven Regional Mutual Assistance Groups (RMAGs) that include sharing of restoration workers, critical equipment or materials, and inter-regional mutual assistance agreements. In Hurricane SANDY (2012) which impacted 10 million customers across 24 states, 80 utilities from almost every state and Canada assisted through RMAGs in the grid restoration process. See Edison Electric Institute, Understanding the Electric Power Industry's Response and Restoration Process, June 2016; and Miles Keogh and Sharon Thomas, Regional Mutual Assistance Groups: A Primer, NARUC, November 2015. For further discussion of "mutual assistance" see infra, pp. 53-55.

[51] See Chapter VI of this Guide.

[52] See Presidential Policy Directive PPD-41, United States Incident Coordination, Section IV(B) Asset response activities; and Section V(B), National Operational Coordination, issued July 26, 2016.

equipment that is difficult to replace (e.g., transformers and control buildings) is likely to be cost-effective.

Another prudent step is to use remote detection technology to provide surveillance to the substation without the cost of deployment of personnel. Security cameras, floodlights, and motion detectors are commonly used techniques in the security industry. The same is true with large generating facilities. While remote surveillance may not be able to stop an attack, rapid response may provide the ability to minimize the damage and operational impact by permitting operator action to remove equipment from service prior to causing widespread outages. Public vigilance is also important regarding suspicious activities around substations. State police have established call lines for reporting such activity.

A more general response to increased resiliency is to provide more network redundancy such that individual equipment, substations, or transmission lines do not become "critical" single points of failure, thereby sustaining service in local areas and, more importantly, preventing wide-scale outages or interruptions. Loop power line configurations offer major advantages over hub-and-spoke connectivity. In the substation, resiliency may mean use of additional, lesser capacity transformers to provide the same capacity, albeit at additional expense. Standardizing equipment while sub-optimizing the performance may be another strategy that will pay dividends in resiliency. Installing additional transmission lines lessens the individual criticality of each line. The same is true with the substation itself and the ability to disperse the risks through additional facilities.

Protection of Control Facilities

Control facilities are vital for electric grid operations, because most transformer substations are unmanned and therefore remotely controlled through Supervisory Control and Data Acquisition (SCADA) networks. Larger substations will have control facilities housed in small on-site buildings. Multiple substations are connected to larger central control facilities that can be very large. Common strategies for control facility protection include:

- *Obscurity*—The location and street address of the control facilities are withheld from public information sources such as phone directories, website pages, and news articles.
- *Redundancy*—Two or more control facilities, in separate locations, can assume full control of the grid network. Redundant control facilities may have 24/7 operational staffs in each location.
- *Defensive perimeters*—Large expanses of property protected by one or more layers of chain-link fences, with security cameras and motion detectors, long access driveways with guardhouses and gates, and armed guards on site. In some cases, control facilities are situated near police stations.

With expanding terrorist and foreign adversary threats, enhanced protection for the most critical control facilities may be necessary. For example, control facilities may be shielded against radio frequency weapons. During time of increased threat, police or National Guard troops may be dispatched to protect control facilities.

Protective Actions for Cyber-Attack

Increasingly, computer systems used to operate electric grids are being interconnected with the public internet. As a result, adversaries can implant malware that can take over grid control systems in grid control facilities. In some cases, communications among control facilities, substations, and generation facilities take place via the public internet, adding yet another layer of vulnerability.

In 2014, Russia tested a complex attack scenario (Havex/BlackEnergy2) against the North American Grid. Incidents such as this offer unparalleled opportunities to assess vulnerabilities, threats, and existing and projected risks.[53]

What are the lessons learned as they affect cyber-security? One of the major surprises was penetration of vendor Industrial Control System (ICS) and SCADA supply chains; infecting vendor products routinely installed in the electric grid without further testing. By late 2015, Russia was ready to test its improved cyber-attack system on a vulnerable target, the Ukrainian national grid, taking down three of six distribution utilities for over six hours and shutting down power to about 230,000 customers.[54] The attack on the electric grid was accompanied by a distributed denial of service attack on call centers. This attack disrupted situational awareness while taking complete control of electricity control centers. The Russians did no permanent damage to hard-to-replace equipment; it was obviously not their objective.

U.S. national authorities convinced Ukrainian authorities not to overreact to this event, denied public attribution to the government of Russia, and evidently encouraged the U.S. electric utility industry to minimize any association with the 2014 Russian incursions into the U.S. grid. This was clearly a U.S. foreign policy decision. The Ukraine incident indicates the slippery slope upon which U.S. grid cyber-security rests. The Secretary of Energy, armed with new cyber-security authority under the FAST Act of 2015, should not minimize ongoing cyber vulnerabilities of the U.S. energy sector.

Steps to protect against cyber-attack could include:

---

[53] On Havex, see https://ics-cert.us-cert.gov/advisories/ICSA-14-178-01.

[54] The remotely engineered Ukrainian grid blackout occurred on December 23, 2015. On March 18, 2016 the Electricity Information Sharing and Analysis Center (E-ISAC) and the SANS Institute jointly issued a public report, Analysis of the Cyber Attack on the Ukrainian Power Grid: Defense Use Case, with some details of the methods of attack and Ukrainian grid restoration process. For further analysis, see Jake Styczynski, Nate Beach-Westmoreland, and Scott Stables, When the Lights Went Out: A Comprehensive Review of the 2015 Attacks on Ukrainian Critical Infrastructure, October 2016, p. 3.

- For cyber events, consider encrypting the communications of the control facilities, some which are directly or indirectly connected to the public internet. Encryption could protect SCADA devices managed by control facilities. Encryption devices are not expensive. (The July 1, 2016, FERC Order No. 822 requires securing communication links between control centers, but not between control facilities and electric substations.[55])
- Limit on-site access to data systems to trusted employees. Require card and pass code or biometric access to sensitive areas. Keep access lists current—purge names quickly when employees leave or transfer.
- Limit remote access. The industry depends heavily on remote access by vendors to Industrial Control System (ICS) instrumentation and SCADA systems. However, for security purposes, this access should be limited.[56]
- Reduce or eliminate system vulnerabilities to single point failure of SCADA and control systems.
- Minimize use of the internet communications for SCADA and control systems.
- Enhance access control and fire-walling of systems.
- Provide extensive anti-phishing training to all individuals with system access.
- Establish a 24/7 operational cyber-security monitoring program. There can be no grid-wide cyber-security 24/7 situational awareness possible without such a system.
- Establish "whitelisted" grid and industrial control system equipment as part of a broader effort to protect cyber supply chains.[57]

See Appendix 4 for a discussion on Industrial Control and SCADA Systems.

As part of this awareness and in an attempt to increase community engagement, the U.S. Department of Homeland Security (DHS) established the Industrial Control Systems Cyber

---

[55] The July 21, 2016 FERC Order No. 822 requires securing communication links between control centers operated by Reliability Coordinators. NERC does not at present support cyber-protection requirements for electric substation communications and control equipment. See Joseph M. Weiss, "The NERC CIPs continue to expose the grid to significant cyber vulnerabilities even after the Ukrainian hack," Control: Unfettered Blog, October 10, 2016. See also "The use of protective relays as an attack vector—the cyber vulnerability of the electric grid," Control: Unfettered Blog, July 22, 2016.

[56] Frank Koza of PJM suggests "Dramatically reduce or enhance remote access to protection and SCADA systems. Remote access permits technicians to access the protection devices and SCADA from remote locations to facilitate response. However, the Ukraine event was facilitated by the theft of credentials that allowed access to SCADA with remote access. Remote access appears to be a weak link in the protection of the grid control assets." Specifically, "a malware tool. BlackEnergy3, designed to enable unauthorized network access, then used valid user credentials to move laterally across internal systems, and ultimately shut down electricity distribution using the utilities' native control systems." When the Lights Went Out: A Comprehensive Review of the 2015 Attacks on Ukrainian Critical Infrastructure, Booz Allen Hamilton, Oct. 2016, p. 1.

[57] See FERC Order No. 829, July 21, 2016, a final Rule on Cyber Supply Chain Standards for the bulk electric system.

Emergency Response Team (ICS-CERT) in 2009. It is an organization within DHS's National Cyber Security and Integration Center (NCCIC). The ICS-CERT unit serves as the industrial control systems focus for the United States Computer Emergency Readiness Team (US-CERT) program.[58]

ICS-CERT provides several key resources to assist with ICS security, which include:

- Incident response and security guidance
- Community membership portal
  - Community message boards
  - Alert and document repository
  - Acceptance of, and security of, PCII data
- Email notifications and alerts
- Training activities

Cyber-Attack Vulnerabilities

Readers should be cautioned that ICS-CERT alerts and related warnings do not include analyses of cyber malware penetrations of industrial control systems that are not reported as causing actual cyber or control system damage or identifiable degradation of critical infrastructure performance.[59]

Western infrastructure is a target for several kinds of "threat actors" including nation-state hackers, cyber-criminals, cyber-terrorists, and hacktivists. Protection of critical infrastructure is a pillar of any government's cyber-strategy. The cyber-space is recognized

---

[58] "About the Industrial Control Systems Cyber Emergency Response Team." Department of Homeland Security, US-CERT. n.d. Accessed September 30, 2016. https://ics-cert.us-cert.gov/About-Industrial-Control-Systems-Cyber-Emergency-Response-Team.

[59] Many cyber operations result in delayed ICS-CERT reporting. For example, since at least the year 2006 a Chinese cyber-attack program within the 2nd Bureau of the 3rd Department (3PLA) of China's People's Liberation Army (PLA), led by Wang Dong with internet handle "UglyGorilla," designed and executed malware operations affecting industrial control systems within the energy sector of the U.S. and Canada. Cyber-attacks by "UglyGorilla" and PLA associates targeted an advanced nuclear power plant designed by Westinghouse and energy pipeline designs, including control and compressor systems for gas pipelines upon which U.S. electric utilities rely for about 33% of net electric generation as of year 2016. See David E. Sanger, David Barboza, and Nocile Perlroth, "Chinese Army Unit Is Seen as Tied to Hacking Against U.S." New York Times, Feb. 13, 2013. For additional background on Chinese cyber operations against U.S. critical infrastructure see U.S. Department of Justice, Indictment of Wang Dong, et al., District Court, Western District of Pennsylvania, May 1, 2014, Criminal Case No. 14-118. For a broader review of cyber vulnerabilities of U.S. energy infrastructure, see Nell Nelson, with Rob VanderBrink, Advisor, The Impact of Dragonfly Malware on Industrial Control Systems, SANS Institute, 2016. DRAGONFLY also known as ENERGETIC BEAR, targeted aviation and defense industries and since year 2012 the U.S. energy sector. This SANS Institute report explains that associated HAVEX software "enabled the [Russian] espionage group to collect network and equipment information valuable for the execution of a later attack." For additional information on foreign cyber targeting of the U.S. energy sector see FBI Special Agent William E. Ebersole, "Pipeline Cybersecurity Issues from Marcellus and Beyond," Pipeline & Gas Journal, Vol. 243, No. 9, Sep. 2016.

as the fifth domain of warfare, and militaries around the globe are improving their capabilities in order to protect national assets from cyber-attacks.

The expanding cyber-attack threat space now includes a sophisticated malware "dropper" originating in Russia, designated by Western European security analysis as Stealthy Furtim Malware (SFM). Furtim (Latin for *stealth*), has been identified as operating within energy and other critical infrastructures by at least March 2016. Though first widely reported in Europe in May 2016, the DHS ICS-CERT public-facing website through September 2016 provides no warnings or indications of Furtim capabilities and characteristics.

Furtim may represent a new generation of malware designed to perform a reconnaissance of cyber-attack detection and defense capabilities; to serve as a decision-aid to select malware appropriate for non-detectable intrusions; and to enable malware insertions and persistence during an extended period without target system detection. In fact, Furtim will not install itself if it identifies on the target machine one of an extensive list of security products (both common and esoteric), sandbox, or virtualization environments.

A new generation of non-detectable malware targeting industrial control systems could be an indicator that the scope, duration, and residual damage from cyber-attacks on the energy sector and other critical infrastructures may be more comprehensive than is generally assessed.[60]

Protective Actions for Solar Storms
Solar storms, also known by the technical term Geomagnetic Disturbance (GMD), disrupt electric grid operations by inducing harmful current—Geomagnetically Induced Current (GIC)—in long-distance transmission lines and the high-voltage transformers at the ends of these lines. GIC saturates transformers, causing harmonics and overheating. Resulting reactive power consumption can cause voltage collapse. Hard-to-replace high-voltage transformers may catastrophically fail. Protective actions for solar storm include:

- Install GMD monitoring and/or blocking devices at select locations, based on network vulnerability analysis.
- Provide additional spare equipment to selected substations.
- Standardize, to the greatest degree possible, major equipment to facilitate replacement.
- Replace vulnerable large power transformers with modified designs that are more resistant to GIC.
- Shed load to reduce transformer reactive power consumption and overheating.

---

[60] See Joseph Landry and Udi Shamir, "Malware Discovered—SFM: Furtim Malware Analysis," July 14, 2016; J. P. Buntinx, "New Furtim Malware Can Shut Down European Power Grid Facilities," Merkle News, July 19, 2016; and Yotam Gottesman, "Analyzing Furtim: Malware that Avoids Mass-Infection," Breaking Malware, May 16, 2016.

Protective Actions for an Electromagnetic Pulse Attack

When a nuclear weapon is detonated in the upper atmosphere, it generates a series of electromagnetic pulses that radiate downward, covering a circular area at ground level within the line of sight of the blast. A very short but intense pulse, the "E1" pulse, causes conductors attached to electronic equipment to act like antennas, coupling transient pulses with peak amplitudes in the thousands of volts.[61] A long-duration, low-amplitude pulse, the E3 pulse, induces currents in long-distance transmission lines. Induced currents can saturate high-voltage transformers. Risk factors for EMP include:

- The most troublesome aspect of an EMP attack to the power system is the E1 pulse, the extremely high-amplitude, but ultra-short-duration pulse that has the potential to damage solid-state electronics. The majority of protective relays on the transmission system are digital (hence, solid state) and the old, traditional electro-mechanical relays are being replaced by digital devices. Electro-mechanical devices are thought to be immune to the E1 pulse, but they are only minimally in service and spare parts are equally difficult to obtain.
- The degree to which the digital relays would be damaged in an EMP attack is unknown. Some testing of digital relays has been done, but no comprehensive testing program has been completed.

If the digital relays undergo damage or upset requiring manual reset as the result of an EMP attack, the ability to provide protection to the major transmission equipment would be compromised, if not eliminated. The challenge at that point is whether the equipment could be operated or removed from service. Obviously, removing a large number of power system elements threatens the operational viability of the network.

Given the complexity of the electric power grid, it is unlikely that the entire grid can be protected against EMP effects with confidence. Thus, a limited, protected monitoring and control architecture is needed to support decision making on what generating and transmission and load-balancing assets within the grid (including generation "grid islands" and "cranking paths") need priority "hardening" for interoperability. Considerations in prioritizing should include public safety, affordability, relative importance to grid recovery operations, synergies with priorities for recovery of other critical infrastructures, and conservation of scarce fuels. These decisions should also take into account protection against other threats to the grid (i.e., physical and cyber attacks). Note that protection against man-made EMP threats will ensure protection against natural EMP threats (solar storms)—the converse is not true. Specific protective actions for EMP could include:

---

[61] International Electrotechnical Commission (IEC) Standard 61000-2-10, HEMP Conducted Environments.

Transformer protection, both neutral ground blockers and transient voltage suppression devices (metal oxide varistors known as "MOVs" or spark gaps) are used for E3 and E1 protection, respectively.[62]

Mobile command centers are EMP-protected and could back up and, if needed, take the place of burned out control systems.

SCADA systems are EMP-protected and cyber-protected, replacing the current systems that are vulnerable to both EMP and cyber-attack.

Digital Relays to increase the ability to survive an EMP attack, shielding should be considered. It is possible to house the relays in Faraday cages to shield them from the E1 pulse. Also, spare relays could be stored in Faraday cages to ensure that they would be available after an attack. The issue of shielding the control cables that bring the data from the sensing devices to the relays is more troublesome. The control cables are often copper and provide a convenient antenna to conduct the pulse to the relays. Control cables could be replaced with fiber optics to eliminate the threat. Absent replacements, some alternative methods to isolate the cables from the relays should be investigated.

Protective relays are usually installed with redundancy, meaning that there are backup relays standing behind the primary protection schemes. Given the threats associated with EMP, it would appear prudent to either protect (shield) the back-up relays, or consider replacement with electro-mechanical relays.

FLEX warehouses are EMP-protection supporting equipment for nuclear power plants, or hardening of the spare equipment, or some combination thereof.

Manual generator restart procedures should be developed and practiced. Many generation stations depend exclusively on electronic industrial control systems to operate and restart generators. If manual restart procedures do not already exist or if they have been forgotten, generator operators should develop and regularly practice manual restart protocols.

Large load centers are used because generators cannot restart unless they have a large enough connected load. Identification and protection of large load centers such as pumping stations or factories would expedite recovery. In some cases, installation of protected load banks may be necessary.

---

[62] Installation of protective devices to block ultrafast E1 pulses may increase the magnitude of E3 pulses experienced by transformers without neutral blockers installed. It is essential to "take into account all EMP pulses (E1, E2, and E3)" to avert "unintended gaps in protection." See Idaho National Laboratory, Strategies, Protections, and Mitigations for the Electric Grid from Electromagnetic Pulse Effects, INL/EXT-15-35582, January 2016, p. iv and p. 23.

Steps to Aid Grid Recovery

No protection of electric grids from physical attack, cyber-attack, solar storms, and electromagnetic pulse can be 100% effective. Therefore, emergency planning should include steps to aid grid recovery. Such steps could include blackstart equipment and procedures, backup generation, stocking of spares, mutual assistance agreements, priority protection of cranking paths to nuclear power plants, and resilient microgrids. Modeling of electric grids under scenarios of equipment damage and broken connectivity should be conducted before any emergency.[63]

These restoration steps should be guided by architectural decision-making associated with priorities established among and within various "grid islands" of the electric grid, so as to ensure the best possible utilization of limited resources. Nuclear power plants should be assigned a high priority because of: (1) the potential radiation threat if the safety measures, cooling capabilities, and control systems are not restored in a timely way; and (2) the extraordinary generating capacity that can be enabled by use of on-site nuclear fuel assemblies, for months or years through conversion of nuclear fuel into baseload electrical energy once the power reactors are brought back on-line.

Blackstart Equipment and Procedures

Under grid reliability standards, electric utilities are required to establish blackstart equipment and procedures. Hydroelectric plants, coal-fired plants, and gas-fired plants are commonly used for blackstart. "Cranking paths" are then employed between blackstart plants and other generation facilities such as nuclear plants. However, blackstart equipment may not be protected against EMP or cyber-attack. The blackstart process requires that generators have adequate loads, which means that a minimum set of load systems will need to be protected or quickly restored. Regular practice of blackstart under scenarios that include equipment damage is important.

Backup Generation

Backup generation is commonly available for critical infrastructure. However, availability of diesel fuel for generators is one of the most important issues facing the power sector if there is a long-term widespread power outage. Diesel fuel cannot be kept for long periods of time. It becomes moldy, oxidizes, or otherwise degrades without special additives. Generally, businesses keep enough diesel fuel for one to three days of generator use. Nuclear power plants generally have a minimum of seven days of diesel fuel, and since the SAFER program took effect in year 2012 most nuclear power plants have significantly expanded on-site diesel storage capacity. Military installations may have 10 days of fuel;

---

[63] See Vladimir Gurevich, "Protecting power systems from destructive electromagnetic fields," Transmission and Distribution (2015): 36-37 on planning for equipment sparing.

and military facilities designated as Tier 1 facilities have significant resiliency programs underway to extend base operability after loss of commercial grid power.

Commonly stored quantities of diesel fuel would not protect critical infrastructure sectors through a long-term outage (LTO) lasting weeks or months. Consequently, in preparing for an LTO and taking into account that communications will be very difficult, it would be beneficial to have a plan in place that would automatically be executed when the power fails in a region:

- Emergency stocks of fuel would be prepositioned.
- Tanker trucks would be filled with fuel; truck models should be tested to ensure operability following E1 exposure.
- The trucks could deliver the fuel to the priority customers that may include prepositioning of emergency stocks of fuel.
- Emergency stocks of fuel would be prepositioned.
- The trucks could deliver the fuel to the priority customers that may include:
    - Water and wastewater treatment plants;
    - Control facilities for electric grids;
    - Blackstart generation facilities;
    - Critical telecommunications nodes;
    - Nuclear power plants and other nuclear infrastructures with hot fuel rods;
    - Prisons;
    - Hospitals and healthcare facilities; and
    - Government buildings used for emergency management, including the National Guard, police, fire stations, and operations centers.

Stocking of Spares

Not all electric grid facilities can be preemptively protected on a cost-effective basis. In these instances, stocking of spares and pre-positioning may be the best strategy. For example, large electric utilities have worked together to form Grid Assurance LLC, a company that stockpiles large power transformers, circuit breakers, and other critical grid equipment. The Fixing America's Surface Transportation (FAST) Act (Pub. L. No. 114-94), signed into law in December 2015, requires the U.S. Secretary of Energy to submit to Congress a plan for a Strategic Transformer Reserve.

Mutual Assistance

Mutual assistance among utility companies is an emergency measure with proven success for weather-related outages. Edison Electric Institute (EEI) coordinates Regional Mutual Assistance Groups (RMAGs) for investor-owned electric utilities in seven regions of the United States (see Figure 9). Each region receives communications backup support from other designated regions. However, for wide-area outages caused by physical attack, cyber-attack, solar storms, or EMP attack, mutual assistance cannot be assured.

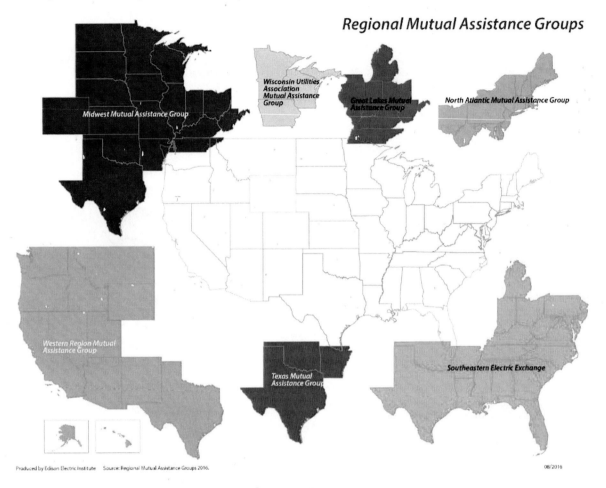

Figure 9: Regional Mutual Assistance Groups (RMAGs) as of October 2014.[64]

Beyond the Regional Mutual Assistance Group system for regional blackouts, Edison Electric Institute (EEI) coordinates and supports a National Event Response Plan, via a National Response Team, in the event of a nationwide system blackout. EEI also supports the Electric Sector Coordinating Council (ESCC) of the Department of Homeland Security, which can provide intelligence and other information sharing and federal emergency assistance. The various RMAG regions provide backup communications and logistics support to each other. EEI has a National Power Restoration Plan to address larger grid blackouts. However, with extended geographic scope and duration of a projected grid outage, how realistic is the National Power Restoration Plan in the absence of more

---

[64] Map produced by Edison Electric Institute's Project Support Group, as published in <u>NARUC, Regional Mutual Assistance Groups: A Primer</u>, November 2015, reformatted courtesy of Edison Electric Institute, Aug. 2016.

extensive pre-outage protections for vulnerable grid equipment with long replacement times?[65]

Mutual assistance between companies during emergencies takes several forms. During more routine emergencies (e.g., high loads due to extreme weather or loss of a large unit), neighboring NERC Balancing Authorities (BAs) have emergency assistance provisions for capacity and energy, per mandatory NERC standards. These are bilateral and trilateral agreements between private companies that are generally not publicly available.

In addition to one-to-one assistance, a number of entities have joined together to form Reserve Sharing Groups (RSGs), which allow sharing of emergency assistance among multiple companies. An example is the Northwest Power Pool.[66] Most NERC regions publicly post summaries of RSGs. The SERC region has several RSGs summarized in its Contingency Reserve Policy.[67]

For storm restoration efforts that are primarily distribution-related, but can also include transmission and generation if impacted, mutual assistance organizations have been in place for decades. The most notable mutual assistance agreement for storm restoration is the Southeastern Electric Exchange (SEE). Started in the 1930s, the SEE name is a bit misleading today in that participants range from New Mexico to New York and Florida to parts of Michigan and Illinois.[68]

For Bulk Electric System (BES) facilities, mutual assistance is covered by other organizations and groups. A good public resource for information about these is the NERC report on its Spare Equipment Database System (SEDS).[69] Although the report was published in 2011 and therefore does not include information on new groups like Grid Assurance LLC, it provides a good description of the SEDS and also describes and links other efforts (e.g., Edison Electric Institute's STEP program).[70]

Resilient Microgrids

Local power generation and storage could become essential for the survival of most technology-based communities in the event of a long-term regional or nationwide power outage. However, there is a broad range of how microgrids might be defined, designed, financed and built. Microgrids must be specifically planned to be operational during the worst-case, high-impact threats.

---

[65] For the Edison Electric Institute overview of the electric grid system restoration process, see Understanding the Electric Power Industry's Response and Restoration Process, June 2016. 7 pp.
[66] See http://www.nwpp.org/our-resources/NWPP-Reserve-Sharing-Group.
[67] See http://www.serc1.org/docs/default-source/program-areas/standards-regional-criteria/regional-criteria/serc-reg-criteria_contingency-reserve-policy-rev-6-(10-28-14).pdf
[68] For more information about SEE, reference http://www.theexchange.org/aboutus.html.
[69] Available at http://www.nerc.com/docs/pc/sedtf/SEDTF_Report_Draft_PC_Meeting_2.pdf.
[70] For more information on Grid Assurance, see http://www.gridassurance.com.

Moreover, if microgrids are to be relied on to provide blackstart services that aid in restoration of the bulk electric system, the microgrids could be designed to support grid stability during the system restoration process. In particular, such microgrid assets should be designed to counteract conditions of under-voltage or over-voltage, or under-frequency or over-frequency conditions.[71]

Here is a simple worst case scenario: Imagine a 6- to 18-month nationwide power outage where no help is coming to a community or facility from areas outside since adjoining areas will have their own problems. In the case of a no-notice EMP or cyber-attack, a key way to survive might be to have local power and energy storage, such as microgrids, and networks of microgrids that are protected from the very threat that brought down the regional power grid.

In the case of an EMP or cyber-attack, the electronic controls that could be used by power utilities to disconnect or "grid island" local facilities would likely be damaged themselves. A way a facility or campus can be assured that they can continue to operate is to be already pre-islanded, which means that it can be manually separable or separated instantly and protected from the very threats that impact the regional grid to which they are connected.

Under current Nuclear Regulatory Commission safety regulations, rapid shutdown of U.S. commercial power plants is required in the event of loss of outside power, known as a "LOOP event." The immediate problem then becomes how to provide limited power to ensure the nuclear plant is safe until sufficient power is available to restart normal power reactor operations. Equipment requiring electricity includes the control facilities, the security systems, and spent fuel cooling and monitoring systems. Blackstart ("system restoration") plans, with allowable cost recovery, are operational components of the bulk power system, supported by exercises and training.

The U.S. military already has EMP protection approaches that are tested and well-understood. For more than a half-century, military-installed command and control systems for nuclear response have been protected against EMP attacks. Regional civilian grids have not yet been designed for this capability, nor have the majority of commercial microgrids.

Were microgrids to seek participation in blackstart programs, they would require both tested resilience and capabilities to meet system restoration reliability criteria previously adopted by NERC and approved by FERC. Most microgrids presently lack the capability and regulatory approvals needed to participate in blackstart of the bulk electric system.

The potential benefits of EMP-protected civilian microgrids underpin a May 2015 request for proposal (RFP) from the Defense Threat Reduction Agency (DTRA). This RFP asked for

---

[71] Presentation by Gerry Cauley, CEO, North American Electric Reliability Corporation, Electric Infrastructure Security Summit VII, London, July 18, 2016.

solutions to civilian critical infrastructure on which military bases and defense critical infrastructure depend (see "Island-Mode Enhancement Strategies and Methodologies for Defense Critical Infrastructure"; SBIR Topic DTRA 152-006). Military bases not only need to ensure that their critical applications and power sources are EMP protected, but they need to be certain that the civilian applications on which they depend are also protected—despite the military's lack of control over civilian infrastructure and financing to pay for it is protection.

Resilient microgrids should have on- or near-site power generation sources and storage. Sources could be from solar, wind, geothermal, or hydro, while storage could be from batteries and other power storage methods. These local (on- or near-site) sources should have the protections discussed in this chapter just like is recommended for the centralized grid. Critical functions could be continuously powered by a microgrid so that those functions would operate automatically if the centralized grid were to fail. These critical functions could be powered from the microgrid on a permanent basis as well.

Planners could start local. A core system is one that can be built and operated entirely within the property lines of a given organization. This is the simplest way to start and might be all that is needed. A modular design can take future modules and expansion into account. A single property microgrid can also be linked with others next to them or in their community into a larger microgrid that can share resources. Once connection to a neighboring property is undertaken, management, technical, and often regulatory issues need to be addressed, most often through the participation of a utility or energy cooperative. As noted above, microgrids associated with nuclear power plant operations could constitute an important initiative.

It is essential to build a microgrid system from the bottom up with a clear understanding of user requirements, environmental constraints, and reliability standards for interconnections. Individual systems can be built that are inherently capable of being islanded in real time without the assistance of outside network or power management systems that might be disrupted or damaged. Most so-called "smart grids" might be damaged before they can switch local power sources into a grid island mode. The most efficient and resilient way to have microgrids operate in grid island mode is to have that protection built-in.

Basic methodologies for microgrids are already available. Local communications and power systems that meet military standards such as the MIL STD 188.125 have EMP filters at the demarcation between the EMP-protected facility and the non-EMP-protected grid or communications system. This protection, if not bypassed inappropriately, can prevent a pulse from being carried through a conductor to the protected power or communications system. Similarly, every single conductive penetration into that protected environment needs to be assessed, protected, or eliminated, and to be inspected from time to time to ensure system integrity.

With proper protection, microgrids can continue to operate without interruption during EMP events, shedding non-essential loads and relying on local generation and storage. In the future, microgrids that utilize renewable generation capabilities may be able to facilitate blackstart of regional electric grids.[72]

Transforming Nuclear Power Plants: From Blackstart Liabilities Into Blackstart Assets

The Nuclear Regulatory Commission has an opportunity to develop a Demonstration Program to authorize back fitting and augmentation of existing nuclear power plants, associated blackstart generating facilities and "cranking paths" to ensure reliable blackstart re-operation of nuclear generating facilities. To meet safety requirements, applicants are likely to be required to demonstrate availability of reliable on-site and off-site backup electric power to ensure safe shutdown, protection of spent fuel pools, and reliable operation of control and security systems. Appropriate criteria for cost recovery may involve both the Nuclear Regulatory Commission and the Federal Energy Regulatory Commission (which authorizes blackstart cost recovery), and state public utility commissions.

---

[72] See Chapter VI on microgrids and Appendix 5 on Blackstart. NERC CEO Gerry W. Cauley recently cautioned that microgrid operators seeking to participate in system restoration of the bulk electric system need to: provide adequate reactive power; offset under-voltage or over-voltage conditions when interconnecting; and offset frequency discrepancies. Without stabilizing capabilities to support grid interconnection, and without adequate training and system restoration exercise participation, off-grid renewable generating facilities may inadvertently cause the collapse of system restoration. See remarks of Gerry W. Cauley, Electric Infrastructure Security Council, London, July 18, 2016.

Chapter V: Enhancing Preparedness of Other Critical Infrastructures

This chapter is devoted to a select number of the 15 Critical Infrastructure (CI) Sectors. This subset serves to illustrate the preparedness needed in all CI Sectors because they are all dependent on electrical power and, in turn, impact the availability of the electrical power.

As discussed in Chapter III, Presidential Policy Directive (PPD) 21, issued by President Obama in February 2013, established the "policy of the United States to strengthen the security and resilience of its critical infrastructure against both physical and cyber threats." Of particular note, the National Infrastructure Advisory Council (NIAC) subsequently identified the energy, water, communications, and transportation sectors as "lifeline sectors" that warrant consideration as top priorities for strengthening resilience.

Consistent with the above NIAC designation, this chapter addresses lifeline sectors water/wastewater, communications, and transportation. The chapter also discusses several additional sectors, including agriculture/food, public health and medical, finance, and emergency services–security.

Water & Wastewater

Various studies, such as the Regional Catastrophic Preparedness Grant Program (RCPGP) Supply Chain Resilience Project, have found that a long-term loss of the water sector (drinking water or wastewater) could prove to have particularly catastrophic consequences.

The water sector in is highly, if not totally, dependent upon the commercial electric grid. Large pumps, motors, and other equipment needed to treat and move water require large amounts of electricity, often making water and wastewater utilities the largest electricity user in a particular jurisdiction. In many cases, without commercial electric power, large pumps and other equipment stop and can be difficult to restart.

Chapter II of the Report to the President by the National Infrastructure Advisory Council on "Water Sector Resilience: Final Report and Recommendations", July 2016, highlights interdependencies and the rapid degradation of other critical infrastructure sectors if the water sector loses either water utility service, wastewater service, or both.

The District of Columbia Water and Sewer Authority, known as "DC Water," provides more than 600,000 residents, 700,000 employees, and 17.8 million annual visitors with water and wastewater treatment services. They also treat wastewater from an additional 1.6 million people in Maryland and Virginia. Due to the size of their operations, DC Water is the largest electricity user in the District, and their Blue Plains Advanced Wastewater

Treatment Plant alone uses roughly 25 megawatts of electricity to pump, filter, aerate, and disinfect about 370 million gallons of effluent every day. This is about the same amount of electricity needed to power 16,250 residential homes (assuming 1MW can serve about 650 residential homes).

Lessons learned from Hurricane Sandy include that, as the lack of electrical power continued for days:

- Generators started to break down, because most generators are not created for continuous use for days or weeks;

- Competition for generators increased as the outage continued;

- Some emergency managers did not understand the need for the water sector to have generators;

- Fuel became a serious issue;[73] and

- In the eight hardest-hit states, about 11 billion gallons of untreated and partially treated sewage (including 3.45 billion gallons of raw sewage) flowed into rivers, bays, canals, and, in some cases, city streets.[74]

Note that Sandy's effects lasted several weeks, not months. The American Water Works Association (AWWA) in their after action report on Hurricane Sandy stated that giving the water/wastewater sector priority for generators and fuel during power outages is important.[75]

One of the goals during a long-term power outage would be to keep people in their homes. In a severe scenario, there would be no place for the population to flee because no reachable destination would have power. If water and wastewater are available, people are more likely to remain in their homes. Without water, there could be a "tipping point" beyond which lives will be lost. FEMA Administrator Craig Fugate has remarked that loss of

---

73 See EIS Council (EPRO) Handbook II, Vol. 1—Fuel, July 2016, pp. 26-29, 52, 60, 94-97, 126-144; and EIS Council (EPRO) Handbook II, Vol. 2, Water July 2016, pp. 73, 179, 183-185, 198, 218. Available at http://www.eiscouncil.com/App_Data/Upload/7f41c325-654e-4c67-be3d-6941645f4485.pdfhttp://www.eiscouncil.com/App_Data/Upload/7f41c325-654e-4c67-be3d-6941645f4485.pdf.

74 Storm surges flooded sewage treatment plants. See Alyson Kenward, Daniel Yawitz, and Urooj Raja, Sewage Overflows from Hurricane Sandy, Climate Central, 2013.

75 E-Pro Handbook II Volume 2, Water, ibid., p 222

water service threatens lives and urges, "Keep the water on." [76] Ideally, the highest priority for generators, fuel, chemical distribution, and maintenance materials would be the water/wastewater systems.

There are more than 160,000 water and wastewater systems.[77] Only 8 percent of Americans get their water from small Community Water Systems, while 92 percent get their water from only 410 large Community Water Systems. Likewise, only 383 wastewater systems serve the large population centers, while there are over 11,000 private works serving small-population cities.[78] Concentrating on these large systems would serve most of the population. Many of the water utilities have found it very cost effective obtain generators "just-in-time" as they are needed in lieu of owning them. Unfortunately, obtaining "just-in-time" generators may not be possible in the scenarios described in this book.

Funding resilience is a significant issue because of the other competing demands on funding for this sector. Aging equipment requires substantial investment, and the costs can run in the hundreds of billions[79] (e.g., recent water crisis in Flint, Michigan). It will be important that citizens understand how important the funding is for water/wastewater, and that approvals for these investments are required from utility boards of directors and various government officials. It is also important to realize that the American public pays less for their water/wastewater than other developed nations.[80]

There are different ways that the Water and Wastewater Sector can be more prepared. Backup generators for drinking water and wastewater increase system resiliency. Generators (or alternative capability) large enough to provide the minimum amount of water needed for 72–96 hours are essential, but far from sufficient for long-term outages. Ideally, there should be generator capacity and fuel for 30 days at a minimum.

As noted above, many water systems have now found that "just-in-time" generators are more cost effective than owning their own generators. Key points in this regard include the following:

---

76 Ibid pp. 107-113

77 Ibid p. 190

78 Ibid pp. 123-125

79 E-Pro Handbook II Volume 2/Water

80 Ibid pp. 94-100

- In addition to adequate generator capacity, there should be generators and repair parts on hand to repair or replace generators that break down during sustained use.

- Dual-fuel generators (i.e., diesel and an alternate fuel) should be used when possible. Unfortunately, these generators are being replaced and less common.

- Generators fueled by natural gas tend to have issues during power outages because their compressors and industrial control systems require electric power. Thus, prioritizing gas system restoration is another important preparedness item.[81]

- Another issue is the limited number of emergency generators in key inventories. For example, FEMA has 400 generators for their 10 regions. The U.S. Army Corps of Engineers has 25 locations with 30 generators each. To provide context for these numbers, there are 160,000 water/waste water systems. Other associated challenges include identifying skilled people capable of installing the generators and handling the logistics of getting the equipment to the right locations.[82]

Scenarios in which utilities have generator outages (or at least an emergency response plan or playbook) for longer than 30 days are recommended. This is a capability that could be developed if not already planned. According to the "EIS Council (EPRO) Handbook II, Vol. 2, Water", the playbook could contain goals, set minimal levels of service, establish emergency plans, and define policy changes required.[83] The National Infrastructure Advisory Council's "Water Sector Resilience Final Report and Recommendations" discusses developing mitigations for water disruptions by analyzing and mapping the risks, fortifying response and recovery capabilities, increasing federal funding for resilience, increasing technical and financial resources, and strengthening federal leadership, coordination and support.[84]

During a long-term or wide-scale power outage, utilities relying on contractors, FEMA, the U.S. Army and/or others for installation of emergency backup power may recognize that they would be competing against numerous other facilities for the same backup power

---

81 Ibid pp. 21

82 Ibid pp. 187-196

83 Ibid pp. 55-58. See also the EIS Council EPRO Handbook II, Vol. 1, Fuel, especially Section 3, "The Structure of the Natural Gas Industry and its Dependence on Electric Power," and Section 4, "Resilience Initiatives within the ONG and Electric Subsectors."

84 National Infrastructure Advisory Council Water Sector Resilience: Final Report and Recommendations, p 4-5 https://www.dhs.gov/sites/default/files/publications/niac-water-resilience-study-draft-06-09-16-508.pdf

resources. Advanced planning ideally would be done by the water sector to develop a strategy for addressing competition for these critical emergency resources.

Where feasible, water and wastewater systems could explore the development of on-site generation, Combined Heat/Power (CHP) systems, and microgrid technology that allows grid or resilient community islanding during a power outage. Microgrid operations can allow for sustained water and wastewater treatment during a long-term power outage, and sometimes provide opportunities for additional benefits (e.g., peak-shaving, re-use of treatment by-products such as biogas, etc.). These resilient systems ideally would be protected from the threats (i.e., cyber, physical and EMP) and would have local power generation and storage. Note that gas supplies may also be integrated in these scenarios.[85]

Shortage of fuel for water sector backup generators was a problem experienced during Hurricane Sandy (2012) and other events. This lesson learned highlights the need for fuel resupply plans are at the state/regional/national level. Such plans ideally would acknowledge the importance of the water sector to public health and safety and to national security. A fuel mitigation strategy could focus on replenishment of fuel stocks—specifically, quickly re-energizing pipelines and related critical infrastructure, and then utilizing current legal authority and relationships to direct available fuel to priority customers. However, the priority customers for an event of this duration will be different than those currently identified for a short-term event.

Delivery of chemicals needed for drinking water and wastewater treatment will likely become very difficult during a long-duration power outage. Treatment chemical resupply plans are needed at the state/regional/national level. Such plans ideally would acknowledge the importance of the water sector to public health and safety and to national security.

The capability to provide ongoing maintenance of the utility systems is paramount. Proper maintenance management practices that include adequate onsite parts bin supplies are integral to any solid plan. Adequate fuel, generators, and chemicals would be no use if the actual water and wastewater equipment fails. Physical maintenance manuals and parts catalogues should be on hand to back up electronic documents.

---

85 The July 2016 NIAC Water Sector Resilience Final Report, explains at p. 20: "The Water Sector relies on energy, specifically electricity, to operate its pumps, treatment facilities, delivery systems, and processing. Long-term power outages can overwhelm a water utility's backup energy supply or deplete fuel reserves. This scenario is worsened if the outage is systemic, in that multiple energy utilities in a region are shut down or multiple water utilities in a region have to compete for scarce backup resources. In addition, energy prioritization—the order in which disrupted sectors obtain energy services—may be an issue for water utilities as they work to restore services."

In managing the water supply, a water mitigation strategy could aim at providing just enough water to sustain most of the population without fully energizing the water system. Typically, when communities are without power, the demand on water is reduced because people and businesses are not running water-intensive appliances, such as washing machines, dishwashers, etc. Utilities could also define level of service goals for long-term emergencies (e.g., water quantity, quality, etc.).

One possible level of service goal might be average winter daily demand since this is typically significantly lower than water demand during other times of the year. Emergency response plans/playbooks ideally would reflect these reduced levels of service goals.

- For example, if water & wastewater systems were re-engineered to provide just 20% of capacity, recoverable within 24 hours, one could sustain wastewater system pressure, and support emergency water rationing. Huge waste of water is a cushion. In addition, as California Governor Pete Wilson found, an auction of private potable water would generate additional water supplies.

- The E-Pro Handbook contains a table showing what is maintained at near normal service, reduced service and then at no water. To maintain near normal service would require extensive funding to be prepared for long-term wide area power outages. Having no water service is so devastating that ideally the nation would set a goal to prepare for reduced service.[86] This would mean that fire departments could respond to fires, sanitation services could continue, and hospitals and the military could have service. Citizens would have to treat water for it to be potable. Waivers would be required for this service level.[87]

Local emergency water distribution plans (e.g., bottled water and bulk water) are needed to allow people to shelter in place, avoid a public health emergency, and avoid mass evacuations of large urban areas. Because bottled water would last for a short time, and boiling water would probably not be feasible, water would need to be treated. The Red Cross has recommendations that they could provide to citizens now so that the population

---

86 The July 2016 NIAC Water Sector Resilience Final Report, relying on a Report by Lloyd's and Atmospheric and Environmental Research, Solar Storm Risks to the North American Electric Grid, June 2013, addresses risks of extended electric grid outages in an extreme geomagnetic storm, projecting "widespread impacts that cross State lines and cause severe damage to transformers and other electrical equipment." The NIAC report explains: "The expected duration of the [solar storm-derived] outages could range from 16 days to up to two years depending on the availability of replacement electrical transformers. The associated loss of water service can be expected to be of similar severity." p. 26.

87 E-Pro Handbook II Volume 2, Water pp. 137-150

would have the needed tablets or equipment.[88] The National Guard has a process for treating water.[89] However, it is important to understand the gap between these possible partial remedies and actual population requirements.

Lack of adequate wastewater resources would quickly make home offices, police stations, hospitals, nursing homes, and emergency operation centers unusable. Keeping people in their homes and avoiding the "tipping point" is critical. After the earthquake in Christ Church, New Zealand, they used chemical toilets. This would not be feasible in a severe scenario, however, and thus keeping the wastewater facilities operational is a priority goal.[90]

Enhanced local outreach and education efforts are also needed to encourage individuals to "make a plan" and have their own water resources to sustain themselves for at least 96 hours and, ideally, for sustained outages. The outreach and education efforts could provide guidance on the following:

- How much water is needed per person, per day. The Centers for Disease Control and Prevention (CDC) recommends 1 gallon of water per day for each person and each pet (http://www.cdc.gov/healthywater/emergency/drinking/creating-storing-emergency-water-supply.html)

- How to develop a personal water supply for long duration events (e.g., home potable water and non-potable water purification systems, portable water pumps, etc.).

- How to protect human health and the environment by constructing a provisional toilet.

Excellent information about emergency water supply preparation, sanitation, and hygiene can be found at: http://www.cdc.gov/healthywater/emergency/drinking/emergency-water-supply-preparation.html

Degradation or loss of ordinary communications capabilities will affect water and wastewater services. A communications mitigation strategy could accept the long-term failure of most normal communications channels and focus on extensive pre-disaster preparedness activities by decision-makers and the general public.

---

88 Ibid pp. 146-148

89 Ibid p 116

90 Ibid pp. 210-213

State and federal government have an important role to play in setting priorities and creating the needed waivers. For example, the Clean Air Act standards would need to be modified to allow waivers in the event of a severe scenario.[91] The E-Pro Handbook had several suggestions for creating functions that could address the water/wastewater planning and needs. One would be creation of a "National Emergency Power Council (NEPC)" to plan, survey and determine needs.[92] Another is to create a "National Emergency Utility Consumables Council (NEUCC)" that would concentrate on plans for critical infrastructure giving priority to water, wastewater, and chemicals.[93] Department of Homeland Security and FEMA could examine the Stafford Act to determine if modifications for public and private utilities would be helpful.[94]

A nationwide rain barrel contingency water storage program, backed by revised state and federal legislation, might be helpful because several states do not allow harvesting of rainwater due to local aquifer and other concerns.[95]

Communications

Americans are accustomed to instant communications and continuous communications in an emergency. Yet without electrical power, how will people communicate and learn what is happening in a major emergency?

> *Basic AM/FM Radios:* Everyone, either individually or as member of a household, should have a basic AM/FM radio that uses batteries or ideally is hand cranked. In addition, cars also invariably have basic AM/FM radios. Given that the internet will likely not be operational, in emergencies, citizens would use these AM/FM radios to receive information, primarily from community stations with emergency broadcasting capabilities. Transmission power for these stations is typically limited, so reception ranges are also limited.

> *Point-to-Point Radios:* Some individuals may have low-power point-to-point radios for two-way communications with others in the immediate vicinity. Effective receiving distance may be a mile or less.

---

91 Ibid p 20

92 Ibid p 218

93 Ibid p 223

94 Ibid p 102

95 See S. A. Loper, Rainwater Harvesting: State Regulations and Technical Resources, Pacific Northwest Laboratory, Report PNNL-24347, June 2015; National Conference of State Legislatures, "State Rainwater Harvesting Laws and Legislation," May 13, 2016.

Citizen Band Radios: These unlicensed two-way radios are useful on a campus or in immediate neighborhoods.

Amateur (or Ham) Radios: These two-way radios, used for non-commercial purposes, provide another communications option. Use requires passing a test to obtain the needed license, but the process is comparatively easy if the applicant goes through local radio clubs sponsored by the Amateur Radio Relay League. Ham radios may be used for short, medium, and long distance, with transmitting power and the type of antenna as the key variables. Note: in WWII amateur radio was not allowed, and many Ham radio operators helped the government using their equipment. That might happen again in a major disaster such as an extended grid failure. As one recent example, in Joplin, MO, on May 22, 2011, amateur radio operators helped to re-establish communications in the aftermath of the devastating tornados. To learn more about amateur radio, go to <u>www.AARL.org</u>.

Radio Amateur Civilian Emergency Service (RACES): RACES is an emergency communication protocol created by FEMA. The protocol is widely used to train amateur radio operators and other volunteers who support emergency communications relied on by local governments.

Civil AIR Patrol (CAP) and the U.S. Coast Guard Auxiliary: Both volunteer organizations have significant communications capabilities and could be called upon for emergency communications.

Military Auxiliary Radio System (MARS): This is supplemental communication system for DOD. MARS is similar to Ham radio, but uses separate frequencies reserved for military purposes and restricted to those licensed to participate.

FEMA National Radio System (FNARS): FEMA created FNARS to provide robust high frequency communications capability in emergency continuity of operations scenarios. FNARS links the U.S. military and most federal public safety agencies with most of the states. FNARS also enables the President to access the Emergency Alert System.

SHARES: The SHAred RESources (SHARES) High Frequency (HF) Radio program, administered by the DHS National Coordinating Center for Communications (NCC), provides an additional means for users with a national security and emergency preparedness mission to communicate when landline and cellular communications are unavailable. SHARES members use existing HF radio resources to coordinate and transmit messages needed to perform critical functions, including those areas related to leadership, safety, maintenance of law and order, finance, and public health.[96]

Other Communications Options: Highway road signs powered by solar panels and batteries and deployed strategically are another alternative for communicating emergency messages. Another possibility is dropping leaflets from planes, but limited fuel supplies would likely be allocated to higher priorities. One of the best overall approaches could be having people go to

---

[96] DHS website: www.dhs/SHARES

neighborhood sites for the critical news they will need at various times during the extended emergency.

Transportation

Transportation has many different modes, all of which need to be prepared for terrorism and other high impact disasters. The sector getting critical supplies—including food, pharmaceuticals, fuel, and materials to restart the grid—to their destinations in predictably difficult conditions. For example, during a long term power outage, gangs could try to hijack transportation assets or break into transportation facilities in order to obtain fuel, food, supplies, etc. Consequently, transportation assets and facilities will need protection.

Major ports would be extraordinarily important in an extended grid failure scenario. Relevant considerations include the following:

- Many ports contain hazardous chemicals that could explode or contaminate the environment. In scenarios involving a sustained loss of power to the port, the Coast Guard may exercise its authority to close the port to prevent or contain hazardous conditions. Guidelines for restoration of port operations are typically addressed in Coast Guard contingency plans.
- Intermodal transfer safety considerations would also be significant (e.g., Liquid Natural Gas (LNG) shipments).
- Cranes are essentially indispensable for offloading cargo, and they are typically powered by diesel. In part to reduce air pollution, owners of large cranes in most seaports are substituting all-electric cranes for those operated by diesel fuel or LNG.
- Ships make their own power, but federal air quality regulations restrict them from using their own power when in a port. Governors would have the authority to provide emergency relief from many regulatory constraints on ship-based electric supply to critical port operations. Ports may need to be pre-configured and pre-planned to safely accept ship-based power before an emergency involving an extended regional or national electric blackout.[97]
- Coast Guard and other government officials could exercise existing emergency powers to give priority access to, or authorize mandatory cargo removals from, ports for reasons

---

[97] Port transportation planners "have begun to re-evaluate their emergency preparedness and recovery plans and incorporate new features for ensuring that power generation is either maintained or quickly recovers following a major disruption to power lines or to the electric grid. Loss of regional grid-based power supply can become a 'single point of failure' issue in some ports (note: no power means no fuel pumps working)… All respondents mentioned the importance of power at ports, and some port authorities have begun to discuss options such as reversing cold ironing capabilities (the practice of providing shore power to a ship so the ship may shut down primary and secondary combustion engines while in port) to allow vessels to power the marine terminals."

 "One possible option suggested for consideration involved drawing power from nuclear powered Navy ships (or submarines). However, the process of how exactly to tap into this ship power safely and to the satisfaction of the power companies has yet to be solved. "National Cooperative Freight Research Program, Making U.S. Ports Resilient as Part of Extended Intermodal Supply Chains, Transportation Research Board of the National Academies, 2014, Report No. 30, pp. 35-36.

related to safety, continuity of operations, availability of emergency supplies and/or the flow humanitarian aid. As one example, there may be circumstances in which a port could delay the entry of a car carrier to ensure there is an open berth for an incoming ship with medical supplies.

Still in the maritime realm, sailboats should not be overlooked as a largely energy-independent way to move cargo and fish for food.

Out on the roadways, most traffic signals will not operate without electricity. Powering key traffic signals by solar and/or configure them for portable generator power could prove a wise a capital investment.

Airports are like a small city dependent on electrical power for air traffic control, landing lights, and radar, as well as the terminal operations. Landing lights are mandated by the FAA, and they are ideally powered by diesel. Airports often have their own fire and police departments, or detachments from local jurisdictions. Humanitarian aid may come via air, and key major airports would need to continue operations at some level. Airports could have their own microgrid powered by an alternate source[s] of power. Already major airports (e.g., Denver) are moving in this direction.

Rail is potentially an excellent transportation option in extended grid outages. Many rail systems today depend upon electricity to power trains; others operate on diesel, so availability of diesel will be a major factor. Rail is also dependent on communications, signals and switches. If these are not operational, the rail use can be greatly impeded. In planning for contingencies, it would be important to determine if signals and switches can be manually operated. If so, a policy could be instituted as to when and how. If not, signals and switches in major corridors could be replaced with ones that have a manual override. Also, in various areas around the country, there are tourist railways and museums with coal/wood burning steam engines that could be pressed into service using existing railways to deliver needed supplies.

Interstates will be essential in transporting fuel and other critical supplies. (See State Executives in Chapter VIII– early control of the Interstates early will be important to getting critical supplies to needed locations.) If used by everyone, people may run out of fuel and abandon their vehicles, thus clogging the highways (similar to what often occurs during major snowstorms when private vehicles impede plowing operations). Another consideration is that interstates may have tolls, which are often collected electronically and could have been financed by bonds (entailing legal ramifications if tolls are not collected).

It could be beneficial to amend federal regulations now to restrict the use of Interstate highways in disasters so that the transport of fuel and other critical supplies has priority and to authorize "clearing" transportation arteries for efficient emergency operations.

Also, it could be beneficial for governors and state emergency managers to review and, as needed, to amend state regulations to suspend toll collection in emergencies and/or revise bond language to allow for the suspension of toll collection during a governor or presidentially-declared disaster. Both federal and state authority exists to extend truck driver hours of service and overweight/oversize permits to operate during emergencies. Pre-crisis planning could avert needless implementation delays in actual emergencies.

Tanker trucks often have nozzles that only work with large container tanks at filling stations. The filling station must have a generator to be able to pump gas. If the tanker trucks had exchangeable nozzles and optional lower pressure pump settings, they could pump gas directly into emergency diesel generators, hospital storage facilities, and emergency vehicles. Some states that experience hurricanes have enacted such legislation.

Agriculture/Food

Access to food is often a critical need for those who find themselves impacted by a disaster, whether it is a severe storm, an earthquake, flooding, or some other emergency. To ensure disaster victims have access to food and are provided with enough nutritious food to eat following an incident, the USDA's Food and Nutrition Service (FNS) coordinates with state, local, and non-governmental organizations to:

- Provide shelters and mass care sites with adequate food supplies;
- Distribute food packages directly to households in need; and
- Approve the operation of the Disaster Supplemental Nutrition Assistance Program (D-SNAP).

By engaging in these ways, as part of the National Response Framework, the FNS is able to provide nutrition assistance to those most impacted by a disaster or emergency. In coordination with states, the FNS is also able to provide food supplies to the non-governmental organizations involved in mass care feeding operations or household distribution, such as the Salvation Army and the American Red Cross.

Food intended for use in the USDA National School Lunch Program are most often used for mass care feeding. FNS, in coordination with FEMA and other disaster relief organizations, may also be able to provide infant formula and baby food following a major disaster to support children in shelters.

Disaster relief organizations sometimes have access to USDA foods in small quantities to provide to individual households following a disaster. These smaller packages are mostly obtained from state and recipient agency inventory intended for The Emergency Food Assistance Program, the Commodity Supplemental Food Program, and the Food Distribution Program on Indian Reservations. States must get prior approval before distributing USDA foods from these programs to disaster survivors.

70

FNS also provides food assistance to disaster victims through its Disaster Supplemental Nutrition Assistance Program (D-SNAP). This program provides electronic benefit transfer cards to disaster survivors. During the 2008 hurricane season, USDA and FNS working in conjunction with the Farm Service Agency were able to coordinate with local food distributors and vendors to ship food products to where they were most needed—in some cases, within hours of the requests (USDA/USDI Program Aid No. 1821, March 2011).

Food Banks may also provide an important resource to help meet the food needs of those impacted by a disaster. Food Banks may participate in the Emergency Food Assistance Program or they may work through state agencies to request approval through FNS to operate a household disaster food distribution program using USDA foods.

While the foregoing overview captures a number of options for mass food distribution in emergencies, it is critical to note that these assistance programs are <u>not</u> designed for a catastrophic event impacting the Nation as a whole, such as a long term wide spread grid interruption.

Inadequacy of Emergency Food Stocks

Starting in 2008, USDA altered a longstanding program for central warehouse stockpiling of long shelf-life food in specific quantities needed for large-scale disasters. In years 2009-2010, USDA shifted long-life food stocks to 15 regional warehouses, from which food stocks were distributed without equivalent replenishment. It is ironic that the initiation of the substantial draw down of high level stockpiles of emergency foods roughly coincided with declassification of the Congressional EMP Commission report on challenges to critical national infrastructures in the context of man-made EMP threats to the United States.[98]

It is ironic that the termination of high-level stockpiles of emergency foods previously supported in years 2004-2008,[99] roughly coincided with the declassification of the

---

[98] See Report of the Commission to Assess the Threat to the United States from Electromagnetic Pulse (EMP) Attack, April 2008, especially Chapter 7, "Food Infrastructure," pp. 133-144, which recommends at p. 137, "Federal food stockpiles should be sized to meet a possible large-scale food shortage in the event of massive disruption of the national food infrastructure from an EMP attack or other causes." For a subsequent assessment of disruption risks to U.S. food security in the aftermath of an EMP attack, see Maximilian Leeds, Electronic Pulse and the U.S. Food Security Paradigm: Assumptions, Risks, and Recommendations, 2011. For a review of previous defense stockpiling history, see Chapter 2, "Historical Context," and Appendix A, "Stockpile History," in Committee on Assessing the Need for a Defense Stockpile, National Research Council, Managing Materials for a Twenty-first Century Military, 2008.

[99] In the period 2004-2008 the Administration of President George W. Bush stockpiled emergency foodstocks at warehouses in support of Homeland Security Presidential Directive HSPD-9, "Defense of United States Agriculture and Food," issued on January 30, 2004. In year 2008 the President's Homeland Security Council substituted a "Framework" for the preexisting "National Stockpile Plan." In Fiscal Years 2010 and 2011, the U.S. Department of Agriculture transferred stockpiles for "food and agricultural emergencies" to at least 15

Congressional EMP Commission's Report on challenges to critical national infrastructures in the context of man-made EMP threats to the United States.[100]

In an emergency, food supplies could come primarily from existing inventories of USDA foods stored at state, local, and school warehouses and inventories at local Food Banks.

Food supplies distributed as part of the D-SNAP program may not reach recipients until 72 hours after an event and are designed to be available for a limited period of time, usually up to 7 days. The interruption of the nation's transportation networks caused by the failure of the nation's power grid would further adversely impact the distribution of food to those in need.

So what actions can be taken now to enhance national preparedness to maintain essential food supplies during an extended grid failure or other catastrophic event?

In a catastrophic event involving a long-term, nationwide "Lights-Out" scenario affecting power, communication, and other vital infrastructure, it is a virtual certainty that the usual food distribution logistics and supply chains will be significantly disrupted, even while traditional farming may continue to produce for some time. These conditions would result in a daunting national challenge in short order: although humans can generally survive without food for days, and in some cases a few weeks with adequate preparation, casualties will mount rapidly in the absence of vital nutrition.

In an ideal United States, everyone would have a year's supply of food. Members of the Church of Latter Day Saints practice being prepared and having food to last their families for a year and sometimes enough to share.[101] Ted Koppel suggests in his book *Lights Out* that, "Too many families lack the resources to meet even their daily needs. If those who can

---

regional stockpile warehouses throughout the U.S. These emergency food stocks have been largely depleted over ensuing years. A separate system of pharmaceutical warehouses is, however, maintained by the Centers for Disease Control and Prevention and replenished within the Strategic National Stockpile (SNS). There is a separate National Defense Stockpile administered in a system that commenced after World War I. See Clifton G. Chappell, Roderick Gainer, and Kristan Guss, "Defense National Stockpile Center: America's Stockpile: An Organizational History," Defense Logistics Agency, n.d. 42 pp. available online.

[100] See Report of the Commission to Assess the Threat to the United States from Electromagnetic Pulse (EMP) Attack, especially Chapter 7, "Food Infrastructure," pp. 133-144, which recommends at p. 137, "Federal food stockpiles should be sized to meet a possible large-scale food shortage in the event of massive disruption of the national food infrastructure from an EMP attack or other causes." For a subsequent assessment of disruption risks to U.S. food security in the aftermath of an EMP attack, see Maximilian Leeds, Electronic Pulse and the U.S. Food Security Paradigm: Assumptions, Risks, and Recommendations, 2011. For a review of previous defense stockpiling history, see Chapter 2, "Historical Context," and Appendix A, "Stockpile History," in Committee on Assessing the Need for a Defense Stockpile, National Research Council, Managing Materials for a Twenty-first Century Military, 2008.

[101] *Lights Out*, Ted Koppel, pp. 179-208.

afford to take on the responsibility of longer-term survival, supplies available to emergency management agencies can be reserved for the very neediest."

There is a current "prepper" movement involving members who work to be self-sufficient. Actually, if a significant percentage of Americans were to achieve self-sufficiency it would be very beneficial for the country. However, it is unrealistic to think that the majority of citizens would do that, and thus food supply resilience must be a priority national goal.

As an interim measure, the United States could reintroduce emergency stocks of grains, etc., plus a freeze-dried emergency food program. Emergency stocks could be kept fresh using scheduled recycling, with supplies approaching expiration provided to low-income families. Storing emergency stocks in each state would be a valuable approach.

Consideration could be given to broadening the concept underlying the national grain reserve to establish a "food reserve" with emergency stocks positioned locally. The food reserve could be created with: Dried grains and beans ideally with a shelf-life of 30 years could be economical and life sustaining. For example, Mormon food supplies available at their storehouses in different parts of the country include some supplies with a shelf-life of 30 years (https://providentliving.lds.org). Their manual is available at http://thesurvivalmom.com/wp-content/uploads/2010/08/LDS-Preparedness-Manual.pdf

> *Meals Ready to Eat* (MREs) used by DOD have a shelf life of from 4 to 7 years.

> *Freeze dried food* often used by campers could be a source of the food reserve. In addition to commercial-available supplies, there are ways to freeze dry food at home and communities might consider providing this capability to their residents.

> *Canned goods* are another possible source. While their shelf life may be limited to two years, one innovative idea would involve working with grocery chains to buy in bulk so that the canned goods are purchased at a 2-for-1 price; if the "1st purchase" set aside for an emergency nears its shelf life, that can could then be consumed by the purchaser or donated to a food bank.

Certain food production capabilities may under the control of local community governance, with the emphasis on locally grown, year-round access to food with minimal supply chain disruption issues. Set forth below are various recommendations related to these important local initiatives. The recommendations are based on recent trends and evolution of new technologies that are emerging under various labels, such as CEA (Controlled Environment Agriculture), Vertical Farming, Urban Farming or Precision Agriculture.

While at first it may seem counterintuitive, taking plants out of the soil is emerging as one of the modern frameworks for farming. Hydroponics is one such production system, broadly defined as removing plants from soil and more efficiently targeting water and nutrients to their roots. Variations of these methods are generally described as "aquaponics" (which includes fish production in the cycle) and more recently "aeroponics," each of which are otherwise perceived as high-tech greenhouses. Collectively, these farming methods apply modern technologies that offer significant advantages over traditional, soil-based agriculture. While not yet cost-competitive, and not a fully comprehensive solution to all the nutrition requirements, the CEA approach offers at least a feasible means for local food production under catastrophic events (such as described by the "five threat" scenarios discussed in Chapter II).

"Hydroponics" provides a focused example for consideration in evaluating options for local food production, although other variations may be more feasible in certain regions. Hydroponics involves growing plants without soil and letting water deliver nutrients and vital trace elements directly to the roots. While certainly suitable for the countryside, soil-less hydroponic systems can be tailored to fit rooftops, existing buildings, or marginal lands, reducing transportation costs and customizing production to local preferences.

Some of the striking differences between traditional field farming and hydroponic greenhouse farming, especially relevant under the aforementioned catastrophic conditions are:

Local Production: Hydroponics can be established locally to grow a variety of crops year-round (some 80+ types of produce and vegetables have been successfully grown) in these advanced "greenhouses," with no critical dependence on long supply chains. The dependency exception is electrical power, which in most cases can be generated by renewable means (e.g., solar, wind, etc.) at or near the facility.

Yield: Compared to traditional farms, protected and automated hydroponic greenhouse environments can deliver dramatically higher yields per unit area—up to 10 or more times what an identically sized soil-based farm can produce.

Water Use: Hydroponic farms are able to produce an equivalent crop yield with only approximately 10% of the water used by a traditional farm, since most of the water is recovered, filtered and recirculated with the right nutrient mix.

Isolation from Environment: Given an adequate source of energy to produce heat and light (typically renewable sources, local and isolated from the grid), the hydroponic facility could theoretically produce food under any climactic condition, since the dependence on climate is minimized.

Footprint: Hydroponics has a smaller environmental footprint. As a result, many of the externalities imposed on the natural world by traditional agriculture—notably, water and soil degradation, toxic chemical burden, and harms to biodiversity—can be mitigated with higher-intensity agriculture like hydroponics.

Security: Unlike a farm that typically has minimal fencing to keep out intruders, a "greenhouse" type of unit can be effectively secured in a much smaller area, within a structure.

Safety: Unlike soil-based farming which may be subject to contaminants or disease, the controlled environment has much better prospects of filtering and eliminating these risks.

Scalability: With the emergence of new technology, hydroponics has been demonstrated to be scalable on a wide basis, potentially allowing units to be placed on urban rooftops or in similar settings.

As long as adequate electrical power is available, a properly scaled hydroponics facility can continue to produce crops, even in urban environments, during long-term grid outage conditions. It must be emphasized that this approach to supporting food production is most feasible within a certain, limited community, where a finite and secure area is under the control of local governance, and the distribution path is minimal. Of course, in preparation for catastrophic events, such "resilient communities" would need to plan and deploy CEA facilities well in advance to ensure these capabilities were available in a catastrophe. The potential to achieve long-term sustainability in such communities would be greatly facilitated by achievement of local, controlled food production to support the population.

Other actions that could be taken now to enhance food supply resilience, if there was a long-term grid outage, include the following:

Other actions that can be taken now to be more resilient if there were a long-term grid outage:

Food Rationing: In extreme conditions, rationing would be essential, and states could consider enacting legislation now mandating food rationing during grid outages. Exercising this authority every time the power goes out for longer than a very brief period could prove beneficial in terms of public awareness and acceptance of this vital measure in response to long-term grid outages.

Apartment Agriculture: Apartment residents in cities are starting to grow food on their building roofs, often starting with vegetables. Another possibility is growing Swiss chard in an indoor pot; Swiss chard is a good substitute for lettuce and easy to grow. Sprouts such as mung beans can also be grown in apartments with little light and provide essential nutrients and fresh greens to supplement dried grains and canned food.

Victory Gardens: Also called war gardens or food gardens for defense, these were vegetable, fruit, and herb gardens planted at private residences and public parks in the United States, United Kingdom, Canada, Australia and Germany during World

War I and World War II. They were used along with Rationing Stamps and Cards to reduce pressure on the public food supply. Besides indirectly aiding the war effort, these gardens were also considered a civil "morale booster" in that gardeners could feel empowered by their contribution of labor and rewarded by the produce grown.[102] This made victory gardens a part of daily life on the home front. Using this concept could be helpful in such a grid outage disaster. Learning how to garden now would help ensure the feasibility of doing so in emergency conditions.

Local Farmers: Buying from local farmers now is important, and encouraging them to continue and expand could be a key to their continued economic viability.

International Assistance: International assistance could be vital to the survival of the U.S. population if there were a long-term grid failure. Establishing memorandums of understanding (MOUs) with key countries now is critical. Activating such MOUs quickly within the first two weeks could contribute to maintaining civil order and stability (see Appendix 7).

> With no electrical power, plans need to be developed for how food would be delivered from a port to people in that port city and also onwards to other cities. Airlifts of food could also be planned. Planning now for transportation logistics challenges could minimize the corruption often seen when the United States delivers emergency food to other countries.

> Examining the many lessons learned from international assistance programs (e.g., Haitian earthquake relief) would inform domestic planning efforts.

Fishing: Fishing could be of importance to many.

Soup Lines: When soup kitchens first appeared, they were typically run by churches or private charities. By the mid-1930s, state and federal governments were also operating them. Soup kitchens served mostly soup and bread. Soup was economical because water could be added to serve more people, if necessary. Soup kitchens still exist for homeless persons and struggling families across the United States. Being ready to expand this capability in the face of a long-term grid outage would involve challenges, such as how to make the soup and the bread without having adequate food reserves.

USDA has recently joined with 15 regional philanthropic partners to announce a new initiative to bolster the supply chain for local food systems in 10 key U.S. cities. The project, named Food LINC, connects local farmers and ranchers to a regional area's local food businesses, thereby increasing consumer access to healthy foods.[103] This initiative would

---

102 Wikipedia on Victory Gardens. https://en.wikipedia.org/wiki/Victory_garden

103 . Details on this project are found at:
https://content.govdelivery.com/accounts/USDAOC/bulletins/1404f22.

be a worthy candidate for a more robust program involving broader private sector participation.

Public Health and Medical

Modern healthcare relies on an uninterrupted supply of electrical power and access to the internet. Persons who require lifesaving medication (such as Insulin) and/or utilize medical equipment that needs electrical power (such as an oxygen generator) are most vulnerable. Healthcare facilities generally have no more than three days of emergency power capability. Hospitals quickly become dark and dangerous places if there is a prolonged power outage.

Further, disruption of the water sector can render hospital operations unsafe in just hours. As the July 2016 NIAC report on water sector resiliency noted, the inoperability of water or sewer systems causes prompt degradation of hospital services. Between 67% and 99% of the hospitals surveyed, that have self-assessed their facilities, determined that they would need to operate in a degraded condition in just two hours after loss of water sector services.[104]

Recommendations for improving public health and medical preparedness for extended grid outages are set forth below:

- Individuals should strive to stay as healthy as possible. Ideally they would have at least a 3-month supply of all regular medications on hand (which is difficult to accomplish with current health insurance rules). Take a first aid course or, even better, becoming an EMT could literally prove life-saving. Finally, every household ideally would have an extensive first aid kit as a part of shelter in place and/or go-bag preparations.
- Healthcare providers should know their role in disaster scenarios and practice the necessary actions regular drills. Ideally, there would be emergency plans for staff, to include non-medical staff, addressing communications, transportation, and a prolonged stay inside the medical facility. Plans could include provision for possible relocation to a building of opportunity (with temporary power) to continue providing care.
- Healthcare facilities (especially hospitals) could assess the life support and critical load requirement (possibly 30% of the total) required to keep hospitals open. This minimum requirement should be met with renewable energy, ideally involving a microgrid on or near the campus. Surprisingly, many of the most essential elements of healthcare are not medical per se –water, food, clean laundry, waste disposal, security, and non-electronic means of funds transfer are all vital. There could be a plan for reverting back to paper record keeping if necessary, as well as for "graceful" degradation of services in case the facility becomes unable to provide healthcare.
- The Navy has two medical ships, home ported in Baltimore and San Diego. Other Navy ships and special aircraft have medical care capabilities.

---

[104] National Infrastructure Advisory Committee, Water Sector Resilience: Final Report, July 2016, p. 2.

- Planning for safely and appropriately handling fatalities would be essential. Rapid burial could become necessary because embalming may not be possible. Existing plans for mass casualties and pandemics may be helpful in this planning.
- See Chapter VI on Resilience Community Islands for special hospital islands.
- The Strategic National Stockpile, with its extensive yet still limited inventory of medications, is a potential resource to consider in contingency planning

The Navy has medical ships, which are based in Baltimore and San Diego. They could be used to take care of patients. In addition, other Navy ships and special aircraft have medical supplies.

Finance

During extended emergencies, financial transaction may progress through stages, from cash transactions and bartering for essential goods and services to emergency financial credits for goods and services. The Emergency Financial First Aid Kit (EFFAK) published by FEMA[105] is an excellent information resource for individual citizens and small businesses.

Key recommendations for improving financial preparedness for an extended grid outage include the following:

Legislators at the federal, state, and local levels should consider establishing emergency credit and loan guarantee programs to sustain supply chains without electronic payment system operability. The programs need to work top-down and bottom-up. Credit may not be tied to the current financial system (e.g., during the Berlin air lift of 1948-1949, the U.S. and U.K. governments issued both new currency and new ration cards. Congress could authorize emergency credit for at least fuel, food, water/ wastewater, and telecommunications, which may need to exist on good faith at least in the short term.

Corporations and other organizations could consider contingency contracting for priority goods and services.

Individuals could systematically review their overall financial situation and consider the following steps:

- Assemble and safeguard in a fireproof/waterproof container current copies (ideally paper and digital) of all identification, financial, and legal documents (e.g., Social Security cards, passports, birth certificates, etc.), as well as medical information, and household contacts.
- Provide family members, friends, and the family lawyer copies of the most important documents
- Be alert during a disaster with respect to possible scams and fraud attempts.

---

[105] Emergency Financial First Aid Kit (EFFAK) Strengthen Your Financial Preparedness for Disasters and Emergencies, September 2015, FEMA.

- Maintain a reasonable amount of cash on hand—banks may be closed, safety deposit boxes may not be accessible, and ATMs will not function without electrical power. It may also be helpful to have items on hand to barter with (e.g., batteries, toiletries, etc.).

Emergency Services—Security

One of the many crises triggered by a long-term grid outage would be the overwhelming of law enforcement and National Guard forces. Communications and transportation failures would hinder organization, mobilization, movement and resupply. Concern about family members would motivate some personnel to place a higher priority on the safety of their families than strangers.

Among the public at large, the initial onset of the loss of power and communications will soon begin to cause fear, confusion and frustration. This may be exacerbated by the time of year (daylight) and existing weather (hot, cold, mild, precipitation, etc.). In metropolitan areas, the criminal element, particularly gangs, will start taking advantage of the situation to prey upon the weak. Demand for law enforcement could at the same time soar as the lack of food, water and other essential commodities could drive citizens to desperate measures. This situation would be aggravated because, once diesel fuel at some jails/prisons is exhausted, manual locks would be required at certain facilities with automatic security gates to prevent uncontrolled release of some prison populations.

Providing for the safety of one's self, family and community would become a pressing problem. In areas lacking sufficient law enforcement personnel or National Guard personnel, together with sufficient supplies for them, it is easy to imagine how criminal gangs and/or other bad actors would overwhelm individuals and groups unable to protect themselves. As yet, DHS has not published recommendations as to what action citizens could take in such a calamity. The reasonable expectation is that citizens could help themselves to the extent possible, through activities such as Neighborhood Watch and joining forces for self/family protection.

A post-EMP world could necessarily be one of vastly greater local and personal self-sufficiency. Today, individuals outsource most of material needs, such as clean water, food, energy and a trading system. Post-EMP, this situation could change overnight. It certainly follows that safety and security could also suffer the same sort of forced shift from outsourced service to self-sufficiency.

Although solar storms could have global impact, high altitude EMP events would not be global in scope. It thus remains plausible to anticipate priority restoration of international ports and rail transportation, initially for international disaster relief but later for international trade. Much of the global economy may remain substantially intact. Surges in supply chains for essential food, medicine and equipment to reconstitute critical infrastructures might be feasible. With profound scarcity, the entirety of supply chains from the point of origin to the point of distribution could require extraordinary security. Key questions include whether the National Guard and other defense assistance to civil authorities suffice and to what extent approved supply chains could be supplanted by black market alternatives.

The implications of a shift from outsourced security to self-sufficient security are more difficult in many ways than treating one's own water or growing one's own food. Most Americans are not trained in whether, when and how to employ deadly force in their own protection. And, because it is such a politically sensitive subject, people tend to either wish the problem away or simply avoid discussing the issues. Aggravating this overall situation is that the law enforcement community is divided—typically along urban/rural lines—as to whether such preparation would be desirable or feasible.

In areas where law and order break down post-event, any orderly restoration of infrastructure will be seriously retarded or impossible. Criminal gangs and other bad actors would be unlikely to have any respect for, or ability to communicate with, remaining government authorities. One possibility for addressing this serious problem for the Guard and local law enforcement would be to identify, organize, train and equip—now—a cadre of pre-screened civilians willing to be deputized in event of emergency as a force multiplier for lawful authorities. It is essential to develop contingency plans to integrate additional law enforcement personnel so that National Guard and law enforcement have the ability to discriminate between vetted and non-vetted individuals in advance of any catastrophic event. Specialized units with skills to protect critical infrastructures might be pre-selected based upon understanding of which assets require priority protection. Military veterans could be an excellent source of additional volunteers and staff.

One potential beneficial byproduct of such an organizing effort would be the fostering of neighbor relationships necessary for communities to provide for their own security and their own recovery. When people are left on their own, there are disincentives to reveal to the unprepared whether one has a home worth raiding in a crisis. This lack of trust means that creating "whole of community" leadership, bonding, preparation, training, and specialization remains inadequate. A "civilian auxiliary" force has the potential to more quickly break down such barriers between sometimes now unknown neighbors, their skills, and community resources. Sponsorship by the local sheriff, for example, could help reduce the negative or questioning stigma that frequently surround families that today choose to prepare in isolation for worst-case events. More broadly, some of the federal civil defense authorities from the "Cold War" era might be adapted to needs of a 21st century society.

Community Watch can be helpful for communities. Getting involved with this initiative would be helpful in normal times and critical in emergencies to help protect vital goods. It could assist with the planning process for the community. The Citizen Corp and Community Emergency Response Teams (CERTs) members can also provide volunteer services for the community and participate in planning.

Retired police would be another option for augmenting National Guard and current law enforcement personnel during extended grid outages and other catastrophic events. Another possibility is obtaining support from InfraGard members, given that the FBI does a limited check on all members.

Chapter VI: Resilient Communities Islands

The concept of "resilient community islands" is a longstanding planning element for electric grid reconstitution. Recent initiatives include formal modeling of "grid islanded" electric generation to "blackstart" both other "off-grid" electric generation and even components of the bulk electric system. In fact, the concept of grid islands goes back in history.

This initiative's consideration of "grid islanding" concepts started with George Baker's work on blackstart and the concept that the grid would be restarted in a grid island, and then the grid islands would eventually be brought together (see Appendix 5).

That concept started with General Robert Newman's idea for communications and Robert McCreight's thinking about universities being resilient community islands. Others on the Planning Team then took the idea even further to business parks and communities. The ideas set forth below on resilience community islands are an outgrowth of those discussions.

The fundamental goals for resilience community islands are human survival and recovery from the catastrophic event. The underlying approach calls for establishing the required conditions that enable people to work together while enhancing communications and security.

The resilient community island concept entails having places where people can congregate: foremost as communities, with security in numbers and synergies from melding diverse expertise and leadership; then, if necessary, in "recovery islands," where communities come together now to plan for disaster mitigation and sustainable recovery. Ideally, island-committed communities would protect or reconstitute microgrids powered by local or renewable sources, so that they could generate and distribute a sufficient share of required electrical power to enable continuity of critical functions and, over time, community recovery. In so doing, these communities would be helping the environment and positioning themselves to be resilient.

Complementing this core concept of "resilient community islanding" are open-ended concepts for functionally differentiated "resilient community islands." The functionally-differentiated resilient community islands could be organized by specialized expertise or particular manufacturing or repair center skills. These might combine specialty work and associated residential communities; university campuses; business parks; specialized resilient community island complexes, such as urban regions with clusters of medical/hospitals and associated living spaces; teams of telecommunications/cyber experts; or single buildings, like a church, synagogue, or community center.

A community may decide that a network of schools could be the backbone of its resilient community islanded recovery system. In small towns, citizens may work together as a resilient community island. In a large city, the resilient community islanding concept may morph into "resilient community islanded networks," with designated sites in designated neighborhoods, supported by survivable communications.

Obtaining food and having a source of water and wastewater is vital for the resilient community island to accomplish its goals. Keeping the water and wastewater systems functioning would be one of the country's highest priorities, together with public safety, communications, and emergency food supplies. If people have food and water, and training to participate in "resilient community islanding" projects to mitigate and recover from disaster, then knowing what to do in a disaster is important. With an effective plan, people could feel secure about taking the right actions. Even if communications are temporarily disabled, resilient community islanding recovery participants will know where to report and understand some of the tasks supporting recovery.

What are important aspects of a Resilient Community Island?

Families: It would be critical to have families together in the resilient community island. People may want either to stay in their community or go their place of work. If they were to leave their community to go to a different location, the reason would need to be compelling and they would want their family included. Communities may decide on a designated location, such as a school or community center, as the focal point for communication and deliveries of food and keeping families in their homes.

Microgrids: Ideally, a resilient community island would have a microgrid that is:

- Powered from renewable resources;
- Supported with power storage systems;
- EMP-protected so that it could survive even the worst scenario; and
- Protected and isolated from cyber-terrorism attacks.

Communications: It will be easy to communicate within the resilient community island. Communications will be face-to-face. Members can make decisions together and work on issues as they arise. Communications from one resilient community island to another may be possible and important so that the members of the resilient community island do not feel isolated. Letting others know that there is a functioning resilient community island may facilitate access to external sources of food, medications and supplies. Including a HAM operator as a member of the resilient community island would be helpful in communicating with other resilient community islands.

Schools: Active schools would be important to preserving the social fabric and promoting long-term stability. Ideally, there would be teachers among the members of the community.

If not, parents could take on these responsibilities. The children may learn different subjects than they would have otherwise, but it would be important to keep them busy and productively engaged.

Security/Protection: Coming together as a community—whether organized around a university, a laboratory, business, school, church/synagogue, neighborhood, etc. —will invariably be safer than being alone. Working together will help the entire resilient community island survive. Neighborhood Watch can be helpful as part of the resilient community island. The National Guard and/or first responders may be part of a resilient community island with members wanting their families included to afford them peace of mind when deployed to carry out their responsibilities.

Medical: Resilient community islands could obtain at least some basic medical supplies ahead of an emergency. Moreover, owing to the stress of close quarters, loss of "normal" routines, and the emergency itself, community members may exhibit signs of strain, and thus it may also be beneficial for the community to include counselors or other mental health professionals with appropriate training in the event of a long-term grid outage.

Point of Distribution (POD): Major regional and other contingency plans include provisions for focal point to facilitate delivery of food, medications, and supplies. Public Health associations have requested PODs for delivery of critical medications in times of disaster. If the resilient community island is organized and recognized in advance of any high-consequence emergency, the community could then be established as a POD.

Grain/Food Reserves: The Critical Infrastructure Food section (Chapter V) discussed establishing local grain reserves. Resilient community islands could be the perfect place to establish a grain reserve. Such reserves could be joint efforts including local farmers who are willing to set aside a portion of their crops for emergencies. Growing cycles may not produce food at the very time that it is needed, so having a "food reserve" for the resilient community island may prove essential. There are different ways to provision the "food reserve" for the community ahead of an incident. A food reserve could be started by obtaining meals ready to eat (MREs); freeze dried camping food, bulk rice/beans, etc. If food in the reserve is not used and its shelf life expires (4–7 years for MREs; more than a decade for many freeze dried foods), then members would ideally obtain a new supply and ration the current supplies or donate supplies to a food bank or soup kitchen.

Growing Food: If a resilient community island is created now, ahead of a disaster, the members of that resilient community island could work together to gain experience in sustainable gardening and food preservation. As discussed in the Food section in Chapter V, gaining experience in growing food before a disaster might spark interest in the Resilient Community Island concept.

Talents: The various members of a resilient community island could have different and complementary talents that they could bring to the community. These different talents could help the resilient community island function, and might enable designated resilient community islands to refurbish acutely-needed damaged equipment or manufacture supplies, such as water purification systems. Community members could contribute in various ways, such as teaching, food preparation, communications, and medical care. Every resilient island community could have books, operational procedure diagrams, and other references related to survival at the ready.

Formation of Resilient Community Islands

Below are various suggestions on the creation of resilient community islands. Any of the entities discussed could potentially provide the basis for organizing a resilience community island, ideally before the disaster relying on the guidance presented above. Even if the entities did not complete all the preparations for an ideal resilient community, they could still develop a plan for how they would respond to a major disaster. The more people who know where to go and what to do when faced with a long-term grid outage, the more lives could be saved.

Universities: They already comprise a community and usually have dormitories food service. Some universities have research arms associated with them—these may function more like a business park, which is discussed below. Some universities already have microgrids (e.g., the University of California at San Diego and Princeton University).

State Governments: In their continuity plans, state government have predetermined alternate locations to which they would go if they needed to abandon their normal location. In preparing for a long-term grid outage, the state government could expand their plan and adopt the resilient community island concept. The plan might designate the state university as their resilient community island and call for not only state government officials but also the National Guard and their families to locate there. This approach would facilitate full continuity of state governance in a secure environment. Another advantage would be communications because state officials could meet face-to-face at a time when no power, internet, or cell phones, etc., would be available.

Business/Business Parks: Some business parks are installing their own microgrids and could function as a resilient community islands. But even without a microgrid, businesses could become resilient community islands for their employees and their families. They might want to invest in cots or other sleeping provisions or encourage their employees to obtain sleeping bags. They may have cafeterias so that they could prepare food. The resilient community island concept could become part of their business continuity plan. Growing food in these circumstances would prove a challenge businesses might decide to face or ignore. If they decided to start growing their own food, one option might be to repurpose part of their lawn into a garden. Growing potatoes might be unobtrusive, and when harvested the potatoes could be stored as a "food reserve."

Communities: Another alternative is individuals staying in their own homes and simply going to a local school or community center as a meeting place for information and as a point of distribution. Ideally, the community would obtain a microgrid with renewable power and EMP protection. For example, BG&E in Maryland is obtaining microgrids for a neighborhood in Baltimore and a suburban location.

Faith-Based Resilient Community Islands: Within a community, physical structures such as places of worship could serve as focal points to bring people together and as a source of spiritual support. Ideally, faith-based organizations would work to keep their communities together and would also be concerned about disaster preparedness. If several places of worship were in close proximity, they could jointly invest in a microgrid and a renewable power source for the microgrid. There are faith-based volunteer organizations that may want to help lead efforts to encourage preparing resilient community islands or actually join one of these communities.

Functionally Differentiated Resilient Community Islands: The country will need such communities. Key examples include:

Medical Resilient Community Islands: This could involve a single hospital or a group of hospitals in a big city. They could have their own microgrid to keep power flowing. Doctors and other medical personnel with their families could go there, and the community could provide medical care to other islands in the vicinity.

Telecom/Cyber Resilient Community Islands: These would not necessarily be actual physical locations, but rather a group of experts with special knowledge about computers and telecommunication systems. They would need to get these systems functioning and could be called upon by resilient community islands with a functioning grid to provide support. This community may be a subpart of another resilient community island; for example, its members might need or repair equipment in a business park or university or develop markets for repurposed electronic components.

Department of Defense (DOD): Military bases are an example of resilience community islands. Current military base dependency on civilian infrastructure is an issue that DoD is addressing. As the military base becomes more resilient, the local community adjacent could also become more resilient.

Other Critical Infrastructure (CI): The concept of resilient community islands for critical infrastructures has been suggested.[106] Resilient community islands and "temporal coordination" have been used as a way to help CIs work together because of the interdependencies among these infrastructures (see Chapter V). Resilient community islands could help enhances decision-making and communications, as well as control panic. During recovery from the grid outage, if the CIs work with the blackstarted grid islands, they could accelerate their recovery. Eventually, that would expand into networks of resilient communities and grid islands. See Figure 10.

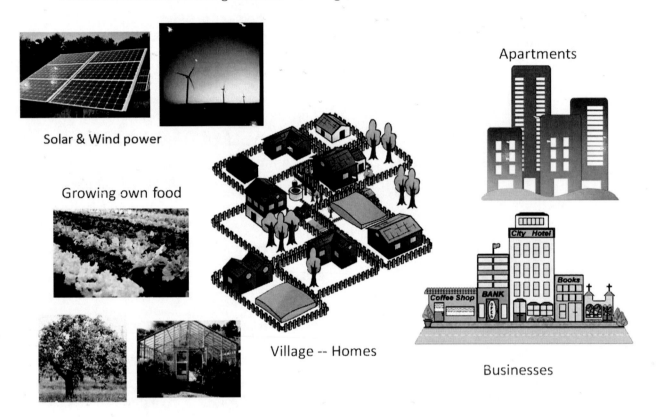

Figure 10: Resilient Community Island Components.

Networking of Resilient Community Islands

Communication among resilient community islands would be increasingly important the longer grid outages extended. Reliable communications links could help in recovering vital resources and preventing the feeling of isolation. Expertise and other talent could be shared more readily with neighboring resilient community islands, including tasking of specialty resilient community islands based on occupational skills or equipment repair capabilities.

---

[106] "Dynamic Islanding of critical infrastructures: a suitable strategy to survive and mitigate extreme events," Jorge A. Hollman, Jose R. Marti, Juri Jatskevich, K. D. Srivastava, 2007; "Dynamic recovery of critical infrastructures: real-time temporal coordination," Jose R. Marti and Jorge A. Hollman, 2008.

As time goes by, resilient community islands could be expanded and joined together. Adjacent or proximate communities within big cities could definitely join together. As more islands join together, the larger resilient community islands could at some point become county-wide communities, which could in turn eventually transition to a state island. In this way, local, state, tribal, and territorial governments, as well as the federal government, could eventually be supported.

Chapter VII: Key Actors

The "Whole Community" approach has been encouraged by many different advocates in both the public and private sectors and is strongly emphasized throughout the federal policy documents that define the current national framework for preparedness and resilience.[107] This chapter addresses the many different participants/actors in this overarching community that needs to mobilize in order to enhance national readiness for extended grid outages.

These actors/participants are the pivotal audience for this Guide, especially the critical infrastructure discussion in Chapters IV and V. All of these individuals and entities have a vital role in preparedness that begins with educating themselves and others, proceeds to orchestration and/or support of deliberate planning efforts, and culminates in real world implementation of significant readiness initiatives.

Such initiatives would enhance national preparedness for extended wide-spread outages and afford the population a meaningful basis for confidence that the nation can survive and recover from a catastrophic event of this nature. To underscore the importance of adequate preparation in every region and sub-region, the geographic scope of such a catastrophe essentially precludes the availability of mutual assistance from outside areas.

The preparedness required to address this daunting challenge must build up from a grass roots level. All actors/participants ideally would inform themselves to the extent appropriate on the threats to the electrical grid, begin to prepare now for a long term wide spread grid outage, and practice prudent responses anytime the electrical power is out. Education about the grid could begin at the elementary school level and continue throughout the educational journey, with an emphasis on such actions as lockdowns, sheltering-in-place, evacuation, and overall preparedness.

Building Blocks for Community Resiliency

The extent of necessary preparations for nationwide high-impact and long-duration threats is far too broad to be centrally planned or controlled. Such preparations are as complex as our society and free-market economy, which have prospered primarily through self-

---

[107] See especially, U.S. Department of Homeland Security (DHS), A Whole Community Approach to Emergency Management: Principles, Themes, and Pathways for Action, December 1, 2011; DHS, The 2014 Quadrennial Homeland Security Review, June 2014, section on "National Preparedness and the Whole Community Approach," pp. 71-74; and National Science and Technology Council, National Space Weather Action Plan, October 28, 2015, explaining at p. 10, Note 7: "Whole Community partners refer to the Nation's larger collective emergency management team and include not only DHS and its partners at the federal level, but also state, local, tribal, and territorial (SLTT) partners, non-governmental organizations such as faith-based and nonprofit groups and private sector industry, and individuals, families and communities." See also FEMA website, "Whole Community", updated June 10, 2016.

determination and limited governance in the form of laws and regulations. Moreover, while a certain measure of top-down government oversight is a current reality, the very nature of a high-impact grid contingency requires that preparedness must occur at every level throughout the nation in a decentralized manner. A solid foundation is essential.

Successful sports teams and the military prepare by starting with individuals while having an organizational understanding of how their future roles fit together dynamically. Individuals are trained with certain fundamental skills and decision-making abilities, and they achieve mastery before being added to a team. Small groups of players accomplish plays that are part of the larger team approach. In the military, individual skills are mastered, then small unit skills (e.g., fire teams and squads), then intermediate-sized unit skills (company), and so on up to the expeditionary force level.

The military and professional sports teams understand how to be ready and stay ready. Likewise, communities across the nation must begin with attention to fundamental individual citizen skills and preparations, followed by household level activity, then street and neighborhood, and on up to town, city, and state levels. Without individual preparations and skills, no entire system can succeed, and, likewise, each level higher must orient to this issue and prepare sensibly. Response and recovery will fail at whatever level this preparation breaks down. For example, if only households and FEMA are ready, then there will be no survivable utilities or larger infrastructure, such as grocery and food distribution operations, available to them.

Citizens

Americans need to know how to survive in trying times. Much will depend on whether they live in a city or in a rural area; whether they have planned ahead and have emergency food and water; and whether their government at all levels has a plan that has been effectively communicated to the citizenry.

Some of the suggestions include:

- Become familiar with all of the threats to the electrical grid, as well as preparedness guidelines and response actions if the grid fails.
- Participate in the "Great Campout" concept that can help families learn how to be resilient and prepared for a grid outage.[108]
- Get to know the neighbors now to lay the groundwork for banding together in times of crisis. Working together to initiate a neighborhood coalition will build the capacity to work together in the future when the imperative may be to stay alive. Collaboration in such circumstances could prove essential (e.g., sharing food preparation and cooking resources).
- Obtain and store food supplies. For example, Mormons plan on having food supplies for months or even a year. Follow their lead and stockpile food that has a long shelf life, such as

---

[108] See Lighthouse Prime website.

rice and beans. Set an initial goal to have a month of non-perishable food on hand for the family, and then increase it each month until you reach a year's supply.

- Keep children in school if at all possible, in order to keep them occupied and learning.
- Create work projects with neighbors or others in the community to stay busy. Volunteering to help others could be rewarding.
- If the local community is being organized as a resilient community island, join in the initiative.
- Participate in faith-based communities as a way of sustaining hope and morale—and also to explore ways to make the place of worship more resilient, possibly to include developing its own microgrid.

Communities—Urban

The photograph below shows the United States as viewed from a satellite at night. It depicts the large U.S. metropolitan areas, some of which are becoming megacities. Survival in a city would be very different from survival in a rural area, and in certain ways more difficult. Consequently, these two living environments have been separated to examine what those living there need to do to be prepared and (in Chapter VIII) what both types of communities will need to do to respond and recover.

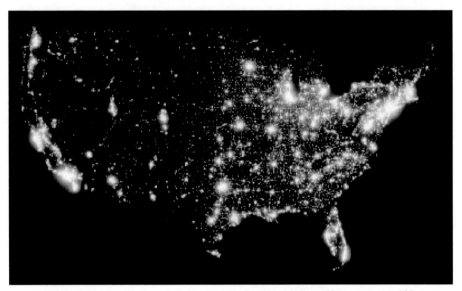

Figure 11: United States Nighttime Satellite View.[109]

If the power is out in the entire country, there will be no place within the country to flee. Evacuation would be fruitless and trigger cascading events that would intensify the catastrophe. Encouraging people to stay in their homes/apartments/condos will be the

---

[109] Source: Satellite images from Defense Meteorological Satellite Program Mission F15, processed by the U.S. Air Force Weather Agency, publicly available on the NOAA website.

safest course. To be prepared for such an event, cities and large metropolitan areas need to plan now ahead of such a catastrophic event.

- Become familiar with all of the threats to the electrical grid, as well as preparedness guidelines and response actions if the grid fails.
- Plan how to communicate with citizens without power. Establish set times each day for communications (e.g., at 9 and 3). This way people know when they will receive information. Being informed helps alleviate fear, panic and rumors.
- Ensure that water and wastewater have the highest priority for fuel and chemical deliveries to keep the water and wastewater systems operating.
- Keep schools functioning? Plan how schools will operate with no bus transportation for students, as well as no heat or air conditioning. If planning reveals that some teachers too far away to commute to the school, arrange for parents to teach.
- Encourage self-sufficiency and resilience by all individuals, to reduce demand on services.
- Identify points of distribution (POD) for critical supplies. Schools, recreation areas and churches could be used as community resource and information dissemination centers.
- Train all community members in food growth, storage, preparation, basic health care, medicine alternatives, and self-security.
- Encourage citizens to buy from local farmers and fisheries in order to help sustain local food sources to rely on in emergencies.
- Encourage citizens to grow some of their own food—so they learn how to do so if there is no local supply available.
- Plan resilient community islands (see Chapter VI) to help people work together and support each other.
- Encourage participation in faith communities or volunteer activities—staying busy helps in multiple ways.

Communities—Rural

A number of people living in rural areas are more self-sufficient, to include growing some of their own food. While their self-sufficiency would be a positive, as a catastrophic grid failure unfolds their isolation may become an issue. Beyond the greater difficulty in accessing medical and other essential services, they may also be confronted by people from the cities fleeing to the rural area and seeking to be fed, housed, etc. Safety could become a major concern; police or National Guard support may not be possible owing to other higher priority requirements.

Some of the steps rural residents could take in order to be prepared include:

- Become familiar with all of the threats to the electrical grid, as well as preparedness guidelines and response actions if the grid fails.
- Install a hand pump to access well water in emergencies.
- Participate in a local grain or food reserve if organized.

- Plan how schools will operate with no bus transportation for students. If planning reveals that some of teachers live too far away to commute to the school, arrange for parents to teach. Consider establishing a school in a centrally-located home.
- Identify Points of Distribution (POD) for critical supplies. Schools, recreation areas and churches could be used as community resource and information dissemination centers.
- Provide training, as needed, to all community members in food growth, storage, preparation, basic health care, medicine alternatives, and self-security.
- Encourage buying from local farmers and fisheries to help sustain local food sources to rely on in emergencies. Encourage more locally sustainable agriculture, hydroponic greenhouses, aquaculture, and emergency fisheries management (see Chapter V: Food and Agriculture).

Preparedness Organizations and Consortiums

This category includes organizations such as the Community Emergency Response Teams (CERTs), the Association of Contingency Professionals, the All Hazards Consortium, and others. These organizations focus on disasters and need to be educated about the consequences of a long-term widespread grid outage.

As one example, CERTs could be an important part of the solution for communities addressing various challenges (e.g., how best to communicate and distribute critical information updates during a long-term grid failure) as they proceed through the contingency planning process. Currently, there are more than 2,600 registered CERT teams.

Typically, a local government agency, often a fire department, police department, or emergency management agency, agrees to sponsor CERT within its jurisdiction. The sponsoring agency liaises with, deploys, and may train or supervise the training of CERT members. Many sponsoring agencies employ a full-time community-service person as liaison to the CERT members. In some communities, the liaison is a volunteer and CERT member.

As people are trained and agree to join the community emergency response effort, a CERT is formed. Initial efforts may result in a team with only a few members, but as the number of members grows, a single community-wide team may subdivide, possibly along neighborhood lines. Multiple CERTs are organized into a hierarchy of teams consistent with Incident Control System principles, most notably the principle of span of control relating to any one supervisor's maximum number of direct reports (see Appendix 2).

In preparation for an outage, CERT teams can play an important role, including:

- Understanding the level of government awareness and preparation in the community;
- Updating local government relating to preparation steps and information from the EMP SIG and Committee;

- Distributing information to citizens to foster greater awareness;
- Identifying citizen resources, such as amateur radio personnel;
- Talking with local companies, such as grocery stores, gas stations, hardware and lumber stores, etc., who could be instrumental in providing necessary supplies; and
- Planning an EMP or high impact scenario exercise.

In addition, if the grid goes out, CERT Teams could be important in the following ways:

- Acting as a liaison between local government (administration, police, fire and emergency management) and the citizens in their community;
- Updating local government on neighborhood developments;
- Providing "extra hands" to handle low-impact issues to free up first responders;
- Identifying and coordinate amateur radio resources;
- Providing emergency medical care;
- Assisting in coordinating supplies, water, and food resources;
- Allocating several meeting or webinars to awareness of the threats and preparedness activities and actions (see Chapter VII and Chapter VIII);
- Encouraging members to have enough food for at least a month;
- Participating in and support resilient community islands.

Individuals concerned about their community readiness for an extended outage should consider joining a local CERT team and talking about how CERT can be a significant force multiplier during an incident such as an EMP. If there is no local CERT program, consider starting one. Information on CERT is available at http://www.fema.gov/community-emergency-response-teams/

Non-Government Organizations (NGO)/Volunteer Organizations

Organizations such as the Red Cross, Volunteers Active in Disasters (VOAD), and American Logistical Aid Network (ALAN) have traditionally been at every disaster helping citizens survive and cope. The Red Cross especially has worked worldwide to save lives and has engendered widespread public trust. VOAD members encompass many organizations that come together to coordinate the response and assistance they collectively provide. VOAD members can also include government representatives.

National VOAD, an association of organizations that mitigate and alleviate the impact of disasters, provides a forum promoting cooperation, communication, coordination and collaboration; the forum also fosters more effective delivery of services to communities affected by disaster. It is the non-governmental leader building community resiliency throughout the disaster cycle, and its members represent a powerful force of goodwill and community service in the United States.

A table listing the National VOAD participant Contacts is provided in Appendix 9.

These organizations typically start their response immediately when the disaster happens. Without electricity, there will be challenges in communicating what assistance is needed where. There could be people who volunteer at the beginning and then leave to take care of their own families as the days of power outage continue. By then, transportation will probably be limited because of the dwindling fuel supplies being allocated to higher priorities and so responding after the first few days will become more difficult.

To prepare for this type of incident, the NGO and Volunteer Organizations could:

- Include long-term regional power outages in their education and planning;
- Participate in local government or state government exercises and develop plans for their volunteers; and
- Plan to participate in a resilient community island (see Chapter VI).

Faith-Based Organizations

These organizations would certainly be needed to help people spiritually and emotionally as they struggle to cope with a long-term widespread grid outage.

To be prepared for such an event, they could:

- Become educated on the implications of this type of disaster; and
- Develop plans which could include:
  - Determining how to communicate with the congregation members when there is no electrical power;
  - Creating a layout of where their congregants live and give everyone in close proximity the contact information for others nearby, which could help ensure that members can help each other when needed in any major disaster;
  - Forming a resilient community island (see Chapter VI);
  - Obtaining a stockpile of long shelf-life foods for the congregation; and
  - Coordinating with other denominations' disaster relief organizations.

Universities and Community Colleges

The response of institutions of higher learning to an extended grid outage will necessarily be dependent to a significant extent on whether classes are in session and whether there are students in residence. During a school term, certain classes (e.g., lectures and seminars) could probably continue, while others (e.g., lab-oriented classes) probably would not with power. In any case, these institutions would have major responsibilities for the safety and security of students, faculty and staff.

To enhance their preparedness, universities and community colleges could consider the following steps:

- Become educated on the threats, preparedness guidelines, and response actions for a long term wide spread grid outage;
- Use an existing long term severe pandemic plan and modify it for an extended power outage, with the assumption that students would stay on campus because there would be no transportation available to get them home;
- Address how to feed students, as well as keep them engaged and learning;
- Consider becoming a resilient community island (see Chapter VI), to include an EMP-protected microgrid powered by renewable sources if possible.

Local Government

Since all disasters, no matter how widespread, are local, local government is critical. Providing local first responders is essential to ensure that public safety and order is kept throughout the emergency. Maintaining public utilities will be vital. And keeping citizens informed will be critical.

Actions the local government could take to be prepared include:

- Plan to protect water/ wastewater facilities and ensure they will obtain fuel and chemicals shipments. Arrange for computer experts to deploy if there is a cyberattack on their SCADA system. This could be the highest municipal priority.
- Work with city water systems to consider wells for microgrid applications and emergency water supplies.
- Create a local grain or food reserve. Partner with the state government to ensure that the local area has access to supplies.
- Conduct a tabletop exercise involving a month-long loss of power and prioritize work on the "After Action" items. Hold another tabletop several months later when the action items have been addressed, only this time consider a two-month scenario. (Local governments could choose one of the predesigned scenarios from the InfraGard EMP SIG, such as the Triple Threat Power Grid Exercise book (See Appendix 9).

Critical Infrastructures

See Chapter V for recommendations on preparations for the critical infrastructure sectors.

Businesses

Business Continuity Planning (BCP) is critical for all businesses. The same type of planning in the government is called Continuity of Operations Planning (COOP). Non-profit organizations also need to plan, and they may use either term to describe their efforts. The common denominator goal, however, is to do as much planning, training and exercising as possible, before an incident occurs, to eliminate as much confusion and as many sub-optimal continuity decisions as possible.

While business continuity plans are important, they are only one facet of the full range of required planning, which also includes incident response and crisis management. Appendix

2 (Planning & Exercises) in this Guide provides background information on continuity planning and could serve as a refresher for those who have done previous continuity planning as well as a primer for those not familiar with the topic.

To be prepared for a long-term widespread grid outage, the following steps are recommended:

- Study the read-ahead material in the InfraGard EMP SIG Triple Threat Power Grid Exercise (Appendix 9) to become familiar with the three scenarios: cyber, solar storms, and electromagnetic pulses. Understanding the threat and the risk it poses is critical to updating or developing a contingency plan.
- Update current plans to address a long-term widespread scenario or develop a new organizational continuity plan for the organization. Appendix 2 (Planning) provides an overview of typical business continuity plan content. The benefits derived from such a plan include:
  - Plans provide a framework for response and identify "who does what when" during an incident.
  - Insurance premiums may be lower if a documented and tested plan is in place.
  - Staff will know what to do and what is expected from them during the response and recovery phases.
  - Communications processes will be identified so that the right people know what to communicate inside and outside the organization, and communicating when there is no electrical power will be addressed.
  - Engage first responders and community leaders to develop an awareness of what steps other key actors will take, thus improving communications and coordination.

- Conduct an exercise as recommended in Appendix 2. This will familiarize everyone within the organization, including the response and recovery teams, about what it would mean if electrical power were not available for an extended period. Following each exercise, revisit the continuity plan to incorporate lessons learned and newly-identified ways to be better prepared for such a long term wide spread grid outage. This Guide can help with the preparations. Key topics to ensure the plan addresses include exactly how communications will be maintained and how interactions with emergency services and critical infrastructure personnel will be organized.
- Ensure the protection of data centers and data. Any establishment of a new data center is an important opportunity to build in EMP and radio frequency weapon protection at the outset, which is invariably more cost effective.
- Evaluate possible installation of a microgrid (see Chapter IV: Microgrids).
- Consider whether the organizational planning process has adequately engaged:
  - Others in the larger community who plan for long-term grid outages;
  - Businesses in the same field that may have developed best practices; and
  - Infrastructure experts who understand the overall level of planning and preparation, if any, that is already in place.

Appendix 2 provides a crosswalk of several planning systems. The last one in the table is one of the BCP standards. The Appendix also includes a section on the Federal Emergency Management Agency (FEMA) National Incident Management System (NIMS). Community emergency management personnel will be using NIMS, and specifically the Incident Management System (ICS). Familiarity with ICS will facilitate understanding the high volume of emergency communications and planning discussions during catastrophic events. Finally, Appendix 3 has a "maturity model" that can be used to track preparedness progress by comparing a current self-assessment to future self-assessments conducted after planning initiatives and exercises.

Supply Chain

Appendix 6 is an in depth examination of supply chain resiliency.

In order for urban communities to survive a long-term national grid outage, people should consider sheltering-in-place within the area rather than evacuating, simply because there is probably no better place to resettle. Supplying the urban area is a major challenge. One of the realities of the U.S. economic structure today is that the more a business can shrink its inventory, the more profitable it could become. This business reality runs counter to what is needed for urban areas to be resilient.

Consequently, one approach could be to start at the citizen level, encouraging each household to stockpile certain supplies (see Food in Chapter V). Each business could also maintain certain critical supplies on hand so as to have at least a minimal inventory at the start of an extended grid outage that would support minimal operations for a limited period. Perhaps 20% would be an appropriate goal. A water company, for example, might commit to maintaining an extra supply of chemicals to keep a minimal water supply operational for as long as possible. Another example is that local governments could establish a local grain or food reserve (e.g., freeze dry food, etc.).

If up and then down the supply chain, there is some inventory, coupled with some capability to respond or surge, then the supply chain may continue work, at least to an extent that might make a critical difference. To help get to this point, three disciplined lines of inquiry can help:

1. **What are the relevant core capacities?** Beginning at the lowest level of Maslow's hierarchy, how are individuals, their communities, and their regions supplied with water, food, pharmaceuticals and medical goods, essential medical care, and shelter? How are waste and other dangerous substances treated and removed? This is a strategic inventory of what is needed to survive. Whether the goal is resilience and recovery or transformation,

understanding what and how much is needed is a first step in strategic preparedness. Answers to these questions basically capture the pre-catastrophic status quo.

2. **How and where are the relevant core capabilities sourced, made, delivered, consumed, and returned?** Once what and how much is needed have been identified, how are those needs currently fulfilled? Where are the sources? Where is the making done? What are the key delivery corridors and mechanisms? Who makes? Who delivers? Who consumes, and where does consumption occur? Where are the nodes and links in the overall system? This is basically a map or set of interconnected maps.

3. **What are the key relationships that enable the core capacities?** Not much is made without electricity. Not much is delivered without fuel, roadways, railways, and such. Not much is consumed without a transfer of funds. What are the relationships—human, technical, financial, physical, contractual, and otherwise—on which the core capabilities depend? How do these relationships work? Are there shared choke points? Are there overlapping nodes?

Conducting tabletop exercise or realistic drills is a way to begin answering some of these critical questions, and widespread implementation of this approach may ultimately serve to improve supply chain resilience across the entire nation and throughout global supply chains.

State Government

In a long-term grid failure, state government must play a vital role. Without the government functioning during such disasters, civil society may collapse. The government will need to establish a framework to rebuild if necessary. If state legislation to strengthen critical infrastructure resilience is enacted before an actual catastrophe, frameworks that are understood and exercised at all levels could facilitate the response of states, local communities, businesses, and volunteer organizations in an event where communication and transportation are difficult. Knowing in advance what to do in a major emergency increases the likelihood that people will take the right actions.

The following suggestions are intended to help state governments prepare for a long term wide spread grid outage:

- Recommended legislation—Particularly given that communications will be limited without electrical power, appropriate laws and procedures need to be established now that will help people take the right actions and minimize confusion in the early stages of a disaster. Several examples are set forth below:
  - Consider rationing food, which could begin immediately if the power is out in a region for more than 24 hours. When the power is restored, remove the rationing. If the law is enforced for minor power outages, the public will be accustomed to rationing which would be vital in a severe power outage.

- Restrict use of interstate highways to critical supplies if power is out in a region for more than 24 hours. When power is restored, lift the restriction. If the law is enforced with minor power outages, the public will be accustomed to not using interstates if the power is out, and this could be vital in a long-term power outage.
- Recognizing that most Governors have emergency powers for only 90 days, provide additional authority to the effect that, if the grid fails and power has not been restored in 90 days, the emergency powers are automatically extended until the power is restored.

- Keeping water and wastewater systems functioning is so vital that this could have the highest priority for fuel allocations. The second highest priority for fuel could be for nuclear power plants.[110]
- Encourage local grain or food reserves. Appointing a state czar to orchestrate this effort would be beneficial. Set aside funds each year for procuring and processing reserves. This will help local farmers, as well as prepare for a severe disaster.
- Update COOP plans to include long-term widespread grid outages and ensure that the plans cover the following:
  - Communications without power;
  - Transportation challenges;
  - Credentialing for utility workers, first responders, critical infrastructure staff, cyber experts, etc., relying on a federal credentialing process if that exists; and
  - A "Government Island" (see Chapter VI)—Ideally, for the resilient community island location, obtain a microgrid powered by renewable sources; install a water filtration capability; and stockpile food and medical supplies.
- The state emergency management agency could hold a tabletop exercise focused on a month-long grid failure for key government leaders and then assign after actions to the correct department. Hold a second tabletop exercise after most of the action items have been addressed with a new timeframe of two months. Predesigned threats can be found in the InfraGard EMP SIG Triple Threat Power Grid Exercise book (see Appendix 9).
- Use existing and/or develop educational materials on a long-term widespread grid outage and provide these materials to the general public.
- Examine the state's fatality management plan and update it if necessary to account for appropriately coping with mass fatalities with no electrical power.

---

[110] Emergency restoration plans for power to federally-licensed nuclear power plants remain under federal jurisdiction. The President, the Secretary of Energy, FERC, and the Nuclear Regulatory Commission participate in priority-setting for "blackstart" of nuclear power plants. The Nuclear Energy Institute has coordinated a (SAFER) program to augment backup power and water resupply resiliency at commercial nuclear power plants. Three regional (FLEX) facilities will provide emergency spare equipment, diesel generators, and diesel fuel to protect nuclear power plants and spent fuel pools during Extended Loss of off-site AC power ("ELAC"). Until the FLEX program and on-site emergency diesel generators at nuclear power plants are certified for EMP and severe solar storm resiliency, retention of U.S. nuclear power plants as a Tier 1 power restoration priority may be essential to avert Fukushima-type radiation releases in event of extended loss of outside power.

The National Guard

Since the Nation's founding of our country, the National Guard has been among the first to respond to serious emergencies in the states. The Guard has historically brought not only essential equipment for rescue and recovery, but also a trained force that can sustain operations to assure the government can accomplish its first mission: protecting its citizens. Today, however, there are many who believe that the Guard is not appropriately trained, equipped, and organized to respond and carry out its fundamental protection mission in an operational environment shaped by an extended grid failure.

A 21st century America without power will find itself struggling to exist and will need the National Guard, in coordination with other emergency responders, to provide order, communications, food, water, medical assistance, and many other necessities. Therefore, the Guard must prepare for operations in a new environment, one where support and assistance from traditional partners is extremely limited or completely unavailable. The increased National Guard focus on cyber and power restoration following an attack is excellent and encouraged.

Yet because a long-term grid failure could be devastating, there is concern that the Guard prepare adequately for off-grid operability so that it is not rendered "inoperative" like most of the country's institutions. Both the states and the federal government will depend upon the National Guard for emergency operational support. This capability may depend in turn upon whole of community support to the National Guard in extended emergencies.

No organization, not even our active duty forces, is adequately planning for such a cataclysmic event. Therefore, it is up to the Guard leadership, both at the National Guard Bureau and in each of the states and territories, to prepare to meet this challenge.

The Guard and its supporting organizations (e.g., state departments of emergency management, FEMA, NORTHCOM, and others) all rely on mutual support during disasters from a resilient, operating society, one that can generate the necessary tools of recovery (i.e., communications, transportation, food, water, shelter and more) to deliver the necessary relief from other parts of the country not affected by the disaster. With the possibility of a large region being affected by wide spread long term grid outage, the support via FEMA or EMACs (Emergency Management Assistance Compacts) might likewise be affected by the event and severely limit or perhaps eliminate any support.

The following steps are suggestions that could enable the National Guard to better respond to such an event:

- Work with experts who are familiar with the debilitating effects, no matter the specific cause, and identify how key systems will be affected and how to mitigate the damage that will be done to those systems in order to conduct the operations necessary for a successful response and recovery.

- Identify critical resources that will be essential to a response, such as power, communications, transportation, food and water.
- Shield these critical resources against an EMP event (see Appendix 9 References).
- Store key supplies that might be hard to secure during an extended emergency. (e.g., food, water, fuel, and ammunition). Anticipate the need for re-supply and develop plans to replenish the stores when they run out.
- Coordinate with local first responders to determine their capabilities and limitations following a long term grid outage. Focus especially on communication and transportation.
- Identify key personnel essential to a response and take steps to ensure their readiness attendance. The necessity to care for loved ones might limit personnel availability, and thus a plan to care for the families of those called to duty would help to ensure units are fully manned and mission-focused. Being part of a resilient community island could be considered and planned ahead.
- Coordinate with neighboring states, NORTHCOM, and FEMA to understand their plans and capabilities and how they might assist. Be sure to understand their limitations as the Guard and emergency management will have to fill the gap.
- Develop microgrids shielded against EMP to ensure a reliable source of power for essential operations. Consider partnering with civilian and Title 10 installations for a more robust, resilient recovery capability.
- Leverage the capabilities of volunteer organizations that could work with the National Guard, such as the National Guard Auxiliary, Coast Guard Auxiliary, Civil Air Patrol, and Neighborhood Watch.

The challenges posed by long term wide spread grid outage can be overcome by foresight and planning. It is up to the National Guard to lead in the preparation for such an event. Guard leaders should fully recognize the magnitude of the threat and the compelling urgency to prepare for an extended grid outage—whether caused by a solar flare, EMP attack, or a cyberattack. Not to prepare for this catastrophic contingency when the warning signs are so clear would be a dereliction of duty.

With respect to the resilience of the National Guard itself, "closed military bases" are potential locations to reposition Guard assets if necessary A substantial number of "closed" military bases have been repurposed as Command, Control, Communications, Computers and Intelligence (C4I) assets, often operated by civilian contractor entities working for the federal government. Some of these facilities include ground stations for space satellite systems that are designed to "operate through" EMP environments. Consequently, if National Guard units relocate to some of these bases, it might be possible to tie civilian emergency operations into DOD telecommunications expected to remain operational in the aftermath of an EMP-type scenario. It is expensive to have civilian infrastructure redesigned for post-EMP operations, and thus National Guard assets might prove a low-cost backdoor channel to link civilian emergency operations at the state and county levels to the DOD/Intelligence Community networks.

State Emergency Management Agencies

The state emergency management agency works with its state government and the National Guard to be prepared for a long term wide spread grid outage. Updating COOP plans and holding table top exercises would be beneficial. State emergency management agencies have primary and back-up sites, which would ideally have EMP protection for their communications and critical data. The state depends on their resilience. They may start planning for participation in a state government resilient community island.

Federal Government

The October 28, 2015 National Space Weather Action Plan, coordinated by the White House Office of Science and Technology Policy, calls for international scientific cooperation to better understand impacts of solar storms and appropriate mitigation measures.[111]

The Department of Homeland Security (DHS) and the Federal Emergence Management Agency (FEMA) play vital roles in being prepared for a long term wide spread grid outage. If the event is nation-wide, neither DHS nor FEMA will be able to respond as they do with other emergencies. They depend on businesses for supplies, and the businesses themselves will be struggling. As with other organizations, FEMA and other DHS personnel will need to care for their own families unless provisions are make for those with family members. The FEMA communications system will be vital in supporting communications throughout the country. Links with the state emergency management agencies will be important to help the federal government monitor what is happening through the country. FEMA's role in orchestrating international assistance providing food, medical supplies and equipment would also be critical.

The following steps are suggestions to help the federal government prepare for a long-term wide spread grid outage:

- Provide immunity for public utilities so they could harden the grid for an EMP, which would also mean they were hardened for space weather.
- Update continuity of operations plans (COOP) to address long term grid outage taking special note of challenges associated with:
  - Limited communications;
  - Travel;
  - International agreements to obtain food and supplies;
  - Supply chains; and

---

[111] 2015 National Space Weather Strategy, White House National Science & Technology Council

- Maintaining order.
- Educate the public and the private sector on detailed preparedness plans to give everyone confidence and knowledge of what to do (use Guide content to help shape educational materials). Establish a nation-wide credentialing procedure so that utility workers, first responders, critical infrastructure staff, cyber experts and others can be on the highways to help restore the grid, keep law and order, and generally restore the nation's operations. Doing this at the national level, not just within a state, would help assure that people can cross state boundaries easily.
- Refine international assistance planning and establish MOUs with other countries to help if there is a wide spread whole of nation incident (see Appendix 7).

Department of Defense (DOD)

The DOD role will be different depending on whether the grid outage is caused by terrorist activity or an act of nature. DOD support will be critical no matter the cause.

Some of the steps DOD could take now to enhance its readiness include:

- Prioritize understanding the complex dimensions of all of the threats to the electrical grid;
- Review prior Y2K plans and update them to today's threat realities; and.
- Conduct tabletop exercises with both terrorist and solar storm scenarios (see the predesigned exercise material in the InfraGard EMP SIG Triple Threat Power Grid Exercise book and Appendix 9). Departmental exercises should involve NORTHCOM participation (see below).

As the designated combatant commander for the homeland, NORTHCOM would coordinate DOD support operations and activities across the country in the event of an extended grid outage.

Steps NORTHCOM could take to enhance its readiness include the following:

- Prioritize understanding all of the threats to the electrical grid, the relevant preparedness guidelines, and the response actions if the grid fails;
- Review prior Y2K plans and update them to today's threat realities; and
- Conduct tabletop exercises involving terrorist and solar storm scenarios (see the predesigned exercise material in the InfraGard EMP SIG Triple Threat Power Grid Exercise book and Appendix 9). NORTHCOM tabletop exercises should involve participation by DOD and other DOD entity stakeholders.

Recruiting, Training and Retaining Critical Volunteer Staff

Many of our current emergency management and disaster response services are provided by volunteers ranging from emergency medical technicians, firefighters, Red Cross volunteers, Coast Guard and National Guard Auxiliaries, Civil Air Patrol and numerous other volunteer and faith-based organizations. Many of these volunteers have professional training and licensing.

However, virtually all of the time, these volunteer groups are understaffed. During difficult economic periods, even fewer volunteers are available because of their need to obtain more financial resources. Ironically, when a major high-impact disaster hits, many of the already understaffed volunteer resources will not be available. Perhaps as many as half or more volunteers will need to focus on their own problems and hence will not be readily available. There will also be fewer volunteers available to travel outside their areas and team up with other volunteers going to a single region of the country caught in a major disaster. Realistically, few mutual assistance commitments will be met. Additionally, the high-impact threat scenarios are the same ones that demand more volunteer resources, far more than a typical local or regional disaster. Yet, after a disaster event, it will be hard to find, vet and train volunteers. For these reasons, it is important to embrace local volunteer organizations now and help them create new ways to recruit, train and retain volunteers now.

An example of how EMP SIG leadership has encouraged volunteer participation is the extension of the program used by the Maryland volunteer fire fighter program that provides state tax incentives for certified training and services rendered and validated during the course of a year. It could be helpful for local jurisdictions and leaders at groups such as the National Governors Association, the National Association of Counties, and the National Association of State Legislatures to develop a triple set of tax incentives ranging from income, property and sales taxes for volunteer services. Tax and financial policy experts at these organizations could determine how much incentive might be given for every dollar of service rendered. By providing sample templates of local and state laws, different jurisdictions could more rapidly develop meaningful incentives for volunteers in their areas. That could also include training and education incentives.

Those interested in this vital topic should consider joining the EMP SIG policy and volunteer working groups considering these policy recommendations. They might also consider initiating discussions of the related issues in their neighborhoods and communities, as well as with local volunteer organizations and elected officials.

Chapter VIII: Response and Recovery in Long-Duration Nationwide Grid Failures

There are different grid failure scenarios. Some scenarios depict catastrophic events, while others could be less severe. In fact, people are accustomed to the electrical power going out and then coming back quickly or in a few hours or even a few days. Hurricanes Sandy and Katrina both resulted in people being without power for weeks.

This Guide is focused on preparations for a long-term grid outage where the grid fails throughout the country. In a nation-wide grid failure, there would be no transporting of generators and their technical support from one part of the country to another as there was during Sandy. The federal government will not be able to rescue most Americans within three days of the catastrophe's commencement.

The matrix in Table 4 presents recommended actions that different key actors could take at different times during a long term outage. All of these sequenced actions would be vital for a severe scenario. However, if the scenario is not so severe and power is restored by the end of the first month, then completing only the actions specified for "2nd/3rd Day" and "2 Weeks" could be considered a "full scale response," and so forth. Taking these recommended actions into account in designing and conducting exercises should help to enhance national resilience if a catastrophic scenario were to occur. Implementing these recommended actions in an actual severe scenario would likely save lives and expedites national recovery.

The philosophy reflected in Table 4's matrix is a bias to take action early before doing so seems absolutely necessary. This approach may prove more likely to minimize cascading events that often make a bad situation worse. For example, if Governors move early to restrict interstate use to transport fuel, food, any supplies for grid restoration, etc., there is more of a chance the highways could be kept open for these critical goods to flow. If the action is delayed, however, evacuees with no safe haven to flee to may overwhelm the highways, with many running out of gas, thus abandon their vehicles, clogging the highways, and delaying recovery.

Anticipatory staging is a time-tested approach for contingency readiness that allows for more immediate response and flexibility. Planners and decision makers could determine and practice sound staging practices. One example could be a policy that, in the event of a complete communications loss, state highway patrol members would mobilize in key locations (such as the capital and along key highway routes) and stand by for further orders that may arrive by courier. Similarly, National Guard units can be staged in locations close to where they are likely to be needed should conditions warrant ordering them into action.

Such staging should also include carefully thought-out stockpiling (caching) of expected critical equipment and supplies such that extended operations may be conducted without resupply. This is commonly referred to as "days of supply" on hand, and it is important to understand how many days of supply are available for each staged and deployed resource. For example, it may be prudent to provide key mobile resources such that highway patrol and utility line workers can maintain three days of supply in their vehicles at all times. This approach would track with the Marine Corps requirement that all units maintain the ability to operate for at least three days without resupply. Additional days of supply could be cached in staging areas or at preset resupply points. Planning for staging could include flexibility for different scenarios such that it balances flexibility with appropriate resource critical mass. Care could also be taken to avoid overly-centralized staging or spreading staged assets too thinly to be effective or protected.

Table 4 includes suggestions to map out recommended actions by key actors as an extended grid outage crisis unfolds. Substantial additional work is required to complete and revise the phasing of proactive and responsive actions, and Guide users are invited to provide their comments and suggestions in this regard.

Proposed actions for the 2nd/3rd day and more extended periods are predicated upon power outages that have continued for the entire state and a larger region throughout the specified time period.

Table 4: Time-Phased Recommended Actions in a Widespread Extended Grid Outage.

Key Actors	2nd/3rd Day of Widespread Outage	2 Weeks	1 Month	2 Months
State, Tribal or Territorial Executive	Consider declaring a State of Emergency as well as: 1. Mobilizing National Guard. 2. Banning travel on Interstates, except fuel, medical, food & critical CI supplies. 3. Rationing food & water. 4. Setting curfews. 5. Assigning fuel priorities for: water & wastewater	If international or other outside food assistance available, determine distribution plan including logistics. If "government island" established, locate government there with National Guard & families – could also serve as a Point of Distribution (POD) for goods.	Reassess known resources & priorities. Determine viability of maintaining population sheltering in place. Identify & take steps to obtain relief for population & key businesses.	Rebuild framework for governance as necessary. Communicate with federal & local governments. Reassess critical capability & ensure monitoring of water supply & wastewater contamination. Encourage local agriculture (e.g., Victory Gardens &

Key Actors	2nd/3rd Day of Widespread Outage	2 Weeks	1 Month	2 Months
	systems, nuclear power plants, prisons & hospitals. 6. Determining need for emergency financing for government & high priority tasks/services. 7. Activating a credentialing procedure.	Inventory & examine fuel set aside for public safety. Initiate request to Strategic Petroleum Reserve.	Determine means to link & expand "resilient community islands."	fisheries). Consider work projects with IOUs as required – or if food, work for food basis. Promote resilient community island networking. Determine how "soup lines" could function.
State, Tribal or Territorial Legislature	Assess whether any emergency laws are needed.	Authorize emergency bonds to fund recovery. Decide whether to go to the state resilient community island with families.	Continue working with Executive Branch to facilitate response and recovery.	
National Guard	Help to maintain law & order as directed. Assess possible use of closed military bases.	Support response & recovery under state direction unless federalized per Title 10		
Title 10 of the U.S. Code details the organization and authority of active duty forces and the reserve forces of each branch of the active military services. Forces under Title 10 authority serve at the direction of the president. When the National Guard is mobilized for its war-fighting mission (such as in Iraq and Afghanistan), they are operating under Title 10 authority.				
Title 32 of the U, S. Code details the organization and authority of the National Guard when under the command and control of the governor of their respective states. Typically, Title 32 is used for missions where the governor, through the adjutant general, exercises command and control over the National Guard mission (such as annual training), but mission operations are paid for by the Federal government. Another status under which the National Guard operates is state active duty (SAD). SAD is ordered and paid for by the state, and typically involves emergencies organic to the borders of a state (e.g., fires, floods, etc.). The governor directs National Guard units on SAD.				
DOD	<u>Note</u>: recommended actions would depend on the event.			
In the event that there was a widespread extended grid failure caused by EMP, DOD has forensics teams to help assign responsibility for this act of war. http://www.army.mil/article/154305/20th_CBRNE_Command_supports_Prominent_Hunt				

Key Actors	2nd/3rd Day of Widespread Outage	2 Weeks	1 Month	2 Months
NORTHCOM	Note: recommended actions would depend on the event.			
State, Tribal or Territorial Emergency Management Agency	Execute normal emergency actions in coordination with local communities & FEMA.	Maintain response and recovery activity.		
Local Government	Keep citizens informed. Maintain law & order. Ensure water & wastewater operations. Activate credentialing procedures as necessary & directed.	Encourage schools to remain open, with parents as teachers if needed. Consider resilient community islanding. Continue information flow. Obtain chlorine for water supplies.	Reassess known resources & priorities. Determine viability of maintaining population sheltering in place. Identify & take steps to provide relief for population and key businesses. Determine means to link & expand "resilient community islands."	Encourage community activities to keep people together.
Local Emergency & First Responders	Secure fuel supplies for water/ wastewater, prisons & hospitals. Protect food & drug warehouses & retail outlets. Provide traffic control.	Facilitate delivery of food assistance from international & other sources to the right people & communities. Protect water & wastewater systems/nuclear power plants/ prisons/healthcare		Ensure that local government is functioning & coordinating with other levels of government. Hold elections as needed.

Key Actors	2nd/3rd Day of Widespread Outage	2 Weeks	1 Month	2 Months
		facilities. Also protect the supply chain is important.		
Power Industry	If appropriate, blackstart via critical cranking paths. Execute FLEX resupplies for nuclear plants.	Review & take advantage of as many regional mutual assistance programs as possible. Allocate available power as per established priority list, particularly water & wastewater systems, hospitals & emergency support. Consider DOE mandatory access rights & interconnections authority (15-day emergency powers).	Grid Islands functioning – trying to tie together? Redirect fuel supplies.	
Telecomm-unications Note: Survivable telecoms would be critical to maintaining public trust.	Use FEMA National Radio System (FNARS) for USG agency communications with state governors & tribal/territorial officials. Rely on community emergency broadcasting systems for radio communications to citizens. Deploy emergency	Continue using emergency broadcasting stations for radio communications for the public. Establish resilient community island communications.	Resilient Community and Grid Island communications of how things are going and what Once resilient communities/ grid islands have power, prioritize establishing a two-way communications	

Key Actors	2nd/3rd Day of Widespread Outage	2 Weeks	1 Month	2 Months
	telecommunication systems as appropriate. Use MARS for DOD communications.		network to exchange information on current conditions, recover status, and available/ needed resources.	
Water & Wastewater	Prioritize systems requiring minimal pumping & pressure. Inventory available fuel on hand, review projected fuel requirements for minimum essential service, and confirm fuel resupply arrangements.	Review & confirm fuel resupply arrangements. Survey all water sources.	Resurvey, protect & seek to augment safe water supplies.	
Food	Even though still in early stages of the event, consider rationing food to promote greater equality of access.	Consider all possible domestic & international sources of food. Initiate appropriate notifications & requests.	Identify food supplies/ sources & distribute bulk food to the extent possible.	Continue food distribution to the extent possible. Encourage people to start growing at least some of their own food. Initiate food growing by Resilient Community Islands.
Transport-ation	Consider enacting a credentialing system for first responders & key CI personnel. Designate transportation logistics coordinators to oversee movement	Keep ports open & operational to the extent possible, in part by relying on ships in port to use their own power. Seek to ensure rail	Continuously reassess fuel and maintenance requirements against available & projected resources.	Prepare to provide transport as rolling blackouts support a return to some limited CI production.

Key Actors	2nd/3rd Day of Widespread Outage	2 Weeks	1 Month	2 Months
	of fuel, food & critical CI supplies. Obtain waivers/ passes as necessary to assure driver access to highways, ports, distribution facilities, etc.	transport available for supplies. If possible, use sailboats for coastal cargo transport and for fishing. Consider the use IOUs in support of supply chain operations.		
Financial	Communicate to the public that the loss of power essentially brings ATM withdrawals & other regular banking to a halt, but that funds on deposit remain safe. Consider establishing an IOU/credit system & announce the initiative.	Encourage exchange and barter for goods and services. Introduce IOU/ credit system if possible.		Monitor & support where possible the ongoing use of exchange, barter, and IOUs/credit as alternatives to normal financial transactions.
Medical & Public Health	Assemble and/or develop public health bulletins on various critical topics to be communicated periodically as necessary.	Deploy strategic national stockpile (e.g., supplies &medication). Set up FMS/field hospitals from storage. Partner with community groups to distribute foodstuffs. Stress prevention over treatment. Employ hospital ships if/when available.	Recognizing that most medical facilities may be closed by this point, continue ongoing survey of open hospitals, clinics & pharmacies to assess level of services available & safeguard supplies.	If not already engaged, consider Medical Reserve Corps, particularly in support of the resilient community islands.

Key Actors	2nd/3rd Day of Widespread Outage	2 Weeks	1 Month	2 Months
		Initiate an ongoing survey of open hospitals, clinics & pharmacies to assess level of services available & safeguard supplies.		
Business	If generator power available, consider printing most vital records and/or initiating an orderly shutdown of computer resources.	If not yet in place, implement Business Continuity Plan. Initiate bartering, IOUs, or some other means of obtaining goods & services.	Participate in a resilient community island if possible	
Supply Chain	Begin coordination with transportation providers to ensure continued flow of cargoes.	If not yet in place, implement Business Continuity Plan. Continue close coordination with transportation providers to ensure continued flow of cargoes, particularly high priority fuel, food, and CI supplies.		
Non-Governmental Organizations (NGOs) Examples include Red Cross & Volunteers Active in Disasters (VOAD)	Review contingency plans for extended grid outages (or other disasters with comparable impacts).	Assist with distribution of food & medical supplies. Assist with communications. If not already linked to and supporting a resilient community island, consider initiating a relationship.	Continue proving support	Provide support for public health efforts & any hospital resilient community islands. If participating in a resilient community island, plan to link & network all resilient community islands within a reasonable distance.

Key Actors	2nd/3rd Day of Widespread Outage	2 Weeks	1 Month	2 Months
Faith-Based Organizations Note: Some of these organizations may be part of VOAD, etc.		Assist with food distribution. Provide gathering place to facilitate distributions, particularly if alternative power is available. Bring people together spiritually, help them see a future recovery, and organize them in helping others.	Participate in resilient community islands	Continue assisting with food distribution. Continue bringing people together spiritually, helping them see a future recovery, and organizing them in helping others.
Universities	Start planning the resilient community islands & decide which students will stay on campus).	Establish resilient community islands. Provide a place for distribution of supplies. Support communications efforts.	Plan for multi-month outage	If participating in a resilient community island, plan to link & network all resilient community islands within a reasonable distance.
Community – Urban	Follow rules on rationing, roads, etc. Listen to radio for emergency information broadcasts.	Stay in the city. Prioritize continued operation of water & wastewater systems. Form Neighborhood Resilient Community Islands for communications. Keep children in school if possible. Rely on Ham radio operators for needed	Stay in the city. Know safe water sources. Maintain neighborhood resilient community islands, to include "community watch" functioning.	Stay in the city. Form networks of resilient community islands. If rolling blackouts provide some electrical power, work for communications at a set time in am and pm. Learn to dry food (fish if OK) to have for the next several weeks. Form teams to help each other – plan ways

Key Actors	2nd/3rd Day of Widespread Outage	2 Weeks	1 Month	2 Months
		communications.		to keep busy & productive.

If an option, stay engaged with a resilient community island & explore networking of resilient community islands. |
| **Community – Rural** | Follow rules on rationing, roads, etc.

Listen to radio for emergency information broadcasts. | Go to schools for information.

Participate in a resilient community island if possible.

Keep children in schools.

Plant if possible to have food for the future. | Know safe water sources.

Maintain neighborhood resilient community islands, especially "community watch" functioning. | Participate in working with & helping others.

Grow as much food as possible. |
| **Citizens** | Follow rules on rationing, roads, etc.

Listen to radio for emergency information broadcasts. | Go to schools (or resilient community island) for information.

Participate in a resilient community island if possible

Determine how to obtain food and water.

Keep children in school if possible to keep them occupied & learning.

Create work projects with | Know safe water sources.

Participate in neighborhood resilient community islands, especially "community watch" functioning.

Start planning for multi-month outage. | Grow as much food as possible.

Help others as much as possible.

If rolling blackouts provide some electrical power, plan activities accordingly.

If in a resilient community island, start working on networking of resilient community islands. |

Key Actors	2nd/3rd Day of Widespread Outage	2 Weeks	1 Month	2 Months
		neighbors or others in community to stay busy – volunteering to help others can be healthy & rewarding. Participate in Neighborhood Watch, Citizens Corps, CERTs, VOADs, faith-based communities, etc.		

Table 4: Time-Phased Recommended Actions in a Widespread Extended Grid Outage.

Chapter IX: Conclusion

At its heart, this Guide is a "**CALL TO ACTION**".

The success of this Guide will be determined by the extent to which Americans are inspired to act now to make their part of the country more resilient. The threats that underscore the importance of resilience are real, and everyone has a part to play.

At the most fundamental level, the answer to this call to action is all Americans preparing themselves, their families, their businesses and their communities to respond to and recover from a widespread extended grid failure or other catastrophic even. Beyond the importance of universal citizen involvement, there are hundreds of thousands of Americans—including first responders, emergency managers, governors, adjutant generals, hospital directors, water systems managers, electric utility operators, transportation coordinators, National Guard personnel, Red Cross officials, and countless others—who have additional roles and responsibilities that are vital to national preparedness and resilience.

It is important to acknowledge that not all Americans have the same amount of time and resources to devote to emergency planning. However, even those less fortunate in these respects may be in a position to take certain basic actions that will likely benefit themselves and, by extension, the entire country in a catastrophic scenario. Examples include simply filling and storing plastic bottles of water (refreshing them every six months) and buying an extra bag of rice or other long shelf-life food item every so often to stockpile for emergency stores. Even these limited actions, taken collectively, represent significant contributions to the entire country's ability to weather the initial stages of disaster and implement the changes necessary to support long-term survival and ultimate recovery.

Ultimately, the daunting task of ensuring national preparedness and resilience will require the commitment of every American. The shared goal should be much greater readiness for catastrophic disasters than is the case today—with the understanding that real progress will undoubtedly not only pay dividends in the many not-so-severe scenarios that will definitely happen, but will also provide the basis for survival and recovery if one of the plausible catastrophic worst-case scenarios ever occurs.

There will be a second edition of this Guide; and reader feedback and suggestions would be greatly appreciated. The InfraGard EMP SIG™ and the many contributing authors all believe the Guide would benefit greatly from readers' experiences in the field, their perspectives on preparedness and resilience, and their candid assessments of first edition content.

The feedback can help with the initial planning for Version 2.0 which includes:

1. Exploring and reporting the risks, costs and benefits of alternative resilient strategies for the lifeline sectors of energy, communications, water/wastewater, food, public health and transportation;

2. Modeling and prototyping the resilient community island concept for urban and rural communities;

3. Capturing the "best practices" of all the critical infrastructure sectors and involving them in taking action to be more resilient; and

4. Involving all levels of government in the quest to become more resilient for long-term, nation-wide grid failures.

Coordinator's Note:

Thank you for reading this Action Guide. "Thank you" to all the authors, those who participated in weekly discussion and especially to Bill Harris, Chuck Manto and Steve Volandt.

Mary Lasky

APPENDIX 1: Acronyms and Glossary

Acronyms

AESO	Alberta Electric System Operator
BCP	Business Continuity Planning
BES	Bulk Electric System
CDC	Centers for Disease Control and Prevention
CEA	Controlled Environment Agriculture
CERT	Community Emergency Response Team, *or*
CERT	Cyber Emergency Response Team
CI	Critical Infrastructure
CIKR	Critical Infrastructure and Key Resources
CIP	Critical Infrastructure Protection (NERC Standards)
CMS	Center Management System
CONOPS	Concept of Operations
COOP	Continuity of Operations Planning
CPG	Comprehensive Preparedness Guide
DHHS	Department of Health and Human Services
DHS	Department of Homeland Security
DoD	Department of Defense
D-SNAP	Disaster Supplemental Nutrition Assistance Program
DTRA	Defense Threat Reduction Agency
E-ISAC	Electricity Information Sharing and Analysis Center
EFFAK	Emergency Financial First Aid Kit
ELAP	Extended Loss of AC Power. A contingency linked to requirements for on-site backup power and security
EMP	Electromagnetic Pulse

EMP SIG	Electromagnetic Pulse Special Interest Group
EOC	Emergency Operations Center
EOP	Emergency Operation Plan
ERCOT	Electric Reliability Council of Texas
ERO	Electric Reliability Organization, currently NERC
FEMA	Federal Emergency Management Agency
FERC	Federal Energy Regulatory Commission
FLEX	Nuclear Energy Facilities Strategy to Enhance Safety
FNRS	FEMA National Radio System
FNS	Food and Nutrition Service
FPDPH	Federal Plan Development Process Handbook
FRCC	Florida Reliability Coordinating Council
GCC	Government Coordinating Council
GIC	Geomagnetic Induced Currents
GMD	Geomagnetic Disturbance
GPS	Global Positioning System
HAM	Amateur radio
HEMP	High Altitude Electromagnetic Pulse
HF	High Frequency
HIT	High Impact Threats
HSEEP	Homeland Security Exercise and Evaluation Program
IAS	International Assistance System
ICS	Incident Control System
ICS	Industrial Control System

IESO	Independent Electricity System Operator (Province of Ontario)
IMT	Incident Management Team
INMA	InfraGard National Member Alliance
IoT	Internet of Things
IP	Infrastructure Protection
IRCG	International Resources Coordination Group
ISO-NE	Independent System Operator, ISO New England Inc.
IT	Information Technology
JIC	Joint Information Center
LNG	Liquid Natural Gas
LOOP	Loss of Outside Power. Generally requires depowering of nuclear power plants.
LTO	Long-Term Outage
MAC	Multi-Agency Coordination
MARS	Military Auxiliary Radio System
MIL STD	Military Standard
MISO	Midcontinent Independent System Operator
MREs	Meals Ready to Eat
MRO	Midwest Reliability Organization
MTA	Mission Tasking Assignment (DoD)
NBSO	New Brunswick System Operator
NCC	National Coordinating Center
NCCIC	National Cybersecurity & Communications Integration Center
NERC	North American Electric Reliability C
NEUCC	National Emergency Utility Consumables Council

NFPA	National Fire Protection Association
NGO	Non-Government Organization
NGAUS	National Guard Association United States
NIAC	National Infrastructure Advisory Council
NIPP	National Infrastructure Protection Plan
NOAA	National Oceanic and Atmospheric Administration
NPCC	Northeast Power Coordinating Council
NRC	Nuclear Regulatory Commission
NRCC	National Response Coordination Center
NYISO	New York Independent System Operator
PEAK	Peak Reliability (separated from WECC in 2014)
PIO	Public Information Officer
PJM	PJM Interconnection LLC
PMU	Phasor Measurement Unit
POD	Point of Distribution
PPD	Presidential Policy Directive
RCPGP	Regional Catastrophic Preparedness Grant Program
RFC	Reliability First Corporation
RFP	Request for Proposal
RFW	Radio Frequency Weapons
RMAG	Regional Mutual Assistance Group
RRAP	Regional Resiliency Assessment Program
SATCOM	Strategic Communications (military)
SCADA	Supervisory Control and Data Acquisition
SERC	Southeast (SERC) Electric Reliability Corporation
SHARES	SHAred RESources High Frequency Radio

SLTT	State, Local, Tribal and Territorial
SOCO	Southern Company Services Inc.
SPC	Saskatchewan Power Corporation
SPP	Southwest Power Pool
SSA	Sector Specific Agency
SSP	Sector Specific Plan
TE	Hydro-Québec TransÉnergie
TRE	Texas Reliability Entity
TVA	Tennessee Valley Authority
UPS	Uninterruptable Power System
USAID	United States Agency for International Development
USDA	United States Department of Agriculture
VACAR-S	Virginia Carolinas (VACAR) South Reliability Coordinator
VOAD	Volunteers Active in Disasters
WECC	Western Electricity Coordinating Council

Glossary

Note: Material for some of the definitions is taken from: the DoD Joint Publication 1-02, November 8, 2010 as amended; Department of Defense Dictionary of Military and Associated Terms, January 15, 2016. http://www.dtic.mil/doctrine/new_pubs/jp1_02.pdf; and from Report on the FERC-NERC-Regional Entity Joint Review of Restoration and Recovery Plans, January 2016, Appendix 4, Glossary, pp. 113-117.

Balancing Authority—The responsible entity within the bulk electric system that integrates resource plans ahead of time, maintains load-interchange-generation balance within a Balancing Authority Area, and supports interconnection frequency in real time.

Blackstart Resource—Generating unit and associated equipment with the ability to initiate start-up without support from the Bulk Electric System (BES) or designed to remain energized without connection to the remainder of the BES, including the ability to energize a bus, meeting the transmission operator's restoration plan needs for real and reactive power capability, frequency, and voltage control; a designated "blackstart" or "system restoration" resource included in the transmission operator's restoration plan.

Bulk Electric System—The electrical generation resources, transmission lines, interconnections with neighboring systems, and associated equipment, generally operated at voltages of 100 kV or higher. Also called BES.

Complex catastrophe—A natural or man-made incident, including cyber-space attack, power grid failure, and terrorism, that results in cascading failures of multiple interdependent, critical, life-sustaining infrastructure sectors and causes extraordinary levels of mass casualties, damage, or disruption severely affecting the population, environment, economy, public health, national morale, response efforts, and/or government functions (DSCA-DoD Directive 3025.18 [2015]).

Consequence management—Measures taken to protect public health and safety, restore essential government services, and provide emergency relief to governments, businesses, and individuals affected by the *consequences* of a chemical, biological, nuclear, and/or high-yield explosive situation.

Cranking Path—A portion of the electric system that can be isolated and then energized to deliver electric power from a generation source to enable the startup of one or more other generating units.

Cybersecurity—Damage prevention, protection, and restoration of computers, electronic communications systems, electronic communications services, wire communication, and electronic communication, including information contained therein, to ensure its availability, integrity, authentication, confidentiality, and nonrepudiation (DODI 8500.01).

Defense Support of Civil Authorities (DSCA)—Support provided by U.S. federal military forces, Department of Defense civilians, Department of Defense contract personnel, Department of Defense component assets, and National Guard forces (when the Secretary of Defense, in coordination with the governors of the affected states, elects and requests to use those forces in Title 32, United States Code, status) in response to requests for assistance from civil authorities for domestic emergencies, law enforcement support, and other domestic activities, or from qualifying entities for special events. Also called DSCA. Also called civil support (DODD 3025.18).

Defense critical infrastructure—Department of Defense and non-Department of Defense networked assets and facilities essential to project, support, and sustain military forces and operations worldwide. Also called DCI (JP 3-27).

Electromagnetic pulse (EMP)—The electromagnetic radiation from a strong electronic pulse, most commonly caused by a nuclear explosion that may couple with electrical or electronic systems to produce damaging current and voltage surges. Also called EMP. See also electromagnetic radiation (JP 3-13.1). It can also be generated by non-nuclear devices with short range. As in a coordinated physical attack, a coordinated use of high-powered microwaves and similar intentional electromagnetic interference (IEMI) weapons could be significant.

Emergency authority—A federal military commander's authority, in extraordinary emergency circumstances where prior authorization by the President is impossible and duly constituted local authorities are unable to control the situation, to engage temporarily in activities that are necessary to quell large-scale, unexpected civil disturbances because: (1) such activities are necessary to prevent significant loss of life or wanton destruction of property and are necessary to restore governmental function and public order; or (2) duly constituted federal, state, or local authorities are unable or decline to provide adequate protection for federal property or federal governmental functions (DODD 3025.18).

Emergency support functions—A grouping of government and certain private-sector capabilities into an organizational structure to provide the support, resources, program implementation, and services that are most likely to be needed to save lives, protect property and the environment, restore essential services and critical infrastructure, and help victims and communities return to normal, when feasible, following domestic incidents. Also called ESFs (JP 3-28).

Emergency preparedness—Measures taken in advance of an emergency to reduce the loss of life and property and to protect a nation's institutions from all types of hazards through a comprehensive emergency management program of preparedness, mitigation, response, and recovery. Also called EP (JP 3-28).

Emergency preparedness liaison officer—A senior reserve officer who represents their Service at the appropriate joint field office conducting planning and coordination responsibilities in support of civil authorities. Also called EPLO (JP 3-28).

Federal service—A term applied to National Guard members and units when called to active duty to serve the United States government under Article I, Section 8 and Article II, Section 2 of the Constitution and Title 10, United States Code, Sections 12401 to 12408. See also active duty; Reserve Component (JP 4-05).

Full mobilization—Expansion of the active Armed Forces resulting from action by Congress and the President to mobilize for the duration of the emergency plus six months all Reserve Component units and individuals in the existing approved force structure, as well as all retired military personnel, and the resources needed for their support to meet the requirements of a war or other national emergency involving an external threat to the national security (JP 4-05).

Governance—The state's ability to serve the citizens through the rules, processes, and behavior by which interests are articulated, resources are managed, and power is exercised in a society, including the representative participatory decision-making processes typically guaranteed under inclusive, constitutional authority (JP 3-24).

Grid island—See "Island, electrical" and Appendix 5.

Homeland defense—The protection of United States sovereignty, territory, domestic population, and critical infrastructure against external threats and aggression or other threats as directed by the President. Also called HD (JP 3-27).

Homeland security—A concerted national effort to prevent terrorist attacks within the United States; reduce America's vulnerability to terrorism, major disasters, and other emergencies; and minimize the damage and recover from attacks, major disasters, and other emergencies that occur. Also called HS (JP 3-27).

Incident awareness and assessment—The Secretary of Defense approved use of Department of Defense intelligence, surveillance, reconnaissance, and other intelligence capabilities for domestic non-intelligence support for defense support of civil authorities. Also called IAA (JP 3-28).

Incident Command System—A standardized on-scene emergency management construct designed to aid in the management of resources during incidents. Also called ICS (JP 3-28).

Island, electrical—An electrically isolated portion of an interconnection. The frequency in an electrical island must be maintained by balancing generation and load in order to sustain operation. Islands are frequently formed after major disturbances wherein multiple transmission lines trip, or during restoration following a major disturbance.

Martial law—The military exercise of government and the military control of occupied areas during the collapse of civil authorities or during military operations of an occupying power. Martial law may involve the suspension of civil courts, and may include the appointment of a military governor. Martial law may be imposed temporarily by the President, by a governor, or by a municipal officer. In the United States, martial law was imposed by Major General Andrew Jackson in New Orleans (1814), by President Lincoln in the Civil War (1861), by the Governor of Hawaii after Pearl Harbor (1941), and by President Roosevelt for Pacific Coast states and Arizona (1942) to enforce curfews and other security measures. Only the Congress has authority to suspend the writ of *habeas corpus*. The military cannot perform law enforcement functions under the Posse Comitatus Act, nor can the military try civilians in states where the federal judiciary is functioning. See also "Defense Assistance to Civil Authorities," whereby armed forces and national guard units may assist civil authorities in lieu of martial law.

National Incident Management System—A national crisis response system that provides a consistent, nationwide approach for federal, state, local, and tribal governments; the private sector; and nongovernmental organizations to work effectively and efficiently together to prepare for, respond to, and recover from domestic incidents, regardless of cause, size, or complexity. Also called NIMS (JP 3-41).

Phasor Measurement Unit—Device that measures the electrical waves on an electricity grid, using a common time source for synchronization. Also called PMU, an element of a synchronized phasor or "synchrophasor network."

Recovery and reconstitution— (1) Those actions taken by one nation prior to, during, and following an attack by an enemy nation to minimize the effects of the attack, rehabilitate the national economy, provide for the welfare of the populace, and maximize the combat potential of remaining forces and supporting activities; (2) Those actions taken by a military force during or after operational employment to restore its combat capability to full operational readiness. See also recovery (JP 3-35).

Reliability Coordinator—The entity that is the highest level of authority responsible for the reliable operation of the Bulk Electric System, has the wide area view of the Bulk Electric System, and has the operating tools, processes and procedures, including the authority to prevent or mitigate emergency operating situations in both next-day analysis and real-time operations. The reliability coordinator has the purview that is broad enough to enable the calculation of Interconnection Reliability Operating Limits, which may be based on the operating parameters of transmission systems beyond any transmission operator's vision.

Resilient Community Island—A community that retains independent infrastructures essential for its functionality. The concept includes functionally specialized islands (see Chapter VI).

System Restoration Plan—Plan required to allow for restoring the transmission operator's system following a disturbance in which one or more areas of the Bulk Electric System (BES) shuts down and the use of blackstart resources is required to restore the shut-down area to a state whereby the choice of the next load to be restored is not driven by the need to control frequency or voltage regardless of whether the blackstart resource is located within the transmission operator's system.

Technical nuclear forensics—The collection, analysis, and evaluation of pre-detonation (intact) and post-detonation (exploded) radiological or nuclear materials, devices, and debris, as well as the immediate effects created by a nuclear detonation (JP 3-41).

APPENDIX 2: Power Grids and Interdependencies

Planning and Response: Frameworks and Tools

Table 5: Cross-Walk of Planning Systems.

Source: Mary Lasky

Federal Emergency Management Agency (FEMA) Developing and Maintaining Emergency Operations Plans Comprehensive Preparedness Guide (CPG) 101	Department of Homeland Security (DHS) Federal Plan Development Process Handbook (FPDPH)	NFPA® 1600 Standard on Disaster/Emergency Management and Business Continuity Programs

Step 1: *Basics of Planning*
 	
   a. Identify Core Planning Team
   b. Engage the Whole Community in Planning
 	
Step 2: *Understand the Situation*
 	
   a. Identify Threats and Hazards
   b. Assess Risk
	Phase One: Understanding the Situation
	
	   1. Initiate Preparation for Planning
	   2. Conduct Research
		Chapter 1: Administration
		   Scope, Purpose
		
		Chapter 2: Referenced Publications
		
		Chapter 3: Definitions
		
		Chapter 4: Program Management
		   Leadership, Finance & Administration
		
		Chapter 5: Planning
		5.1 Planning and Design Process
		5.2 Risk Assessment
		5.3 Business Impact Analysis
		5.4 Resource Needs Assessment

Step 3: *Determine Goals and Objective*
 	
   a. Determine Operational Priorities
   b. Set Goals and Objectives
	Phase Two: Determine Goals and Objective
	
	   1. Information Analysis
	   2. Course of Action (COA) Development
		Chapter 5: Planning
		5.5 Performance Objectives.

Step 4: *Plan Development*
 	
   a. Develop and Analyze Course of Action
   b. Identify Resources
   c. Identify Information and Intelligence Needs
	Phase Three: Plan Development
	
	   1. Course of Action (COA) Analysis
	   2. COA Comparison
	   3. COA Approval
		Chapter 6: Implementation
		6.1 Common Plan Requirements.
		6.2 Prevention
		6.3 Mitigation
		6.4 Crisis Communications and Public Information
		6.5 Warning, Notifications, and Communications
		6.6 Operational Procedures

Federal Emergency Management Agency (FEMA) Developing and Maintaining Emergency Operations Plans Comprehensive Preparedness Guide (CPG) 101	Department of Homeland Security (DHS) Federal Plan Development Process Handbook (FPDPH)	NFPA® 1600 Standard on Disaster/Emergency Management and Business Continuity Programs

Step 5: *Plan Preparation, Review, and Approval*
 	
  a. Write the Plan
  b. Review the Plan
  c. Approve and Disseminate the Plan
	Phase Four: Plan Preparation and Review
	
	  1. Plan Preparation
	  2. Plan Review
	  3. Plan Approval & Dissemination	

Step 6: *Plan Implementation & Maintenance*
 	
  a. Exercise the Plan Review, Revise and Maintain the Plan
	Phase Five: Plan Refinement or Execution
	
	  1. Plan Refinement
	  2. Plan Execution
		Chapter 6: Implementation
		  6.7 Incident Management.
		  6.7.1.1 Emergency Operations Centers (EOCs)
		  6.8 Emergency Operations/Response Plan.
		  6.9 Business Continuity and Recovery.
		Chapter 7: Training and Education
		Chapter 8: Exercises and Tests
		Chapter 9: Program Maintenance and Improvement

<u>Functional Annexes Content Guide</u> Each Emergency Support Function is discussed ESF 1 – Transportation ESF 2 – Communications ESF 3 – Public Works and Engineering with Critical Infrastructure & Key Resources Restoration ESF 4 – Firefighting EDF 5 – Emergency Management/Direction, Control, Coordination including Incident Assessment, Incident Control and Emergency Operations Center ESF 6 – Mass Care, Emergency Assistance, Housing & Human Services ESF 7 – Logistics Management & Resource Support ESF 8 – Public Health & Medical Services		

Federal Emergency Management Agency (FEMA) Developing and Maintaining Emergency Operations Plans Comprehensive Preparedness Guide (CPG) 101	Department of Homeland Security (DHS) Federal Plan Development Process Handbook (FPDPH)	NFPA® 1600 Standard on Disaster/Emergency Management and Business Continuity Programs
ESF 9 – Search & Rescue ESF 10 – Oil & Hazardous Materials Response ESF 11 – Agriculture & Natural Resources ESF 12 – Energy ESF 13 – Public Safety & Security ESF 14 – Long-Term Community Recovery ESF 15 – External Affairs & Emergency public Information including Continuity of Government, Public Sector Coordination, Volunteer & Donation Management		

Business Continuity Planning

Historically, "business continuity" has been used as a generic subject header over a variety of topics that make up the processes of what is called business continuity management. One of the challenges we face is in the definition of the terms we use to describe our industry. Whether we use the term continuity, recovery, risk management, governance, compliance, crisis management, incident management, emergency response, or any others to describe what we do, the goal of business resilience is the same. Our objectives are fairly simple in principle:

- Anticipating the threats we face;
- Understanding the impact (risks) from those threats to our organizations;
- Ensuring we are prepared, that we can respond and recover from the impact of any disruption, ones we can anticipate, and the ones we cannot;
- Developing and exercising plans to provide continuity and recovery for our organizations;
- Building on our capability to adapt to a changing threat landscape; and
- Doing so in a manner that considers regulations, standards, governance, and compliance requirements.

Threats and Risks

Typically, most organizations have organized their risk assessment and planning efforts based on four major categories of threat/risk combination:

- Threats that could impact the ability of data centers or IT services to function, typically focus around loss of infrastructure systems or facility failures;
- Threats that would prevent the use of a facility, whether that be an office, manufacturing facility, hospital, power generation plant, distribution center, or any other brick and mortar establishment;
- Threats that would impact the supply chain, preventing an organization from receiving goods or services critical to their operation including such items as communications, transportation, water/wastewater of the critical infrastructure; and
- Threats to the workforce, either from an act of nature, strike, or other personnel related event.

All of these events have had two major common elements: a localized degree of impact and a fairly identifiable length of outage time.

Moving on from the isolated threat situation, which would impact only one organization at a time, we have seen, over the past several years, an increase in the more regional types of incidents, which have caused contingency planners to broaden their views of how impacts outside their direct control could impact their organizations.

Impacts that can fall into this category would be:

- Widespread natural disasters, like a hurricane, tornado, or earthquake;
- A health-related incident, such as a pandemic;
- A civil disturbance causing a loss of access; and
- A major infrastructure incident, such as a power station, natural gas, or water disruption.

Although these incidents cause planners to step back and consider impacts outside their four walls, they always have been controlled and mitigated within a defined period of time.

What Are Industry Associations Saying About Current Threats?

To provide some substantiation for the view of practitioners in the business continuity industry, it is important to look at a few industry studies.

In its fifth edition, the Business Continuity Institute's Horizon Scan Report tracks risks and threats to organizations through assessing perceived threats as shown by practitioners' in-house analysis. Cyber-attacks such as malware and denial of service retain the top position, with 85% of respondents being "extremely concerned" or "concerned" about this threat. This coincides with findings from other BCI research showing cyber-attacks as the top long-term threat to supply chains (46%). Cyber-attacks and related cyber-security incidents are also one of the top 10 triggers for activating emergency communications plans (28%).

Of the respondents to the BCI survey, 57% said they were extremely concerned or concerned about a utility service interruption. The Horizon Scan's results are documented in the following graphic from their 2016 report.

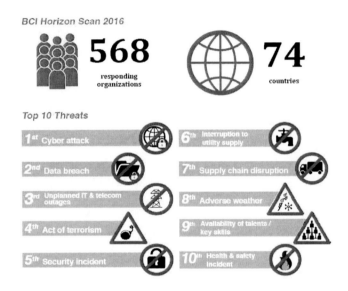

Figure 12: Top 10 Threats to Business Continuity—BCI Horizon Scan, 2016.

Source: Business Continuity Institute, 2016, Horizon Scan Study

Next, the most recent Allianz Risk Barometer study for 2016 is focused on global businesses and risk consultants, underwriters, senior managers, and claims experts in the corporate insurance segment versus business continuity professionals, and as such, it provides more of a business executive perspective.

The Allianz Study provides the following perspective on risks:

				2015 Rank	Trend
1	Business interruption (incl. supply chain disruption)	38%	1 (46%)	-	
2	Market developments (volatility, intensified competition, market stagnation)	34%	NEW	▲	
3	Cyber incidents (cyber crime, data breaches, IT failures)	28%	5 (17%)	▲	
4	Natural catastrophes (storm, flood, earthquake)	24%	2 (30%)	▼	
5	Changes in legislation and regulation (economic sanctions, protectionism)	24%	4 (18%)	▼	
6	Macroeconomic developments (austerity programs, commodity price increase, inflation/deflation)	22%	NEW	▲	
7	Loss of reputation or brand value	18%	6 (16%)	▼	
8	Fire, explosion	16%	3 (27%)	▼	
9	Political risks (war, terrorism, upheaval)	11%	9 (11%)	-	
10	Theft, fraud, corruption	11%	10 (9%)	-	

The fifth annual Allianz Risk Barometer was conducted among both global businesses and risk consultants, underwriters, senior managers and claims experts in the corporate insurance segment of both Allianz Global Corporate & Specialty (AGCS) and local Allianz entities.

Figure 13: Allianz Business Risk Barometer and Rank for Year 2015.

Source: 5th Annual Alliance Insurance Risk Barometer

So once again, cyber incidents (#3) and natural catastrophes such as solar storms (#4) are high on the list, supporting the premise that business continuity professionals need to begin focusing on the triple-threat issues in their planning efforts.

Planning Is the Next Step

Once the threats and risks have been identified, the planning process needs to occur. Following is a potential list of "What's Important?" in a business continuity plan.

First, a document management section, which would include a list of reviewers with review dates and a list of approvers with approval dates, as well as a revision history. This is an early indication as to how current and accepted the plan is in the organization.

Second, every BCP needs a table of contents to enable quick reference to what is in the plan. Many plans do not have this important component, which forces the reader to search for important information instead of going right to it, when it is needed.

Third, a quick reference guide (essentially a 1- to 2-page summary of the action plan, but right up front) provides an obvious reference as to what needs to happen when you have to invoke the plan. These are not the detailed steps, but an overview that acquaints the reader/responder with how the recovery process will unfold.

Fourth, every plan should have a clear and concise scope statement, which provides an overall understanding of the plan's coverage, followed by the objectives of the plan and the assumptions upon which the plan is based. These overview components are important to someone not familiar with the plan—essentially providing a primer on what the plan addresses.

The fifth area is a clearly articulated overall continuity strategy statement that outlines the high-level approach the plan will take, the service levels that operations and shared services (such as IT) have committed to delivering, and the impact on business users during an event and throughout the recovery and resumption phases. This strategy statement is the most concise top-down view of what the plan will do for the business and sets the table for the detailed action steps and the quick reference.

Sixth, a set of timelines and milestones identifies key events that will take place and major accomplishments that should occur during the recovery. This provides an overall roadmap for those directly involved in the recovery process and is useful for measuring progress as the recovery unfolds.

Seventh, a well thought out BCP must also have the ability to address multiple risk types, including disruption or loss of a facility, an IT outage resulting in unavailability of critical applications, a network (voice/data) outage resulting in loss of communications, and finally a workforce outage, such as a strike or a pandemic.

The eighth area of focus, and quite frankly the single most important yet often missing, is a set of detailed actionable steps that this plan will execute. To be effective, the detailed actionable steps need to address 5 simple, but critically important issues:

- What to do.
- How to do it.
- When to do it.
- Who should do it?
- What constitutes complete?

Ninth is that the plan must acknowledge and link to other supporting plans, such as emergency response plans, crisis management plans, IT DR plans, and salvage and restoration plans. A critical aspect of that linkage is to know the triggers from these other plans and triggers to these other plans, so that all of the plans can work seamlessly together and not be overlapping or redundant. Streamlining planning by linking across plans can significantly reduce your level of effort, and other people's level of confusion throughout the entire process.

Tenth is a set of complete and up to date appendices, which include the various lists and forms that are maintainable and referenced as required. Appendices typically include call lists and contact information, recovery requirements that document what is required to successfully execute this plan, a basic explanation of the critical business processes supported by the plan, as well as any required company forms for quick access. And please, do not forget to keep this section continuously updated as changes to the business have profound impact to your business continuity plans.

Lastly, it is very important for a complete BCP to contain test exercise procedures as well as training and maintenance procedures. Including these procedures ensures that your plans are designed from the outset to be tested and continuously maintained as part of an overall program rather than a point in time project.

Here is a quick graphical outline in case it is an easier way to remember all these items:

Figure 14: Guidelines for a Comprehensive Continuity.

Source: Fusion Risk Management Inc.

The true test of a plan is its ability to guide you through an actual recovery regardless of what event your organization may face. A well-formatted, but poorly developed plan misses the mark and is more of a liability than as asset, so make sure you think about the "desired components" when you review or write your next plan.

Enter the Triple Threat!

Up to this point, business continuity professionals have focused on threats and risks that were more easily identifiable and generally definable in terms of length of outage and severity of impact. Now, with the increased awareness of attacks to the electrical grid, which could have wide-reaching and long-term implications, the processes of identifying risks, developing plans, and conducting exercises are no longer adequate. Consider an outage, which has the following implications:

- Loss of electric power across a region, every town, and every building;
- No water flow, no heat or cooling;
- No communications—internet, cell, or landline;
- No transportation if cars and other modes are disabled;
- And on and on.

Essentially, this incident affects all four of the commonly viewed risks of IT, facility, supply chain, and workforce, but all at once. Consequently, traditional plans and strategies, which work great with a limited scope incident, will no longer be capable of addressing the needs of those who would rely on them.

How Can Exercises Help With Preparation?

One of the issues that we all have dealt with over the years is that business continuity and disaster recovery planning is the process of preparing for something we all hope and expect will not happen. So, how do we know if our plans will work when we need them? We do not really, but the best way we can ensure they are as useful as possible is to conduct tests, drills, exercises, or whatever your organization chooses to call them.

Exercises may be the closest we ever get to use our plans and they can go a long way towards giving us and others a sense of confidence that the organization is prepared. All too many people judge the value of an exercise by whether it was deemed "successful" or not and success is judged to be if all the objectives were met and no problems occurred. Success is measured more by the lessons learned and corrective actions taken before a disaster, but we as an industry still have some distance to go in getting alignment of what constitutes success!

The InfraGard EMP SIG has created two different approaches to exercises for the triple threat of cyber, space weather, and electromagnetic pulse (EMP). The material for the two different approaches has been vetted by subject matter experts. The two different exercise approaches are a brief topic overview and a full tabletop workshop and/or exercise.

Use the "Societal Effects of High Impact Threats to Critical Infrastructure" PowerPoint presentation. This simple approach can be conducted in an hour or less and is modeled after work and experience by InfraGard EMP SIG management team members. This approach could be used as a one-time event, or as a starting point in building a team to develop a more in-depth exercise discussed below. This approach requires limited work on your part to conduct the exercise if you wish to use the annotated PowerPoint provided. The introductory slide gives the presenter a place to discuss the presenter's background and the group's perceived needs and requirements. This may be obtained from igempsig@infragardmembers.org

Use the *Triple Threat Power Grid Exercise* (see Appendix References) document with background material and three different scenarios: cyber, space weather, and electromagnetic pulse (EMP). The *Triple Threat Power Grid Exercise* book is designed to establish a learning environment for players to exercise emergency response plans, policies, or procedures and bring awareness of three potential catastrophic scenarios that could adversely impact the electrical grid, resulting in a regional or all-of-nation blackout scenario, impacting millions.

The read-ahead section provides participants a valuable background on cyber-attacks, on what a solar storm is, and on what happens in an EMP. This is valuable background information for anyone interested in participating or even just a quick introduction to the topics.

Each of the three scenarios uses different timeframes. The exercise may use all of them or stop at any point. The timeframes with suggested questions to be considered are:

- 2 weeks
- 1 month
- 3 months
- 12 months (includes questions to consider a new normal)

A set of questions at the end gives the participants time to reflect. Ideally, the participants would then be inspired to use Part 1 of this book to be more prepared and review Part 2 to consider other actions they could take if the grid was indeed out for an extend period.

A facilitator guide has been written to help a team conduct the exercise. The facilitator guide steps through a detailed process or methodology. The steps needed are:

- Obtain a team to help with the exercise;
- Design objectives that you want to accomplish;
- Develop roles and responsibilities for conducting the exercise;
- Use the *Triple Threat Power Grid Exercise* book to choose one of the scenarios and plan the exercise;
- Review and modify the scenario provided by the InfraGard EMP SIG; and
- Evaluate the exercise, etc.

The *Facilitator Guide* may be obtained from: igempsig@infragardmembers.org

Ideally, one of the two exercise alternatives would be used to start your team thinking about one of the scenarios and its cascading events to create a catastrophic event. Then you would use this book to help guide specific actions you can take to prepare and mitigate your risks for such a triple threat to the power grid. Also, study and discuss Part 2 of this book on what actions could be taken if one of the threats takes down the power grid.

Interdependencies Workshop

Simply stated, triple-threat situations most certainly involve external interdependencies, which require that companies not only focus on their own individual recovery plans, but they must also consider major categories of external influences that can significantly impact their ability to recover in a timely manner, or possibly recover at all! See Figure 5 on interdependencies. To address the issue of understanding interdependencies, consider the following steps:

- Identify the potential impact of various external infrastructure and business disruptions;
- Identify the impact of the interdependencies on recovery times and points;
- Identify the various dependencies among private and public organizations;
- Determine potential steps and actions to mitigate or lessen the impacts of outages among the interdependent organizations; and
- Lay the foundation for continual evaluation of external interdependencies.

The better interdependencies are understood, the better prepared to respond to them. The better relationships with public agencies are developed they will strengthen recovery capabilities and reduce the need for inefficient interaction and potential friction when problems arise. Understand the impact on ability to operate or to recover, based on the recovery capability of other companies or businesses.

Consider the interdependencies when planning exercises. Certain people are key to its success, including:

- IT management;
- Facilities management;
- Data center management;
- Business continuity management;
- Security; and
- Representatives from key business units who understand the business-to-business relationships that are critical to conducting business.

In addition, meet with external organizations, both to understand how they would react to an outage, validating or mitigating concerns, as well as to have everyone understand plans and requirements.

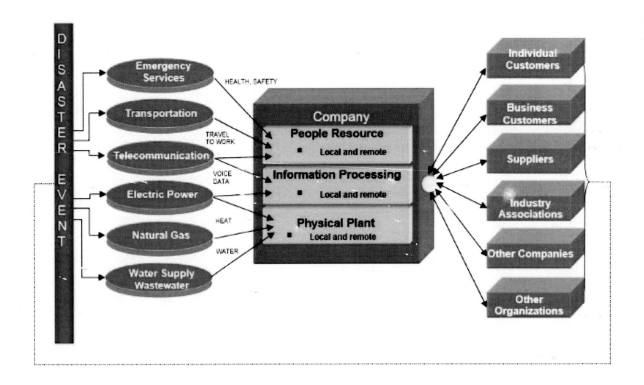

Figure 15: Participants in an Interdependencies Workshop.

Source: John A. Jackson Fusion Risk Management Inc.

In the End, Planning Can Only Do So Much

Having a plan to address what happens if there is no electrical power for weeks or even months will put your organization on an excellent path. See Part 1 section on business continuity planning and Part 2 for business actions.

National Incident Management System

Introduction

Every day, incidents across the United States require public and private sector entities to work together to share resources and take actions to meet the needs of communities before, during, and after incidents. Whether these jurisdictions share borders or are supporting each other from across the country, their success depends on a common interoperable approach for sharing resources, coordinating and managing the incident, and communicating information.

The National Incident Management System (NIMS) is a systematic and standardized approach that guides all levels of government, non-governmental organizations (NGO), and the private sector to work together to prevent, protect against, mitigate, respond to, and

144

recover from the adverse effects of incidents.[112] NIMS doctrine provides responders across the whole community with a common and shared vocabulary, systems, and processes to successfully deliver the capabilities described in the National Preparedness System.[113] This approach provides a consistent foundation for all incidents, ranging from daily occurrences to extreme situations requiring a coordinated federal response. The challenge facing the private sector is taking lessons learned from seminars, conferences, or exercises and transforming that knowledge into action plans with realistic performance outcomes.

Purpose

The purpose of this section is to familiarize the reader with key points from the National Incident Management System and the Incident Command System (ICS) that can be utilized in the event of a major and catastrophic incident that impacts the power grid and interdependent critical infrastructure of the United States.

The objectives of this section are to:

- Describe how the Incident Command System can be used as a command and management tool to the events defined in this framework; and
- Describe potential roles and responsibilities of private sector executives or senior agency officials in relation to activities performed in Emergency Operations Centers, Center Management Systems, Incident Management Teams (IMTs) or Multi-Agency Coordination Systems.

Scope

NIMS is applicable to all state and local government agencies with incident management responsibilities within their jurisdiction. The audience for NIMS includes first responders and other emergency management personnel, NGOs (i.e., faith-based and humanitarian groups), the private sector, and elected and appointed officials responsible for making decisions regarding incident management.

An Overview of NIMS.[114]

Incident management priorities include stabilizing the incident, saving lives, and protecting property and the environment. To achieve these priorities, incident management personnel

---

[112] <u>National Incident Management System Nation Engagement Draft</u>. I.A. Fundamentals and concepts, June 2016.

[113] The National Preparedness System outlines an organized process to help the whole community achieve the National Preparedness Goal. It comprises and builds on existing policies, programs, and guidance to include the National Planning Frameworks, Federal Interagency Operational Plans, and the National Preparedness Report. Refer to the resources and references page at the end of this section.

[114] <u>National Incident Management System, National Engagement Draft</u>, I. A. Fundamentals and Concepts, June 2016.

apply and implement NIMS components in accordance with the following principles: (1) flexibility, (2) standardization, and (3) unity of effort.

Table 6: Defining the National Incident Management System

What NIMS *Is*	What NIMS Is *Not*
• A comprehensive, nationwide, systematic approach to incident management, including the management and coordination of incidents, resource management, and information management	• Only the Incident Command System or an organization chart • Only applicable to certain emergency incident response personnel • A static system
• A set of concepts and principles for all threats, hazards, and events across all mission areas (prevention, protection, mitigation, response, recovery)	• A response plan
• Scalable, flexible, and adaptable; used for all incidents, from day-to-day to large-scale	• Used only during large-scale incidents
• Standard resource management procedures that enable coordination among different jurisdictions or organizations	• A resource ordering system
• Essential principles for communication and information management	• A communications plan

Flexibility

NIMS components are adaptable to any situation: planned special events; local incidents; incidents requiring the activation of interstate mutual aid; incidents requiring coordinated federal assistance; and so on. Some incidents require multiagency, multijurisdictional, and/or multidisciplinary coordination. Flexibility in NIMS allows it to be scalable and, therefore, applicable for incidents that vary widely in terms of geography, demographics, and climate.

Standardization

Coordination and standardization are essential to effective incident management. The National Incident Management System contains standard organizational structures that improve integration and connectivity among jurisdictions and organizations. NIMS and the Incident Management System or ICS use standard practices that allow incident managers to work together more effectively and foster cohesion among the various organizations involved in an incident. NIMS also includes common terminology, which fosters effective communication among jurisdictions and organizations involved in managing an incident.

Unity of Effort

Unity of effort refers to coordinating activities among various organizational representatives to achieve common objectives. Unity of effort enables organizations with jurisdictional authority or functional responsibilities to support each other while allowing each participating agency to maintain its own authority and accountability.

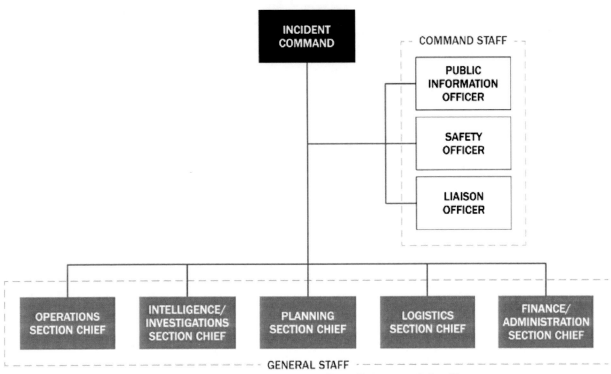

Figure 16: ICS Command and General Staff

Source: National Incident Management System Refresh.

Incident Command Systems (ICS)

ICS is a subset of NIMS. A basic organizational chart is depicted in the above figure. It makes use of an organizational structure for incident management that integrates and coordinates a combination of personnel, equipment, facilities, procedures, and communications. Using ICS for every incident or event helps hone and maintain skills needed to coordinate efforts effectively. ICS is used by all levels of government to include the Department of Defense, non-governmental organizations (NGOs), and private sector organizations. ICS is applicable across disciplines and enables incident managers from

147

different organizations to work together seamlessly. This system includes six major functional areas staffed as needed: a command staff and a general staff, which includes operations, intelligence/investigation, planning, logistics, and finance/administration.

Incident Management Teams (IMT)

An Incident Management Team (IMT) is a group of individuals trained to serve as the command and general staff and other positions in an ICS organization. Pre-established IMTs exist at national, state, and local levels and have formal notification, deployment, and operational procedures in place. In some cases, ad hoc IMTs can be formed at an incident or for specific events from available, qualified individuals (such as the private sector). The level of training and experience of the IMT members, coupled with the IMT's identified response capabilities and responsibilities, are factors in determining an IMT's type or level. Given the standardized nature of NIMS, the needs of the jurisdiction, and the individual's credentials, InfraGard members could serve any jurisdiction across the country as a member of an ad hoc IMT.

Center Management System (CMS)

Operations and coordination centers exist across the nation, at all levels of government, and within jurisdictions and organizations of all sizes (including nongovernmental and private sector entities). Operations/coordination centers are locations from which staff provides centralized and coordinated support to incident command, on-scene personnel, and/or other operations/coordination centers beyond what can be provided at the scene. Primary functions of staff in operations/coordination centers include: (1) sharing, collecting, and disseminating information; (2) supporting resource needs and requests, including allocation and tracking; and (3) coordinating plans and determining the current and future needs of the various jurisdictions and organizations involved in an incident. Additionally, operations/coordination center personnel support public and incident-specific communications, liaise with partners as needed, and support the policy and legal needs of the incident commander and other decision makers.[115]

The ICS and CMS Interface

ICS is used to manage the on-scene/tactical-level efforts aimed at saving lives, stabilizing the situation, and protecting property and the environment by directly applying resources. If necessary, an operations/coordination center is activated to provide an increased level of support and to facilitate coordination among organizations, senior leaders and elected officials, and jurisdictions.

---

[115] National Incident Management System, National Engagement Draft. I. A. Fundamentals and Concepts, Section B, page 31 June 2016

The CMS structure is compatible with the positions and titles defined in the ICS structure. The sections and positions outlined in ICS and CMS are carefully designed to enable personnel working within both structures to perform their duties in coordination with one another. However, the sections and positions are distinct in order to reflect the different roles and responsibilities of ICS versus CMS personnel and to prevent redundancies and confusion in training and type classifying personnel. ICS and CMS personnel coordinate with one another to meet the needs of the incident and fulfill resource and information requests. Together, ICS and CMS describe a comprehensive approach to structuring incident management personnel from the tactical responders on the scene to personnel providing coordination and support in an operations/coordination center.

All types of organizations use operation/coordination centers. These centers are common at the various levels of government (e.g., a county level Emergency Operations Center [EOC], a state command emergency operations center, or a state level regional operations center), as well as with public and private infrastructure owners and operators such as public mass transit organizations, public utility companies, healthcare facilities, NGOs, private businesses, and nonprofit organizations. CMS describes a common organizational structure for staff in these centers.

Configuration of a Center Management System

Effective incident management requires close coordination between the staff at the incident level, organized by ICS, and the staff within operations and coordination centers, organized by CMS. As with ICS, CMS follows the NIMS management and coordination characteristics and the positions (described below) closely align with the ICS structure and positions.

However, the roles and responsibilities of operations/coordination centers are distinct from those of incident command. The center's organization and responsibilities of the individual sections and units reflect those differences. A center director (CD) leads the CMS organization and engages with other leadership to support the incident. Command staff supports the CD and may include a public information officer, liaison officer, and safety officer. The general staff sections consist of strategic operations, information and planning, resource and center logistics, and finance/administration. As with ICS, the structure of CMS is flexible and adaptable to the needs of an incident or jurisdiction. The CD activates individual sections as needed. The organizational structure below shows the command and general staff positions within CMS.[116]

---

[116] A detailed description of the CMS duties and responsibilities are provided in the revised edition of the National Incident Management System, National Engagement Draft, I. A. Fundamentals and Concepts, Section B, page 31 June 2016. Links to this site can be found at the end of this section.

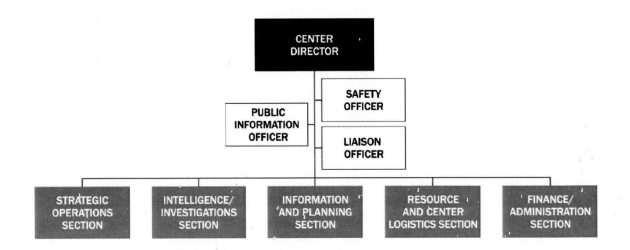

Figure 17: Central Management System.

Source: National Incident Management System Refresh

Activation and Deactivation of Center Management Systems

Centers are activated for various reasons based on support requirements of a jurisdiction or organization, the requirements of an incident commander (IC), the context of a threat, the anticipation of events, or as a response to an incident. Circumstances that might trigger activation include:

- More than one jurisdiction becomes involved in an incident and/or the incident involves multiple agencies and a large geographic area.
- The IC indicates an incident could expand rapidly or involve cascading events impacting critical infrastructures.
- A similar incident in the past required center activation.
- An appointed or elected official directs that the center is to be activated.
- An emergency is imminent (e.g., solar storm or geomagnetic disturbance, hurricane warnings, slow river flooding, predictions of hazardous weather, elevated threat levels).
- Threshold events in the jurisdiction's Emergency Operations Plan (EOP) occur.
- Significant impacts to the population are anticipated.
- The incident commander anticipates the need for support acquiring additional resources.

Multi-Agency Coordination (MAC) Group

MAC groups typically consist of agency administrators, executives, or their designees. It is important that designees be authorized to represent or commit agency resources and funds in support of incident activities. A MAC group acts as a policy-level body during incidents, supporting resource prioritization and allocation, and enabling decision making among elected and appointed officials and those responsible for managing the incident (e.g., the IC).

A MAC group may need a support organization. In some instances, staff in operations/coordination centers provides this support. In other instances, separate organizations are established to support the MAC group by: meeting its logistics and documentation needs; managing incident-related decision support information such as tracking critical resources, the situation status, intelligence, or investigative information; and providing information to the news media and public. The number and skills of personnel vary by incident complexity, activity level, needs of the MAC group, and other factors identified by participating organizations.

A MAC group may be established by organizations at any level (e.g., local, state, or national) or within any discipline (e.g., emergency management, public health, critical infrastructure, or private sector). In many cases, a MAC group can function virtually to accomplish its assigned tasks. MAC group decisions are typically based on a consensus of the members.

MAC groups do not function as incident command nor do they conflict with or replace the role of operations/coordination centers. However, in some communities and jurisdictions, local statutes or delegations of authority limit a center staff's functions and actions, and MAC group authorization may be required to access additional resources and/or provide guidance to EOC staff.[117]

The composition of MAC groups is very important. Sometimes membership is obvious. Organizations directly impacted and whose resources are committed to the incident should be represented. Sometimes, however, organizations that should be members of a MAC group are less obvious. These include business organizations such as local chambers of commerce, volunteer organizations such as the American Red Cross, or other organizations with special expertise or knowledge, such as InfraGard. While these agencies may not have tangible resources or funds to contribute, their contacts, political influence, or technical expertise can be key to the success of the MAC group in supporting incident response and recovery.

Interconnectivity of National Incident Management System and Coordination Structures

NIMS structures enable incident managers across the nation to manage the effects of an incident in a unified, consistent manner. Interconnectivity of NIMS structures is important to allow personnel in diverse geographic areas, with differing roles and responsibilities,

---

[117] Refer to ICS-400: Advanced ICS, Command and General Staff—Complex Incidents, Unit 5, Multi-Agency Coordination, May, 2013

and operating within various functions of Incident Command System and/or the Center management system to seamlessly integrate their efforts through a common set of organizational structures, terminology, and processes.

Table 7: Comparison of Incident Command and Management Structures

	Incident Command	Operations/ Coordination Center	Multi-Agency Coordination Group
Description	• A local or tactical incident management organization established to enable timely, effective, and coordinated operations by integrating a combination of facilities, equipment, personnel, services, procedures, and communications to achieve incident objectives • Organized by ICS	• A central location for interagency coordination and decision making in support of incident management • Organized by CMS	• A group of senior officials organized to coordinate support for incident management through their collective resources, information sharing, strategy development, and policy implementation
Typical Functions	• Command (including Public Information, Safety, Liaison) • Operations • Intelligence/Investigations • Planning • Logistics • Finance/Administration	• Command (including Public Information, Safety, Liaison) • Strategic Operations • Intelligence and Investigations • Information and Planning • Resource and Logistics • Finance and Administration	• Allocate resources in support of operations/ coordination centers and Incident Command structures • Establish decision coordination between jurisdictions and/or organizations • Develop strategies and contingency plans
Personnel	• Incident Command (either single or Unified Command structure) and any assigned supporting staff	• Director and staff plus authorized agency representatives, senior policy makers, and elected and appointed officials	• Agency administrators/ executives or personnel that have been delegated authority regarding allocation of resources
Other	• IC is responsible for overall management of the incident in either a single commander or Unified Command • Area Command may be established to oversee the management of multiple incidents that are being handled by separate ICS organizations or the management of a very large or evolving incident that has many Incident Management Teams engaged	• May be co-located with dispatch, fusion center, and public warning services • In some circumstances may perform Incident Command role	• May establish the priorities for resources among incidents • Harmonize agency policies and provide strategic guidance and direction to support incident management activities

When an incident occurs or threatens, local emergency personnel respond, using the principles and structures of ICS to frame their activities. If the incident is or becomes large or complex, the center management system, county emergency operations centers (EOCs) or other operation/coordination centers activate. The teams working in the various local, state, tribal, territorial, and federal operations and coordination centers are organized and function consistently based on NIMS doctrine. The staff in a Center Management System receives senior-level guidance from multi-agency coordination groups to organize support for the incident. Establishing a Joint Information Center will ensure coordinated and accurate messaging with the public.

If required resources are not available locally, the resources may be obtained under mutual aid agreements from neighboring jurisdictions or from state, tribal, territorial, or interstate sources. The state EOC may activate to support incident management and resource needs. When the resources (personnel, equipment, teams, and facilities) reach the incident, incident management personnel can incorporate them seamlessly through the use of common, standard systems (e.g., ICS, CMS, JIS). Resources, including ICS and CMS personnel, are also typed and qualified in support of a national qualification system that promotes interoperability and the exchange of personnel, equipment, teams, and facilities.

Business Emergency Operation Centers (BEOC)

BEOCs coordinate with businesses to: improve their disaster preparedness; improve communication with business and industry before, during, and after disasters; facilitate public-private information exchange; engage key stakeholders with the ability to supply resources or capabilities and expertise to help manage specific incidents, such as a member of an incident command system or center management system; and help coordinate post-disaster economic recovery.

Federal Support to Response Activities

The majority of incidents are resolved using only the above coordination mechanisms. However, some major incidents may require the capabilities of the federal government. The federal government maintains a wide range of capabilities and resources that may be needed to deal with domestic incidents in order to save lives, protect property and the environment, and ensure the protection of civil rights and civil liberties. NIMS coordinating structures enable federal departments and agencies to cooperate with one another, and with local, state, tribal, territorial, and insular area governments, community members, and the private sector.

The federal government becomes involved with a response when: (1) state, local, or tribal governments need assistance and the governor or chief tribal executive requests federal support assets; (2) federal interests are involved; or (3) if statute or regulation authorizes

153

or requires it. In some instances, the federal government plays a supporting role to state, local, tribal, or territorial governments by providing federal assistance to the affected jurisdictions. For example, the federal government provides assistance to state, local, and tribal governments when the President declares a major disaster or emergency under the Stafford Act. In other instances, the federal government plays a leading role in the response, such as when the federal government has primary jurisdiction or when incidents occur on federal property such as in national parks, or on military installations or bases.

Joint Information Systems (JIS)

Dissemination of timely and accurate information to the public is important at all phases of incident management. Developing and sharing public information is a responsibility of many agencies and organizations at all levels of government. Jurisdictions and organizations across the whole community coordinate and integrate communication efforts to ensure that the public receives a consistent, accurate, accessible, and comprehensive message. Well-developed and coordinated public information, education, and communications plans and strategies help ensure public safety information (lifesaving measures, evacuation routes, threat and alert systems) is coordinated and communicated in a timely, consistent, accurate, and accessible manner. JISs consist of the processes, procedures, and systems to enable this communication to the public, responders, and the media.

Resources and References

NIMS National Engagement Draft, May 2016
https://www.fema.gov/national-incident-management-system/national-engagement

NIMS Training Program
http://www.fema.gov/pdf/emergency/nims/nims_training_program.pdf

Comprehensive Preparedness Guide (CPG) 101: Developing and Maintaining Emergency Operations Plans, Version 2
http://www.fema.gov/plan

CPG 201, Threat and Hazard Identification and Risk Assessment Guide, Second Edition
http://www.fema.gov/threat-and-hazard-identification-and-risk-assessment

National Preparedness Goal
http://www.fema.gov/national-preparedness-goal

National Preparedness System
http://www.fema.gov/national-preparedness-system

National Planning Frameworks

http://www.fema.gov/national-planning-frameworks

Emergency Management Assistance Compact
http://www.emacweb.org/

Fundamentals and Concepts of NIMS
FEMA-NIMS@fema.dhs.gov

ICS Resource Center
https://training.fema.gov/emiweb/is/icsresource/index.htm

APPENDIX 3: Preparedness Maturity Model

The Preparedness Maturity Model provides a sensible and reusable framework that organizations could use as a guide to evaluate preparedness efforts, identify gaps, and achieve readiness. It is helpful to first identify which maturity level your organization currently exists in for each area, and then plan how to proceed to higher levels of maturity. The Mature State (Level 5) can be tailored; however, this is not advisable unless it is made to be more demanding.

Table 8: Preparedness Maturity Model.

AREA	Level 1: Awareness Phase[1]	Level 2: Discovery Phase	Level 3: Planning Phase	Level 4: Implementa-tion Phase	Level 5: Mature State
Policy	1. Key decision makers and stakeholders identified. 2. Plan in place to meet with key decision makers and stakeholders. 3. Meetings with key decision makers and stakeholders are scheduled or have been accomplished.	Existing policy assessed and compared to Preparedness Maturity Level 5.	Determine requirements and construct roadmaps, plans, associated schedules, resource allocations, and budgets to achieve the list of Preparedness Maturity Level 5 objectives.	Gain authority, initiate work, and accomplish plans to achieve the list of Preparedness Maturity Level 5 objectives.	Policy is in place and the organization regularly conducts practice exercises and audits that demonstrate: *Private Sector:* 1. Contractual authority exists to rapidly invoke emergency contingency contracts that include provision of key services and supplies for all critical business operations sectors and their dependencies. Clear proxy and succession lines of authority are defined in writing and authorized by appropriate internal governance authorities. Governance mechanisms that facilitate

AREA	Level 1: Awareness Phase[1]	Level 2: Discovery Phase	Level 3: Planning Phase	Level 4: Implementa-tion Phase	Level 5: Mature State
					immediate priority-based centralized sector control and recovery threshold-based release of control are regularly audited and improved. 2. Event readiness preparations are authorized and continually improved. 3. Mutual support agreements have been optimized and continually improved for Preparedness scenario. 4. Critical services and supply providers routinely and successfully demonstrate improvements to their critical path survivability[2, 5] and, ideally, for 400-day sustainment and recovery plans.[3] 5. All existing and new critical employee participants have taken the oath to uphold and defend the U.S. Constitution against all enemies foreign and domestic. *State and local government:*

AREA	Level 1: Awareness Phase[1]	Level 2: Discovery Phase	Level 3: Planning Phase	Level 4: Implementation Phase	Level 5: Mature State
					1. Elected leader's legal authority to rapidly declare post-event martial law that includes government control and mobilization of all sectors and their dependencies is regularly audited and improved as needed. Clear proxy and succession lines of authority defined and legally authorized. Governance mechanisms authorized to facilitate priority-based centralized sector control and recovery threshold-based release of control are regularly audited and improved. 2. Event readiness preparations authorized and continually improved. 3. Mutual support agreements have been optimized and continually improved for Preparedness scenario. 4. Critical Infrastructure providers routinely and successfully demonstrate

AREA	Level 1: Awareness Phase[1]	Level 2: Discovery Phase	Level 3: Planning Phase	Level 4: Implementa-tion Phase	Level 5: Mature State
					improvements to their critical path survivability and, ideally, for 400-day sustainment and recovery plans. 5. All existing and new implementation participants have taken the oath to uphold and defend the U.S. Constitution against all enemies foreign and domestic.
Governance Process and Systems	Governance process and systems identified that can be used for Preparedness scenario.	The capabilities and limitations of governance processes and systems assessed and compared to Preparedness Maturity Level 5.	Determine desired governance processes and systems required to provide the above policy area requirements and capabilities.	Gain authority and create roadmaps, plans, associated schedules, resource allocation, budgets, and contracts to ensure the above policy area requirements and capabilities.	Contractual and governance processes are approved and in place to support the above policy area requirements and capabilities.

Additional consideration is given to: 1. The governance process to facilitate rapid escalation and triage of urgent priority decision requirements. 2. Essential-information and decision-support requirements and processes documented for all sectors and cross-sector dependencies. 3. Command, Control, and |

AREA	Level 1: Awareness Phase[1]	Level 2: Discovery Phase	Level 3: Planning Phase	Level 4: Implementa-tion Phase	Level 5: Mature State
					Communications (C3) capability that will be seamless between routine and post-event operations. Redundant, can withstand follow-on attacks and failures. Non-electronic backup capability layers are included for all processes. 4. Means to determine how to best ensure that post-event C3 capabilities and limitations are well understood and practiced by all sector participants. *State and local government specific:* 1. C3 aligns with military and NGO structures.
Recovery Command Centers and Bases of Operation	Facilities requirements for Preparedness scenarios addressed by key decision makers and stakeholders.	Assess and compare facilities, related support, sustainment requirements to the Preparedness Maturity Level 5 description.	Determine requirements and construct roadmaps, plans, associated schedules, resource allocations, and budgets to achieve the list of Preparedness Maturity Level 5 objectives.	Gain authority, initiate work, and accomplish plans to achieve the list of Preparedness Maturity Level 5 objectives.	Facilities, related support, and necessary sustainment supplies are ready for no-notice isolated long-term use (up to 400 days).
Situational Awareness	Key decision makers and	Assess and compare the	Determine requirements	Gain authority, initiate work,	Demonstrate the ability to identify,

AREA	Level 1: Awareness Phase[1]	Level 2: Discovery Phase	Level 3: Planning Phase	Level 4: Implementation Phase	Level 5: Mature State
	stakeholders made aware of the requirement for the ability to identify, monitor, assess, prioritize, and disseminate information as described by Preparedness Maturity Level 5.	ability to identify, monitor, assess, prioritize, and disseminate situational awareness to the Preparedness Maturity Level 5 description.	and construct roadmaps, plans, associated schedules, resource allocations, and budgets to achieve the list of Preparedness Maturity Level 5 objectives.	and accomplish plans to achieve the list of Preparedness Maturity Level 5 objectives.	monitor, assess, prioritize, and disseminate information regarding: 1. Crisis and resilience multipliers[4,7] 2. Infrastructure threats 3. Resilience critical path cross-dependency[6] status 4. Consequences from infrastructure reduction 5. Opportunities/ requirements to apply resources and capabilities 6. Real-time/near real-time event/crisis reporting and response-effect reporting
Capability Awareness	Key decision makers and stakeholders made aware of the requirement for capability awareness as descried for Preparedness Maturity Level 5.	Assess and compare the ability to identify, monitor, assess, prioritize, and disseminate capability information to Preparedness Maturity Level 5 description.	Determine requirements and construct roadmaps, plans, associated schedules, resource allocations, and budgets to achieve the list of Preparedness Maturity Level 5 objectives.	Gain authority, initiate work, and accomplish plans to achieve the list of Preparedness Maturity Level 5 objectives.	1. Post-event reliability estimated and published for reference: for each critical item type and infrastructure category. 2. Real-time/near real-time resource, inventory, capability, and location readiness reporting for all infrastructure sectors and critical path dependencies is operational and tested. 3. Resilience multipliers

AREA	Level 1: Awareness Phase[1]	Level 2: Discovery Phase	Level 3: Planning Phase	Level 4: Implementation Phase	Level 5: Mature State
					identified and quantified.
Capability Planning	Key decision makers and stakeholders made aware of the requirements for Preparedness Maturity Level 5 capability planning.	Assess the ability to plan and conduct the list of Preparedness Maturity Level 5 objectives.	Determine requirements and construct roadmaps, plans, associated schedules, resource allocations, and budgets to achieve the list of Preparedness Maturity Level 5 objectives.	Gain authority, initiate work, and accomplish plans to achieve the list of Preparedness Maturity Level 5 objectives.	1. Plans to harness resilience multipliers are in place and tested. 2. Resilience critical path dependencies are identified and quantified. 3. Worst-case capability scenarios are modeled and documented. 4. Plans exist to prepare for worst-case scenarios. 5. Primary and alternate plans exist to respond to worst-case scenarios.
Operations	Key decision makers and stakeholders made aware of the requirements for Preparedness Maturity Level 5 operations.	Inventory and assess existing and reusable operations enablers that can support Preparedness Maturity Level 5 operations.	Determine requirements and construct roadmaps, plans, associated schedules, resource allocations, and budgets to achieve the list of Preparedness Maturity Level 5 objectives.	Gain authority, initiate work, and accomplish plans to achieve the list of Preparedness Maturity Level 5 objectives.	1. Baseline scenarios defined. 2. Anticipatory planning and operations participant, processes, playbooks, and systems have been tested and optimized. 3. Plans to mitigate crisis multipliers are in place and tested. 4. Ability to measure resource and capability gaps, prioritize and redirect based on shifting events and dependencies is

AREA	Level 1: Awareness Phase[1]	Level 2: Discovery Phase	Level 3: Planning Phase	Level 4: Implementation Phase	Level 5: Mature State
					tested and optimized. 5. Minimally acceptable C3 and capability requirements defined and assigned to back-up electronic and non-electronic layers. 6. Ability to mobilize and control minimally acceptable resources and capabilities is being monitored and tested.
Capability Sustainment	Key decision makers and stakeholders made aware of the requirements for Preparedness Maturity Level 5 capability sustainment.	Assess in number of days the ability to support the Recovery Command Centers and Bases of Operation in physical isolation for each of the Preparedness Maturity Level 5 categories.	Determine requirements and construct roadmaps, plans, associated schedules, resource allocations, and budgets to achieve the list of Preparedness Maturity Level 5 objectives.	Gain authority, initiate work, and accomplish plans to achieve the list of Preparedness Maturity Level 5 objectives.	Detailed planning and resource allocation is in place to support the Recovery Command Centers and Bases of Operation in physical isolation for 400 days with no outside support. The following minimal capability categories must be sustained: 1. Personnel 2. Training 3. Force Protection 4. Food 5. Water 6. Sanitation 7. Fuel 8. Medical & medical supplies 9. Equipment maintenance & parts

AREA	Level 1: Awareness Phase[1]	Level 2: Discovery Phase	Level 3: Planning Phase	Level 4: Implementation Phase	Level 5: Mature State
					10. Facilities & maintenance 11. Other supplies 12. Finance & Contracting 13. Law enforcement & judicial 14. Counseling, psychiatry 15. Family care

Table 8: Preparedness Maturity Model.

Notes:

1. *Level Zero:* Organizations that are not yet at Level One are at Level Zero: The Unaware Phase. For example: Most local governments and small business as of the date of this document are not aware of this issue or conducting associated planning.

2. *Critical path:* The core or baseline capabilities, operations, and resources and associated timing required to constitute and maintain the minimally viable sustainment of the organization to conduct its purpose or mission.

3. *400 Days of resilience:* The scenarios discussed in this book allow for power disruption for greater than 400 days. It is improbable that any organization can by itself achieve this for everything it does; therefore, it is imperative that core mission areas, critical dependencies, crisis multipliers, and resilience multipliers be identified and planned for. This planning includes relationships with external organizations that your organization is dependent on and those who rely on your organization.

4. *Resilience multipliers:* Capabilities that, if ensured, create far more solutions than the cost of problems created by their absence. For example: Maintaining sewage treatment plant capabilities via emergency generator fuel; and stockpiling treatment chemicals that if they last several months would dramatically reduce deadly waterborne disease caused by untreated sewage entering surface water supplies.

5. *Resilience critical path dependencies:* An item whose absence creates a cascading impact to critical capability availability. For example: A lack of robust cooling pump power and equipment for nuclear waste fuel rods could be the cause for waste rod overheating and catching fire.

6. *Cross-dependency:* Dependency outside of an organization's control. For example: The State Highway Patrol/State Police and National Guard are dependent on fuel for their vehicles. They must be resupplied from external sources or their operations will be halted or hindered.

7. *Crisis multipliers:* Dependencies or near-term issues that if not resolved create problems greater than the cost to mitigate them. For example: A nuclear waste rod fire caused by a failure in the cooling system will create deadly fallout to the downwind population, rendering areas uninhabitable (e.g., Fukushima), create a refugee crisis, and force transportation routes to bypass them.

The following figure is provided to facilitate planning discussion and provide insight into critical path cross-dependency issues.

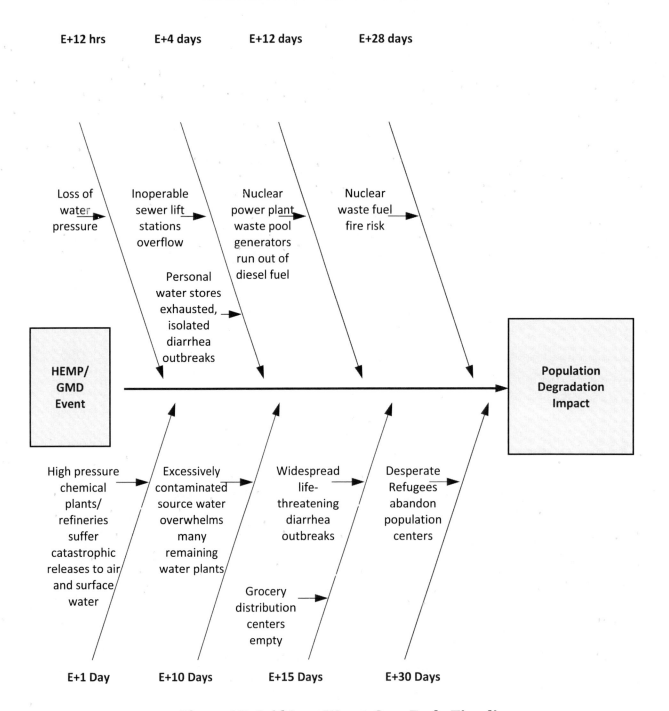

Figure 18: Grid Loss Worst-Case Early Timeline.

Source: Stephen Volandt, Auroros Inc.

166

APPENDIX 4: Guidance on Cybersecurity and Industrial Control/ SCADA Systems

Disclaimer

This information is intended to provide a general guide to basic information and systems security with the intent of helping to start the conversation around systems security; and to provide a set of basic suggestions. These suggestions should be evaluated in the context of the organization and maturity of your cyber-security programs.

ICS-CERT is a valuable resource, but it is only one aspect of what a holistic cyber-security program should include. ICS-CERT is largely business and ICS community driven, which also means there is a chance for political and business motivated failure to provide timely disclosure of security issues and data provided always runs the risk of being inaccurate. The information provided by ICS-CERT should be used to supplement risk analysis and threat management around industrial systems, while taking on a holistic approach that considers everything from the end point and ICS/SCADA systems to the networks (wired and wireless) that they run on, the servers they interface with, and the vendors that may interact with them, both when on-site and remotely.

Cyber Security

Information systems security is an extremely important component of both private and public computing today. Every day new threats are identified, new vulnerabilities are found, and it is everything the information security industry can do to keep up with the pace of these discoveries. Over the past several years, the non-vendor publication of serious Zero-day exploits (ones that are not currently identified by protection systems) has dropped significantly. In correlation, as systems become more complex and security controls are implemented, successful exploits have become increasingly valuable. These vulnerabilities and associated exploits are potentially worth millions of dollars, in turn, reducing the incentive for researchers to publish them and instead, turn them into monetary gains. As this trend increases, basic security principles become ever more important.

Industrial Control/SCADA Systems

Information and system security is ever changing and continues to increase in complexity. As threats are relatively mitigated, new methods to circumvent security controls are uncovered. In a recent 2015 SANS research publication on Industrial Control Systems

167

security, a survey indicated that 32.3% of respondents confirmed breaches with a larger percentage, 48.8%, unable or unwilling to answer directly yes or no (Harp & Gregory-Brown, 2015).

In general, this indicates a lack of visibility and awareness into the risks to industrial control systems. These systems still control much of our utilities, national infrastructure, and operations at many manufacturing companies; including critical infrastructure.

These systems suffer from limitations in not only what they can provide technologically but also, due to being simpler technology, limitations on what measures can be taken in order to secure them. Given the technology limitations, it can be difficult to even identify what lead to compromise and even further, who was responsible for and what that ongoing risk may be.

As such, for these systems, it is much better to attempt to secure the systems through the basic concepts of least privilege access and system isolation. As technology and capabilities increase, this may change in the future at which time this guidance should be reevaluated.

The National Institute of Standards and Technology (NIST) and The Industrial Control Systems Cyber Emergency Response Team (ICS-CERT) provide in-depth documentation around Industrial Control Systems/SCADA risks, threats, vulnerabilities, and some protective guidance. While the recommendations below are valuable to begin work, they will not provide the comprehensive information that may be needed long term. Two such publications are: Common Cybersecurity Vulnerabilities in Industrial Control Systems and Guide to Industrial Control System (ICS) Security, U.S. Department of Homeland Security, 2011; and Stouffer, Pillitteri, Lightman, Abrams, & Hahn, 2015).

The Industrial Control Systems Cyber Emergency Response Team (ICS-CERT) System

Cyber-attack vulnerabilities of critical infrastructures require awareness, training, warning, and adaptation of defenses. The importance of focusing on those risks and communication about them continues to rise. As part of this awareness and in an attempt to increase community engagement, the U.S. Department of Homeland Security (DHS) established the Industrial Control Systems Cyber Emergency Response Team (ICS-CERT) in 2009. It is an organization within DHS's National Cyber Security and Integration Center (NCCIC). The ICS-CERT unit serves as the industrial control systems focus for the United States Computer Emergency Readiness Team (US-CERT) program.[118]

---

[118] "About the Industrial Control Systems Cyber Emergency Response Team." Department of Homeland Security, US-CERT. n.d. Accessed September 30, 2016. https://ics-cert.us-cert.gov/About-Industrial-Control-Systems-Cyber-Emergency-Response-Team

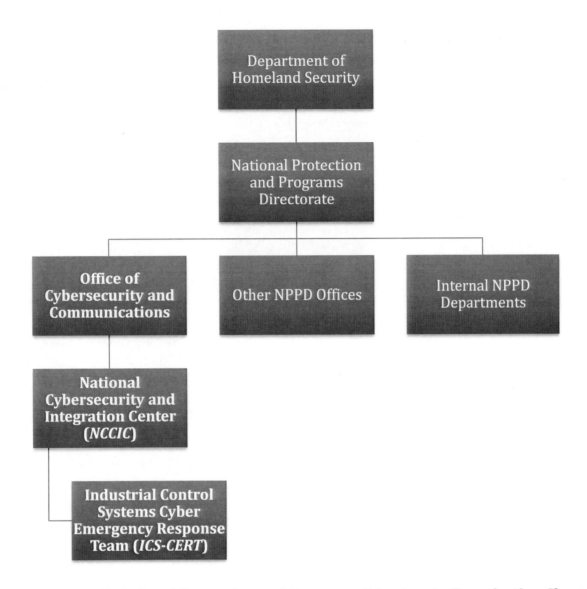

Figure 19: DHS National Protection and Programs Directorate Organization Chart, December 2014.

ICS-CERT provides several key resources to assist with ICS security, including:

- Incident response and security guidance
- Community membership portal
  - Community message boards
  - Alert and document repository
  - Acceptance of, and security of, PCII data
- Email notifications and alerts
- Training activities

This team is responsible for security as it pertains to ICS/SCADA systems and most specifically, has a role in assisting with security incidents in this space. This includes an online community-based web portal and the ability to respond to ICS security incidents with on premise resources if appropriate and requested. Both the US-CERT and ICS-CERT groups offer web portals, which are intended to assist in the dissemination of communication within those communities between both public and private partners. The membership base includes companies working with equipment, or providing ICS related solutions, Information Sharing and Analysis Centers (ISAC), cyber-security companies, government agencies, and other members with relevance in this area.[119] [120]

ICS-CERT membership is limited to critical infrastructure owners and operators and on a case-by-case basis to others who are directly engaged in or responsible for cyber-security of critical infrastructure control systems. This is important as some of the information provided through ICS-CERT is designated "For Official Use Only" (FOUO). However, even without membership, ICS-CERT provides a significant amount of valuable, publicly available information on its site.

The portals provided allow members access to one another through message boards which help to facilitate the discussion of industry topics that focus on the CERT goal. This is a particularly useful tool as it facilitates access to communicate with industry experts across different sectors, including posting to the full audience of members so that anyone with the appropriate input and expertise can see and respond.

One of the most significant benefits that ICS-CERT provides is email alerts relating to different emerging threats. These alerts may be forwarded alerts from FBI-related bulletins or US-CERT-related indicator bulletins that provide members of the community with breaking information about threats they may face in their environment. The cadence for communications of this nature is around two notifications per week. In many cases, these will contain: "hash values" of suspicious and malicious files that enable owner-operator search for implanted malware. These alerts may also explain tactics-techniques-procedures (TTP) used by the attackers; and in some cases, industry accepted structured threat information expression (STIX), formatted files that can be used with security platforms that support their import, which helps to streamline the response time to these types of communications.

In addition to messaging boards and email alerts, ICS-CERT provides a document library containing a variety of information and archives about alerts, advisories, indicator bulletins, and other documents related to ICS security. This document repository contains valuable cyber-security information that can be used in conjunction with security tools, such as Intrusion Prevention/Detection Systems (IPS/IDS), Security Information and Event

---

[119] "US-CERT | United States Computer Emergency Readiness Team." Department of Homeland Security, US-CERT. n.d. Accessed July 24, 2016. https://www.us-cert.gov/
[120] "ICS-CERT." ICS-CERT. n.d. Accessed July 24, 2016. https://ics-cert.us-cert.gov/

Management systems (SIEM), and others that can help in both detection and prevention of ICS threats where these technologies intersect.

ICS-CERT provides training that can be accessed on its website (https://ics-cert.us-cert.gov/Training-Available-Through-ICS-CERT) and is also responsible for accepting and safeguarding voluntarily submitted critical infrastructure information as a part of the DHS Protected Critical Infrastructure Information Program (PCII), which was established as part of the Critical Infrastructure Information Act of 2002 (CII Act), this information is submitted to them by members of the ICS-CERT community.[121]

While ICS-CERT provides several valuable resources, it is important to note that not all ICS systems have the capacity to interface appropriately with modern-day detection technology and ICS-CERT may only contain information about a single attack vector when multiple vectors may be present. ICS-CERT resources, the communications it facilitates, and the data it provides, should constitute a component of a larger ICS and organizational cyber-security strategy.

Contact Information

US-CERT Contact: (888) 282-0870; info@us-cert.gov

Postal Address:

DHS/US-CERT
ATTN: NPPD/CS&C/NCCIC/US-CERT
Mailstop: 0635
245 Murray Lane SW Bldg. 410
Washington, DC 20528

ICS-CERT Contact: (877) 776-7585; ics-cert@hq.dhs.gov

---

[121] "Critical Infrastructure Information Act." H.R. 5005-11, 107th Congress. 2002. Accessed July 24, 2016. https://www.dhs.gov/sites/default/files/publications/CII-Act-508.pdf.

Organizational Strategy

The information security profession has steadily moved through the following states with respect to the ability to enact security in computing environments:

- We will secure our systems, so they cannot be breached.
- We will do our best to secure our systems, but a breach is inevitable.
- We assume our systems are already breached and actively search for attackers.

In many ways, this ideology is progressive in nature and currently, a few, well-developed security programs take the third approach, while the majority of programs identify with the second. Most security programs no longer believe that systems can be absolutely protected against intrusions.

Protection Principles

While it is not possible to ensure total protection, some core principles can help reduce risk and make it significantly harder for an attacker to be both successful and undetected.

- *Establish a strong password policy:* This should include regular changing of passwords, requirements for complex passwords, requirement for current hashing and encryption technologies (MD5 and SHA1 are not acceptable). Encryption key use, such as SSH, should also be rotated on a regular basis. Most importantly, change ALL default passwords and regenerated default keys. On Industrial Control Systems and firmware based systems be especially aware of any factory default, hard coded, passwords that may be in use. Find out if they can be changed or updated; reach out to the manufacturer to get them to update the products. If these cannot be done, consider other products or compensating controls to prevent use of default/hard coded access.
- *Establish a monitoring system at least for critical systems:* Being breached is bad, not being able to identify when, where, who, or even that you have been breached is even worse. Having a proper monitoring system in place can help identify when an attack has happened and details about that attack. Ideally, this will reduce the time that attackers have access to any systems. Do not forget to turn on logging components on the various devices and configure them to properly talk to the monitoring system.
- *Use industry accepted security controls:* Firewalls, antivirus, and antispyware software are all important. Many information security professionals consider antivirus a legacy technology, but it still serves to mitigate some threats so should not be overlooked unless compensating controls are truly in place and validated to be effective across the system spectrum. A combination of firewall, antivirus, and advanced endpoint protection solutions is currently the recommended approach.

- *Establish good computer user security policy:* Computer operators and end users should not browse the open internet, use email, or install software (unless specifically required for the system) through sensitive systems such as servers, systems containing sensitive data, and control systems, etc. Consider whether systems, especially end-user systems should be "always on." Consider implementation of education and awareness training around use of computer systems in a more secure way. User understanding and acceptance of policy will increase compliance, notification of possible threats, and, as a result, overall security.

- *Perform regular backups and updates:* These are absolutely critical components to IT programs in general and even more important for security programs. Backups can protect an organization in the event of an equipment failure or serious security scenario where data is maliciously modified or removed. Backups should always be stored off-site and encrypted. Updates are a must, the correct systems problems as well as implement new security features, patch vulnerabilities, and more. An aggressive patching schedule will help to mitigate many new threats.

- *Take a least privilege approach:* Not all users need all rights to all systems. In many cases, most users need very few rights and system privileges in order to do their jobs. You should evaluate and establish security policy around this principle and only grant user's access to the systems and at a level required to do their jobs. Not only will this reduce insider threat risk, but it will also reduce the risk that an attacker can leverage a given users credentials for attacks across the environment. In turn, this may also aid with detection, mitigation, and remediation activities since the incident may be isolated.

- *Reduce and restrict external to internal access:* Many companies and organizations successfully utilize VPN technology to allow remote workers to do their jobs more effectively and more conveniently. While this does enable extended functionality, it is important to evaluate the need for remote access against the possibility of the system, user, or user account being exploited in a manner that grants an attacker remote access into those systems. Whenever possible Multi-Factor Authentication should be implemented and used, especially in cases of remote access. Furthermore, Industrial Control Systems and other systems should not be connected to the open internet. A recent article about printers connected to the internet helps demonstrate why this should be avoided; at the time of publication 21,000 devices were found on the open internet (Vickery, 2016).

- *Consider network segmentation to isolate sensitive systems:* Allowing remote access in some cases may be necessary, if so, properly configured, VPN technology should be used. In addition, isolating different parts of the network from other areas should also be considered. An important example of this is Industrial Control Systems. Due to the challenges faced by many ICS systems, it is often not appropriate or secure to directly connect ICS devices into a network shared by other non-Industrial Control Systems not involved in the operation of the overall component. VLAN separation may be a solution as long as the risks are reviewed and deemed acceptable. Consider implementing Network Access Controls to prevent unauthorized devices from physically connecting into network ports; wireless, phone, and voice communications networks should be included in these considerations.

- *Consider vendor security controls:* Some of the largest hacks have involved access through trusted third-party networks run by organizations other than the one ultimately targeted. It is important to review and understand the security controls that suppliers have in place to protect you as their customer.

- *Consider what else is connected and how it can be exploited:* With the onset and growth of the "Internet of Things" these devices are quickly becoming the latest frontier of new risk to individuals and organizations alike. You should consider what devices you are providing or being provided and how they interact with the other systems on your network. Evaluate and understand the risks around misuse, misconfiguration, and use with malicious intent. Do NOT forget about non-wired devices, Bluetooth, Wi-Fi, and other wireless connection methods are potentially more dangerous than even wired devices. Consider if they can be isolated from other networks and devices.

- *Consider advanced technology, but also what you can successfully support:* Advanced technology such as next generation firewalls can be an important security component to help reduce risks in many environments. The same goes for advanced end-point protection, threat intelligence, incident response, and other current technologies. While these can be positive additions, consideration should also be taken as to whether the long-term support and maintenance of those systems is possible within budgetary, staffing, and skillsets currently available. A security solution implemented but not maintained properly can actually increase your risk instead of reducing it.

- *Code development security:* Systems security is extremely important, but an often overlooked security component is in the very code that is being used in applications. With software driving more and more of what we do the importance of good development practices and secure coding techniques has risen to epic proportions. Take for instance long-running security flaws within Flash and Java products, which have led to significant security problems over the years. A SDLC program that incorporates code review from a security perspective should be considered.

Important Follow-Up Questions to Consider

Several questions that can help to further map out and understand what risks you are protecting against are:

- What is the risk?
- What is your security goal?
- What is the impact of the system being utilized by unauthorized access?
- What is the impact of the system if it is taken out of service?
- To what extent can you identify unwanted/malicious activity?
- What other systems interact with the one that I am concerned about and what security controls are in place at that level?
- What is my risk from human exploit, insider threat, corporate espionage, etc.?

APPENDIX 5: Blackstarting the Electric Power Grid

Following an EMP attack, solar superstorm, cyber-attack, or coordinated physical attacks, a blackout of large regions of North America electric power grid is possible. The process of restoring electric power following a blackout is referred to as "blackstarting" the grid. The systems used to restart the grid, known as "blackstart" resources, are defined by NERC as generating units and their associated set of equipment that have "the ability to be started without connection to the remainder of the [electric power] system," and that has been included in the transmission operator's restoration plan. Most blackstart generation resources today are hydroelectric plants, small gas peaking units, small oil fired peaking units, and diesel plants. NERC guidance may be found in NERC Reliability Standards EOP-005-2 (System Restoration from Blackstart Resources) and EOP-006-2 (System Restoration Coordination) available from the NERC website (www.nerc.com).

The basic steps associated with blackstarting the grid or portions of the grid following a triple-threat blackout are as follows:

1. The first step in recovery is identifying the geographic extent of the blackout and nature of the damage to the system. This process is greatly simplified if grid monitoring and control centers remain operational—unlikely following intentional attacks. Following an EMP or cyber-attack, control centers and remote telemetry will likely be disabled until repair is possible, thus boots on the ground may be needed to assess the state of the grid. Pre-planning is important for grid surveillance and repair operations including priority task schedules for different contingencies and human and system resources required. Trained technical and force protection personnel and a reservoir of spare parts will be needed.

2. Because restarting the entire grid at once will not be possible, disconnecting the larger network into smaller independent "grid islands" must occur first by automatic or manual isolation breaker tripping. Some locales are already set up to do this; others will need to take steps to enable "grid islanding" themselves.

3. Within each grid island, blackstarting begins with repairing and restarting one (or more) smaller generation stations to bootstrap the rest of the grid. Hydroelectric plants are ideal "blackstart stations." Where hydroelectric stations are not available, combustion turbine generator stations can be used provided a sustainable fuel supply is available. Typically, there will not be many blackstart stations. Recovery at most locations will need to wait for other areas to restore power and then be reconnected increment by increment.

4. Within each grid island, principal transmission lines and substations between the blackstart stations and other generation resources and user loads are then repaired and energized. Special attention should be devoted to ensuring that nuclear power

plants have power for their cooling systems to avert Fukushima type catastrophes.[122] High priority must also be given to security and life-support locations such as 911 centers and hospitals.

5. Within grid islands with larger generation plants, available generator station power could be used to start larger nuclear or fossil-fuel-fired base load plant(s).[123]
6. The power from the base load plants is used to restore power to all grid island loads
7. Once individual grid islands have achieved stable operation, coordination of reconnecting them can occur to restore the larger grid.

Although NERC regional operators have blackstart plans for limited blackout contingencies, there is presently no national plan addressing restoring the grid following a large-scale, "long-term outage" (LTO) blackout contingency.[124] The LTO phenomenon has been defined by the President's National Security Telecommunications Advisory Panel (NSTAC) as an interruption of electricity and/or communications for a period long enough, and over a large enough geographic region, to hamper providing electric power and communications even by alternative means.[125] Triple-threat blackout contingencies will be particularly challenging, given that large numbers of bulk power system generation and transmission equipment may be damaged. In these circumstances, existing regional blackstart plans may not be adequate. An LTO contingency has not yet occurred in North America.

The absence of a U.S. national-level blackstart plan makes it more important for regional and local power companies and their surrounding communities to plan for electricity restoration using regional and local resources.[126] Instead of a top-down blackstart approach, a bottom-up approach will be needed.[127] Towns and cities should develop the ability to isolate themselves from the rest of the grid and run priority infrastructure on an adequate supply of local generators. With regard to local generation, note that diesel

---

[122] The NERC Reliability Standards require that nuclear be given highest priority to insure public safety.

[123] In most cases, every grid island will have at least one large generator. This may not be true in triple-threat contingencies) The grid island could not be built out unless it had enough generation to support the load (note that when cold load (load that has been off for several hours) is added, the start-up load can be up to 10 times the normal amount of that load. A general rule of thumb in restoration is to limit each incremental load pick-up to 5% of available generation.

[124] Note that, following the loss of 25% of their national grid in 1987, the United Kingdom developed a national blackstart plan that includes pre-event financial incentives for utilities to develop and improve their blackstart capabilities.

[125] National Security Telecommunications Advisory Committee, Telecommunications and Electric Power Interdependency Task Force, People and Processes: Current State of Telecommunications and Electric Power Interdependencies, January 31, 2006.

[126] See the Report on the FERC-NERC-Regional Entity Joint Review of Restoration and Recovery Plans, January 2016, on local and regional system restoration plan assessments by industry and FERC staffs.

[127] The power industry is trending toward a "top-down" blackstart approach using larger combustion turbine generation plants to restart the grid. Triple-threat contingencies will need a "bottom-up" approach using smaller generation plants to restart the larger plants. For an example, see ISO New England Letter to FERC Commissioner Kimberly Bose, Revisions to the ISO New England System Restoration Plan, 30 December 2011, p 7.

locomotives can be used as mobile power plants. There are both AC and DC locomotives, so it will be important to have conversion issues resolved beforehand. They can be used for big loads like hospitals, defense locations, banking, and communication hubs. At port locations, ships can (and have been) also used to supply emergency power.

Communication planning is essential to expedite the blackstart process. Utilities, in cooperation with local government officials, should establish lines of communication from local to regional to national authorities with attention to both electric power interconnections and the communication systems that are most likely to be available.

Communities should work with utilities to develop priorities for who gets power first (e.g., military bases, 911 centers, police stations, fire departments, and hospitals). Nuclear power plants must continue to receive electric power whether or not they are operational, because they require electricity to circulate cooling water within the reactor vessel and spent rod cooling pools in order to prevent release of radioactive material.

Local utilities should identify primary blackstart generation facilities.[128] Hydroelectric power plants are ideal blackstart power sources because their turbines continue to turn in most threat conditions and they require very little initial power to restart (just enough to open the intake gates and the excitation of the generator field coils). These can rapidly energize transmission lines to enable restarting large fossil-fueled or nuclear stations. Also, certain types of combustion turbines can be configured for blackstart in areas where hydroelectric power plants are not available. Care must be taken in planning for LTOs to ensure that a long-term, uninterruptible fuel supply is available for combustion turbines.

To be prepared, local utilities should also assess their networks for single point vulnerabilities with respect to EMP, solar storms, cyber-attacks, and coordinated physical attacks. Most single point vulnerabilities will be the same for multiple threats. Assessment teams should address generator station, transmission system, and distribution system operators.

Protection of blackstart resources is crucially important in advance of contingencies. Protection of blackstart generator stations is the highest priority; without generator output voltage, nothing else will work. E1 can damage generator startup and operational control electronics. Aurora-type cyber-attacks can cause generators to self-destruct. Protection efforts must address the generators themselves, generator station step-up (GSU) transformers, and associated industrial control systems. Protection of the transmission system is the next priority. Transformers can be damaged by EMP or solar GMD effects if not protected. Delivery time for a single large transformer today is typically one year. There are roughly 2,000 transformers in use in the transmission system today at 345 kV

---

[128] Identification and regular testing of blackstart resources is required by NERC Reliability Standards

and above with many more at lesser voltages.[129] Note that, if generator stations are working, it is possible to work around failed transmission substations by stringing bypass lines on the ground.

The blackstart process is a race against the clock. Plans should include a premium on restarting tripped-off generators before they cool, within 2 hours if possible. As generators cool, the shafts are prone to lock-up due to thermal deformation.[130] The process involves detailed step-by-step coordination between grid control centers and field operators. There is a premium on reliable communication systems. Grid equipment damage and shock-hazards are possible unless tight coordination of connections and switch positions occur from the control center to the field operators. Land mobile radios are likely to continue to function following an EMP event and can be used over grid island regions. It is likely that crews will be working within isolated grid islands for quite some time.

Utilities should practice the blackstart sequence in real exercises.[131] During exercises, blackstart teams should demonstrate their ability to isolate and reconnect grid islands. Within grid islands, teams should practice the blackstart sequence in field exercises at least from the generator stations to the first layer of substations downstream of generators. Teams should practice working around damaged main components (e.g., re-configuring around failed substation transformers). Some issues worth noting regarding blackstart capabilities include:

1. It is important to have a clear chain of command in place,[132] agreed on at all levels, beforehand among utility company principals and public officials.
2. Without power, there will be public disorder that will require special protection for restoration teams. There will likely be a need for National Guard assistance with law enforcement and force protection. Substations may be used as command post locations to coordinate restoration team activity and provide protection. National Guard communication systems may be helpful to restoration teams in coordinating their step-by-step recovery process.

---

[129] Report of the Commission to Assess the Threat to the United States from Electromagnetic Pulse (EMP) Attack: Critical National Infrastructures, ch. 2, "Electric Power," April 2008.

[130] Shaft deformation can occur even without the thermal stress. All generators of significant size (vertical shafts excluded) must keep their rotors turning slowly to prevent deformation. This is one reason that re-powering generation resources for at least the amount of power required to turn the shafts is a priority.

[131] Many utilities already practice for limited blackouts. NERC Reliability Standards require all certified personnel to have a minimum of 32 hours of emergency operations training annually. This training includes drills/exercises within each utility and between the utilities in a given region. However, large-scale blackout drills will require additional tasks due to unavailability of operational adjoining region generation plants.

[132] NERC Reliability Standards prescribe this for the utilities for limited-scale blackouts. For example, the individual Transmission Operator (TOP) is given overall authority (over Balancing Authorities, Generator Operators, Load Serving Entities, etc.) within its service area. Coordination between TOPs is under the authority of the Reliability Coordinators (RCs). For long-term national-scale blackouts, the chain-of-command will need to be re-evaluated and augmented.

3. Unlike generation station recovery, blackstart of the transmission grid will require wide-area communications because coordination between remote locations is necessary. Communications assets used for this purpose under normal conditions include cell phones, dedicated microwave systems, and satellite systems. Following an EMP attack, it is likely that only land-mobile radios and possibly UHF SATCOM may be available.

4. As controls and other critical components of the electrical transmission and generation system suffer damage, so do similar components on the production, processing, and delivery systems providing fuel to the electric generators. Restoration of the electrical power system is not feasible on a wide scale without a parallel restoration of these fuel processing and delivery systems. Many utilities are now switching their primary blackstart facilities from hydroelectric to natural gas plants. This trend is counterproductive from a national resilience standpoint because natural gas pipelines supplying fuel for gas turbine generators may shut down quickly at the outset of triple-threat contingencies.[133] Hydro-plants, coal plants, geothermal, and nuclear plants have longer duration latent fuel supplies, which can play a major role under LTO conditions. Beyond hydroelectric and geothermal, coal plants typically have significant stockpiles of fuel so the delay in rail and other delivery systems for even a month is not an issue for coal fuel.

5. At present, NRC rules require nuclear plants to be shut down under blackout conditions. This requirement should be re-evaluated given the multi-year energy output capacity (without reload) of nuclear fuel. Nuclear power plants serve as a strong base power source for avoiding blackouts or restarting other portions of the grid should a blackout occur. Re-engineering of these plants to enable them to operate through[134] or rapidly restart would add significantly to blackstart resources and avoidance of Fukushima-type catastrophes.[135]

6. It will take considerable time to restore the grid. Balancing generation and load and then reconnecting each new increment are a reasonably difficult and time consuming process in the best of circumstances. A "new normal" interim situation should be anticipated with local grid islands as the main electric power supply for

---

[133] Most combustion turbines designated as blackstart resources are dual fuel units—capable of running on either gas or oil. It is expected that these units would initially start on oil. The need for re-establishment of gas supply is still critical since the oil on hand is a limited resource.

[134] Rapid restart is possible. Operate through is challenging because a substantial amount of load would need to remain connected to balance the large amount of generation from these units. A protected backup load would need to be available including, for example, pumps to replenish hydro reservoirs or dedicated scalable resistive load banks.

[135] One significant geomagnetic storm could replicate the Fukushima disaster ten times over in the most densely populated region of the U.S. Evacuating the population in this area would be impossible in the best of times. A massive power outage, combined with transportation problems, would make an evacuation inconceivable. The only viable way to prevent massive loss of life would be the rapid restoration of power to cooling pumps at the nuclear facilities.

some months. Power will be available within geographic pockets and the electric supply will not operate 24/7 in many of these locations.

7. Because triple-threat continental scale blackouts are possible, a North American blackstart plan is needed. The plan could identify utilities that are most likely to sustain generator operation (e.g., high complement of hydroelectric plants) or restart generators quickly. As an example, in the event of a North America-wide blackout, New England grids can be more easily divided into smaller grid islands and are richer in hydroelectric plants, thus they may be restarted more quickly and provide the energy basis for restarting other parts of the grid. Hydroelectric plants are most prevalent in the Northeast and Northwest.[136]

---

[136] In the event of a complete national blackout, all grids will need to initiate blackstart from the outset. However, the New England may be able to be restored the most quickly and then be leveraged to bootstrap other areas. The New England grid is divided into much smaller grid islands than the rest of the U.S. grid. These grid islands usually contain more than one interconnection node, reducing the incidence of single point failure locations. Because New England experiences a cold winter climate, it is prudent to restart this region first during winter to avert cascading effects on the population and critical systems due to cold temperatures. The New England power grid serves a large, concentrated population, so restoration of service in the region would provide the greatest good to the largest percentage of the population. From experience, grid breakers and relays in the New England grid behave oddly in cold weather; they are more difficult to restart once tripped. Substations often have DC battery packs that can run equipment for a limited amount of time, but cold weather can reduce the period that batteries will last without recharging. However, the most significant benefit to restarting the New England grid first is preventing cooling problems at nuclear power plants. There are a large number of nuclear power plants within the New England network (the nation's most densely populated region), presenting an urgent threat to human life.

APPENDIX 6: Supply Chain Resilience

If supply chains are resilient, catastrophe is less likely. If supply chains fail, catastrophe is much more likely. The supply chain is how water, food, pharmaceuticals—all the essentials and many of the non-essentials of modern life—are sourced, made, and delivered to large populations.

Over the past three decades the supply chain has been revolutionized. It has been transformed from a largely supply-oriented push system to a much more demand-oriented pull system. This revolution has had significant benefits for producers and consumers. But the recent emergence of demand-pull—rather than supply-push—presents particular challenges in case of a potentially long-duration outage of the electrical grid.

For most of human history—and it is still true in most of the world—supply has been limited by geography, climate, logistical limitations, and other externalities. While demand has always affected supply, the influence has traditionally been muffled and delayed by time, space, and a whole host of frictions impeding the expression or perception of demand.

Today in the United States and other consumer-driven economies across the planet demand can often be said to create supply. The superstructure on which the U.S. economy is built is the demand-pull supply chain.

In 1900, there was only one city in the United States with a population of more than 1 million. As recently as 1950, there were only five U.S. cities with more than a million residents. Today there are 10 million-plus cities and 33 U.S. metropolitan statistical areas with more than 2 million residents. These dense concentrations of people require high-capacity and high-functioning supply chains to meet demand for food, pharmaceuticals, medical goods, fuel, and other key resources. Over the last generation, 5,000 years of supply finding demand has been overturned by demand specifically shaping supply. Since 2014, a second revolution in demand and supply networking has begun.

Recognizing these shifts will be fundamental to any effective adaptation in the event of a long-term outage of the electrical grid.

Supply Chains and Complexity

Emergency management and homeland security professionals give considerable attention to critical infrastructure and key resources (CIKR). The electrical power grid is a key feature of critical infrastructure. The supply chain is one way to engage several key resources. There are also multifaceted mutual dependencies between the supply chain and critical infrastructure.

The supply chains for water and food depend heavily on dependable electric power. Electric power depends on the supply chain for coal, natural gas, and other crucial commodities. Which comes first, the chicken or the egg? In the case of supply chain and critical infrastructure: which is the chicken, which is the egg?

The modern supply chain is a complex adaptive system. No one owns the system. There are many owners (and tenants and squatters) many of which both depend on and compete with each other. No one controls the system. Yet the system can be exquisitely responsive to any subtle shift in supply or demand.

William Eggers, Executive Director of Deloitte's Public Leadership Institute explains,

> *Consider: Who is in charge of getting the right number of chickens to Manhattan every day? After all, few chickens live there, but a lot of chickens get eaten there. The typical Manhattanite downs about sixty pounds of chicken a year, in every imaginable form, from chicken chow mein to chicken nuggets, from organic chicken to those little cubes that float in your can of chicken soup. Untold thousands of people participate in providing for Manhattan's ever-changing chicken needs, from truck drivers to restaurant owners, from grocery store managers to Arkansas chicken farmers. Who is in charge? Who makes sure that New York City winds up with the right amount of the right kind of chicken?*
>
> *The answer is: No one. The chaos of the uncontrolled buying and selling of the market produces an orderly pattern of exchanges that coordinates the activities of independent yet interdependent participants. The result, without any central planning, is an adaptable and ever-changing arrangement that generally meets the needs of Manhattan's chicken eating public. The government provides certain oversight and context for the market. The U.S. Department of Agriculture watches over chicken farms and the city's Board of Health licenses and inspects restaurants. Chickens are hauled over public roads and contract disputes between chicken farmers and truckers are resolved in public courts. But when it comes to the essence of the chicken delivery system—how much chicken, of what kind, at what price—it is the invisible workings of supply and demand that align the productive activities of a loose network of thousands of people (and companies) in making sure New Yorkers get their chicken potpie, chicken vindaloo, and extra-spicy buffalo chicken wings.*

Author Francis Fukuyama believes we are just beginning to understand the paradox of how chaos can create order. In *The Great Disruption: Human Nature and the Reconstitution of Social Order* Fukuyama notes that, "The study of how order arises, not as the result of top-down mandate by hierarchical authority, whether political or religious, but as the result of self-organization on the part of decentralized individuals, is one of the most important intellectual developments of our time... In an information society, neither governments nor corporations will rely exclusively on formal, bureaucratic rules to organize the people over whom they have authority."[137]

A catastrophe is—among other things—the social interpretation of an unexpected and chaotic event. In a potential catastrophe the always present—but often denied—complexity of human life becomes inescapably apparent. In a long-term grid outage this would include exposing the complexity of supply chains. We usually experience supply chains as simple cause-and-effect mechanisms. To discover this is not the case can be troublesome. To make this discovery in the midst of an already chaotic context is even more troublesome. The complexity of the disastrous event encountering the complexity of the supply chain multiplies our level of uncertainty.

Without electricity the pull-signals on which contemporary supply chains depend are not sent. Without these pull-signals the supply chain is essentially blind and deaf. The immediate reaction by most players in the system is to wait: wait for power and signals to resume, wait for "authorities" to communicate, wait for certainty to return. In this midst of a long-duration grid outage, such waiting actually puts lives at risk.

Being prepared for catastrophe is, at its essence, to be prepared to engage complexity and chaos. This is possible. There are principles of good practice for complexity and chaos. Many of these principles are regularly demonstrated in the behavior of emergency managers, first responders, and average citizens when faced by a crisis. Recognizing, refining, and rehearsing how these principles can be applied to the supply chain will reduce uncertainty and enhance effectiveness in an actual crisis.

Defining the Supply Chain(s)

Is it a supply chain or supply chains? It is each and it is both. The supply chain is the system-of-systems in which individual supply chains operate. There are several ways to describe the supply chain.

In their 2007 text, Tage Skjott-Larsen and Philip B. Schary explain:

> *A supply chain is both a network and a system. The core of the supply chain is a network, a process, and sets of relationships. The function of this network is to convert resources to finished products (including services) delivered to final users/customers... A supply chain is also a system. Systems are specified by their interactions. The system becomes dynamic because of changes, which are made both by managed decisions and actions and by external forces unleashed by the network environment. Because of these inevitable connections, the system becomes both non-linear and dynamic. The system is non-linear in that the efforts to adapt these forces reflect feedback loops... Change is*

---

[137] New York: Touchstone, 1999.

constant, requiring continual adaptation, but a major event, characterized as a strange attractor, can throw the system off balance or even into cataclysm. If the system is sensitive to new influences, then it will ultimately change to meet the challenge. Management occurs at the edge between stability and chaos. (Managing the Global Supply Chain, pp. 349-350)

The Council of Supply Chain Management Professionals (CSCMP) offers that the supply chain:

encompasses the planning and management of all activities involved in sourcing and procurement, conversion, and all logistics management activities. Importantly, it also includes coordination and collaboration with channel partners, which can be suppliers, intermediaries, third-party service providers, and customers. In essence, supply chain management integrates supply and demand management within and across companies. Supply Chain Management is an integrating function with primary responsibility for linking major business functions and business processes within and across companies into a cohesive and high-performing business model. It includes all of the logistics management activities noted above, as well as manufacturing operations, and it drives coordination of processes and activities with and across marketing, sales, product design, and finance and information technology.

Supply chain management "occurs at the edge between stability and chaos." The most successful managers of the supply chain have developed the skills of collaboration, coordination, and creativity that are effective along this edge. This might also be said to describe the most successful emergency managers and homeland security officials. How can these common skill-sets be leveraged?

The Supply Chain Council has developed and advocates an understanding of the supply chain represented in the following process reference model.

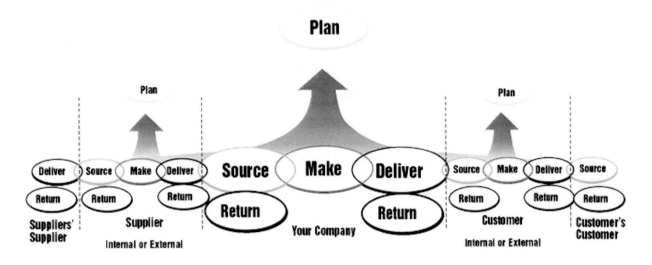

Figure 20: Supply Chain Operations Reference (SCOR) Model.

Source: AIPICS Supply Chain Council.

Especially if the other more obviously complicated definitions are kept in mind, conceiving the supply chain as the outcome of plan/source/make/deliver/return functions is a helpful framework for beginning to deal with this complex adaptive creature we are calling the supply chain. (While the picture may help, this approach is as complicated as any other.)

The five functions (plan/source/make/deliver/return) are as ancient as commerce itself. What has revolutionized the supply chain in the last three decades is the speed by which information on customer behavior is communicated across the functions, and how that information is used to drive decisions regarding the velocity (speed and direction) of the entire supply chain.

An especially important tool in this revolution has been the Universal Product Code or UPC. On June 26, 1974 at a Marsh supermarket in Ohio, a pack of Wrigley's Juicy Fruit chewing gum became the first retail product sold using a scanner and UPC symbol. The use of the UPC and other "bar codes" allows the supply chain to be digitally monitored, mapped, and managed as never before.

Working through a private international standards-setting process a variety of bar codes provide a framework that allows many products, services, and information about them to be pulled across the supply chain. In effect, this information moves the supply chain itself. Increasingly these standards—and the rich information and management resources they make possible—ensure effective, timely, and comparatively friction-free transactions between companies. However it is generated, digital information has transformed the modern supply chain from supply-push to demand-pull.

187

Farmers, miners, and fishermen still matter. Processors, truckers, wholesalers, and retailers still play a crucial part. Ports, railways, and highways are still required. Physical stuff of all sorts still has to move from point A to B (and usually on to points C, D, and Z). But at least in the United States, Europe, the Pacific Rim, and increasingly around the world, the digital signals that are sent along largely determine when and where product arrives.

When this strategic capacity for generating demand-pull information persists, the supply chain is very resilient. Demand-pull is the attractor around which the system self-organizes. But if the digital stream dries up the supply chain goes blind, deaf, and immobile. This has important, and largely unprecedented, implications for catastrophe preparedness.

Given this strategic context we are clearly beyond the typical approach to Mass Care (ESF-6) or Logistics (ESF-7). The Emergency Support Functions are just as dependent on supply chain resilience as any other aspect of modern life. Supply chain resilience is a matter of systemic strategic capacity. If the capacity is resilient, local capability will be restored sooner rather than later. If the capacity is lost, it may be very late indeed until local capability is restored.

To prepare for a long-duration outage of the electrical grid, both public and private decision-makers can begin by asking, what do we know about the sourcing, making, and delivering of key resources? Do existing plans for sourcing, making, and delivering consider catastrophic possibilities? What are the principal supply chain vulnerabilities related to sourcing, making, and delivering? To what extent are these vulnerabilities shared across the supply chain or to what extent are they amplified for specific commodities, services, or geographic locations? Are vulnerabilities threat-specific or are the vulnerabilities generic to all (or most) natural, accidental, and intentional threats?

Principles of Supply Chain Resilience

Given the complexity and capacity of commercial supply chains, any sustained failure in a dense urban area, or multiple urban areas, will not be addressed in a timely manner through replacement. In individual cases or contexts involving less dense populations, external sources of supply can temporarily replace lost supply capacity. But to serve dense populations over an extended period of time will require the resilience of some significant proportion of preexisting supply chain capacity.

The mid-Atlantic Regional Catastrophic Preparedness Grant Program (RCPGP) Project on Supply Chain Resilience developed five principles of good practice:

- **Awareness**: Observe and engage the full context;
- **Connectedness:** Recognize and engage our full range of relationships and dependencies;

- **Realism:** Differentiate between cause and effect, capacity and capability, novelty and continuity;
- **Agility:** Expect change in context and relationships, remain creatively open to change, and actively embrace change; and
- **Flexibility:** Expand the operational space where and how turbulence can occur without threatening the supply chain system's fundamental identity.

In case of a long-duration outage of the electrical grid, readiness to engage these principles would be very helpful to saving lives.

If leaders, decision makers, contingency planners and others can establish a reasonably accurate picture of their full context, they are more likely to recognize when the event—and the social interpretation of the event—is beginning to cross the boundary into a non-recoverable catastrophe. This level of shared awareness will allow more informed choosing regarding recovery or transformation. This is much more than a common operating picture, which focuses on tactical conditions in real-time.

Parts of the supply chain are connected and interdependent. The supply chain is deeply interdependent with power, telecommunications, financial, and other systems. The more parts of a connected system are destroyed or contaminated, the more likely a catastrophe. In Japan an early indication of catastrophe was when both the lack of electricity and the lack of fuel—and a sustained period with reduced supplies of each—signaled a whole host of connected activities would be affected, such as water system repair, food delivery, medical care, and shelter.

Is the public and are leaders able to be realistic regarding consequences? Recognizing and understanding key interdependencies can help us differentiate between a short-term challenge and long-term failure. Is the underlying capacity for recovery destroyed or only disrupted? Is the difference discernible? Do key decision makers share a common understanding? Will the public believe the assessments of leadership, of the media, of experts?

How can we be effectively prepared to accurately assess the changes in context and underlying relationships?

Command, control, and communications (C-cubed) are fundamental to tactical success. Strategic success can be said to depend on context, connections, and courage. Those who observe reality, are oriented to see it accurately, and choose to decide and act in a manner well-matched with reality are most likely to survive and thrive, regardless of what has happened. These are the prerequisites to agility and flexibility whether in restoring the status quo ante or moving into a new normal.

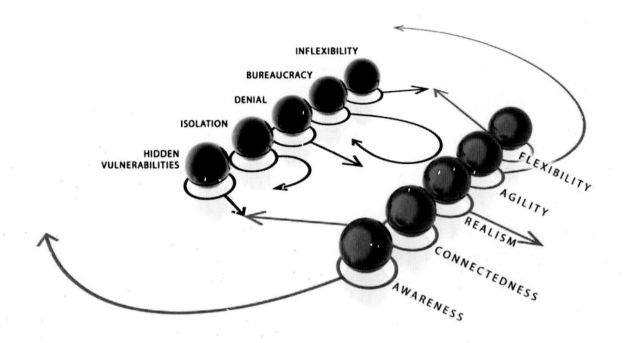

Figure 21: Five Principals of Good Practice for Supply Chains.

Source: The mid-Atlantic Regional Catastrophic Preparedness Grant Program (RCPGP) Project on Supply Chain Resilience

Being able to recognize the full context and the connectedness built into our social systems and having the courage to see when, where and why a fundamental shift has occurred may be the principal value emerging from any approach to catastrophe preparedness. How do we cultivate a shared capacity for resilience and transformation? Three disciplined lines of inquiry can help:

- **(1) What are your core capacities?** Beginning at the lowest level of Maslow's hierarchy, how are you, your community, and your region supplied with water, food, pharmaceuticals, medical goods, essential medical care, and shelter? How are waste and other dangerous substances treated and removed? This is a strategic inventory of what is needed to survive. Whether the goal is resilience and recovery or transformation understanding what and how much is needed is a first step in strategic preparedness. This is basically a list reflecting the pre-catastrophic status quo.

- **(2) How and where are your core capacities sourced, made, delivered, consumed, and returned?** Once you have identified what and how much is needed, how are those needs currently fulfilled? Where are the sources? Where is the making done? What are the key delivery corridors and mechanisms? Who makes?

190

Who delivers? Who consumes and where does consumption occur? Where are the nodes and links in the overall system? This is basically a map or set of maps.

- **(3) What are the key relationships that enable the core capacities?** Not much is made without electricity. Not much is delivered without fuel, roadways, railways, and such. Not much is consumed without a transfer of funds. What are the relationships—human, technical, financial, physical, contractual, and otherwise—on which the core capabilities depend? How do these relationships work? Are there shared choke points? Are there overlapping nodes?

Many—perhaps most—of these relationships are not explicit. Often the relationships are hidden in plain sight, taken for granted even by those who are most dependent on the relationships. There is a level of unrecognized "precariousness" where, if a set of relationships falters, the current equilibrium will have to be reset.

While the core capacity list and related maps will help, the full set of relationships—and their implications—will only be exposed in action or, at least, through anticipation of action. **Tabletops, exercises, and other realistic drilling** are ways to make explicit the key relationships. Once the relationships are recognized and better understood steps can be taken to mitigate vulnerabilities and strengthen the resilience of the relationships.

The tabletops, exercises, and other drills are a way to peel the onion of multilayered relationships on which the modern world depends: intergovernmental, interagency, private-public, and more. Through this form of action-research, context becomes clearer, connectedness is mapped, and the courage to act is given essential direction in the midst of crisis.

[This Appendix draws on prior work published in the *Strategic Playbook: Regional Catastrophic Preparedness and Supply Chain Resilience*. It was adapted by Philip J. Palin, one of the authors of the Strategic Playbook and a Senior Fellow in Homeland Security at the Graduate School of Rutgers University.]

APPENDIX 7: International Disaster Assistance

Background

Looking back at the 2005 Hurricane Katrina disaster that devastated so many areas inside the United States, we understand that some catastrophic events may be so disruptive and calamitous they actually set the stage for considering temporary offers of assistance and relief from foreign governments. Major catastrophic disasters likely to unfold in the future should also be assessed in light of the Katrina experience. This is also very likely given the traditional practice of sending our own search and rescue teams, and supplies, overseas in cases where a major disaster struck. Reciprocal offers from allies as friends may be offered and the United States government needs a coherent policy and system for accepting, storing, and deploying those goods as effectively as possible.

Since then, it has become the norm for the U.S. government to receive offers of aid following notable domestic disaster events. Global collaboration in emergency management has become the norm and made more realistic the relatively new phenomena of country-to-country offers of assistance, often before a complete picture of the impacts of the disaster and the needs of the survivors are fully identified. The United States is no different; however, the unique system in place should be understood for its current strength as well as its limitations.

Several federal agencies are deeply involved in orchestrating the acceptance, storage, and internal transfer of donated goods, relief supplies, and equipment. The Federal Emergency Management Agency (FEMA), the Department of State (DOS), the U.S. Agency for International Development (USAID), the Department of Health and Human Services (HHS), and a few other U.S. government regulatory agencies have created the International Assistance System (IAS).

As part of the IAS there is also a Concept of Operations (IAS CONOPS) to review and accept or reject foreign offers of assistance. The IAS CONOPS, which is only utilized following a Stafford Act declaration by the President, establishes standard operating procedures for:

- Reviewing international offers and determining whether to accept or decline these offers;
- Managing the logistics of transporting, receiving, and distributing international donations; and
- Procuring resources internationally when deemed necessary by FEMA or a FEMA mission-assigned (MA) agency.

Under most likely disaster situations, including many types of crisis situations, the U.S. government is usually in a position to be able to fulfill its disaster response requirements domestically and no foreign assistance is expected or needed. Typically, the U.S. government will not find it necessary to utilize the IAS, except under extraordinary circumstances when the U.S. government determines it is necessary to request or accept international offers of assistance for a catastrophic disaster response and if FEMA needs help managing the offers of assistance.

However, in some circumstances the United States can accept financial contributions to voluntary relief organizations, which are often the most useful form of assistance that can be provided following a disaster. In recognition of this, and to minimize offers of in-kind assistance from foreign governments, the U.S. government will recommend that donations be in the form of financial contributions to organizations working in the affected area. FEMA will provide to the Department of State information on relief organizations active on the scene of a disaster for dissemination to potential donor nations.

Major Features of the IAS CONOPS

The IAS CONOPS delineates the roles and responsibilities of key agencies and groups. It specifies the various federal agencies involved and which ones have the lead in determining how certain disaster relief requirements will be met if the decisions are made to accept them. For example:

- FEMA determines potential requirements, decides on acceptance or rejection of international donations using its gift acceptance authority, or initiates acquisition procedures for assistance not available through domestic channels, and, once notified that international response supplies or personnel are available at the port of entry, coordinates the logistical activities involved in receiving and distributing such donations by utilizing internal and inter-agency resources as necessary.
- To ensure coordination and management across the entire IAS spectrum, FEMA will also activate an International Resources Coordination Group (IRCG). The IRCG, normally co-located with the National Response Coordination Center for Level I or II events, coordinates all acquisition, shipment, receipt at appropriate ports of entry, obtaining appropriate clearances, and notifying the Response Section Chief of the National Response Coordination Center (NRCC-RSS) of the availability of supplies, equipment, or personnel once clearances are completed.
- State Department will document all offers of international assistance, utilizing the International Assistance Tracker and serving as the official medium of communication between the U.S. government and countries or international organizations making offers of assistance, officially notifying donor nations or organizations of U.S. government decisions.

- If a specific domestic relief mission inside the United States is assigned under the Stafford Act, USAID assists FEMA with logistical support, when requested. This support may include: managing flights and ground transportation for inbound assistance; coordinating regulatory agency clearance of international resources, prior to arrival; and establishing and managing a Reception and Departure Center (RDC), should international responders be accepted by the U.S. government.
- U.S. government regulatory agencies provide guidance on offers of assistance and expedite customs clearance for accepted resources. They may deploy personnel to various ports of entry to facilitate clearance pursuant to notifying FEMA NRCC-RSS that items are cleared for pickup and transfer to International Response Staging Areas (IRSA) or other FEMA designated distribution points. See the International Assistance System Concept of Operations.
- The Department of Defense (DoD), when issued a Mission Tasking Assignment (MTA) by FEMA, may provide logistical assistance to support IAS operations, to include use of military bases to host and operate the International Response Staging Area.

In overall terms, to ensure the IAS is properly supported, FEMA may mission assign State Department, USAID, DoD, HHS, and other agencies as needed, using Stafford Act funds. Once an MTA has been issued, FEMA's International Affairs Division (IAD) will collaborate with these agencies via the International Resources Coordination Group (IRCG) to successfully support the U.S. government's response to a major disaster.

IAS interagency operational issues and challenges remain in terms of ironing out the role of private sector donations and coordinating arrangements along with Department of Defense issues on certain aspects of in-kind military equipment or related emergency relief logistics.

The IAS CONOPS Is a Dual-Natured Support System

The IAS CONOPS addresses both the critical needs of the response operators to be able to function effectively with limited distraction and the diplomatic considerations that may be an element in a domestic crisis. Thus, if the U.S. government determines that the domestic situation and international response to that situation requires the utilization of the IAS, the U.S. government will accept international resources only in the following limited circumstances:

- When there is an operational need in responding to the disaster that cannot be fulfilled domestically ("pull"); or

195

- When FEMA determines it can accommodate and accept certain goods from offering countries in the interest of foreign policy ("push"). In creating a "push" and "pull" system, the IAS attempts to balance operational needs and diplomatic interests.

The "pull" system is based on needs identified by local, state, tribal, or federal officials in the disaster area. It originates with a request from an authorized federal response agency for resources that are urgently needed but not available within the United States in either the time or quantity required. FEMA, DOS, and regulatory agencies will utilize the IAS to find international sources for the purchase of the needed capability, or in some cases, accept the donation of the item from a foreign nation or international organization.

The overall "pull" system, by contrast, accommodates U.S. government Diplomatic Interests. In some cases, FEMA and DOS may determine it can accommodate and accept select offers in the interest of diplomacy. In this situation, FEMA will use the IAS to officially accept and receive such resources. Under "Push," the U.S. government will only accept commodities that can enter the country without significant regulatory agency oversight or inspection and that can readily be used by the agencies and organizations involved in the disaster response.

While there are many ways donated goods might enter the U.S. (e.g., from nongovernmental organizations or private citizens), the IAS CONOPS applies only to formal transactions between foreign governments or international organizations and the U.S. government. All FEMA-approved, donated resources ("pull" or "push") will be accepted through FEMA's gift acceptance authority under the Stafford Act and, as such, will become FEMA property. FEMA approves the consignment of all donated goods to response agencies and state, local, or tribal governments. Resources accepted by an agency under its own authority will become the responsibility of the accepting agency, including responsibility for ultimate disposition of that resource and any associated costs.

The IAS/CONOPS Is Part of the National Response Framework

The National Response Framework (NRF) and its International Coordination Support Annex (ICSA) are "always in effect, and elements can be implemented at any time... Selective implementation of National Response Framework structures and procedures allows for a scaled response, delivery of the specific resources and capabilities, and a level of coordination appropriate to each incident" (NRF, page i). Similarly, the IAS is a survivor-centric system that is always available to support the needs of survivors, and is built to be scalable and flexible in integrating international assistance with domestic capabilities. For clarity's sake, the three levels of operations for the IAS are described below.

Level 3: Watch/Steady State

Following news of a major disaster in the United States, the U.S. government may receive spontaneous offers of assistance from foreign countries or international/multilateral organizations. Both FEMA's National Watch Center (NWC) and the Department of State's Crisis Management Support (CMS) office in the DOS Operations Center monitor possible international interest in a U.S. domestic disaster. All inquiries from abroad are routed to CMS for resolution.

Level 2: Operations Level 2

Following a Stafford Act Declaration, if FEMA agrees to accept an international offer of assistance in support of U.S. government diplomatic interests or when FEMA requests specific items of assistance unavailable through domestic resources, FEMA may elevate the IAS to Level 2 and convene the International Resources Coordination Group (IRCG) at a minimal level to ensure that the accepted resources are transported and cleared appropriately into the United States. If other federal agency support is required, FEMA may utilize the authority in the Stafford Act to issue MAs to those agencies.

Level 1: Operations Level 1

Following a Stafford Act Declaration, if multiple offers of assistance are accepted, or requests for disaster relief assistance available only from a non-U.S. source are anticipated, FEMA will elevate the IAS to Level 1. Level 1 will require robust IRCG activity and coordination, and will likely require additional support from other federal agencies. The IRCG will operate from FEMA HQ in close coordination with the National Response Coordination Center (NERC). FEMA's International Affairs Division will serve as lead for the IRCG.

Other Relevant Issues

- Direct, in-kind donations that flow directly to private sector firms and organizations are outside the normal coverage of the IAS system for the time being. However, pending interagency doctrinal issues regarding the overall coordination and disposition of these items has not yet been fully agreed upon and clarified. Areas of ambiguity and overlap will need to be aligned to ensure that in kind offers are closely coordinated with IAS entities.
- In the same vein, direct defense items may be accepted and processed by the Defense Department under a separate, but coordinated, approach that has not been fully defined in relation to the existing IAS process agreed in July 2015. However, it is equally important to note that several federal agencies have independent authorities to declare disasters or emergencies and could potentially be in charge of

any non-Stafford Act incident response. Thus, the IAS CONOPS can serve as a paradigm that other agencies may wish to use when addressing international disaster assistance or resource requirements. Already some may do so through the development of memoranda of understanding and/or interagency agreements with other agencies that specify those agencies' roles and responsibilities for that incident.

- The IAS remains a significant interagency mechanism for accepting, storing, and distributing foreign donations and services in the event of a major disaster. Not all issues associated with such disasters have been finalized or clarified. One such issue is the introduction of foreign experts, physicians, emergency workers, and other personnel who would need authorization to operate in crisis and disaster relief situations in coordination with U.S. agencies and selected state and local governments. These issues, along with others, will be eventually resolved as the doctrine, policy, and procedures related to major catastrophes are clarified and understood.

NOTE: For further information, please refer to the following IAS CONOPS document, or forward any questions or comments to FEMA's International Affairs Division at https://www.fema.gov/international-affairs-division.

HIGHLIGHTS OF STATE RESILIENCY LEGISLATION
REGARDING ELECTROMAGNETIC PULSE (EMP)
AND GEOMAGNETIC DISTURBANCES (GMD)
by
William R. Harris
Foundation for Resilient Societies™
October 2016

Legislation in years 2013 through September 2016 that is **enacted** and legislative resolutions that are **approved** are indicated in **bold italics**. Other bills that were filed but not enacted are summarized in non-italic black.

2013: *Kentucky H.B. 167 Enacted* as Acts of 2013, Ch. 32, Rep. Tom Riner (House-Dem.) Establishes the Kentucky Office of Homeland Security in the Office of the Governor, with a Working Group purpose to identify risks and needs, and to assess the preparedness of Kentucky to respond to acts of war or terrorism, including nuclear, biological, chemical, electromagnetic pulse, agro-, eco-, or cyber-terrorism. Study required on electromagnetic pulse and geomagnetic disturbances via an Inter-agency Working Group, including review of state preparedness to respond to acts of war or terrorism, including electromagnetic pulse and other acts of war or terrorism.

2013: Maine: *H.P. 106* L.D. 131. ***Enacted*** May 28, 2013. Rep. Andrea Boland (House-Dem.) and other sponsors required the Maine Public Utilities Commission to assess vulnerabilities and to develop costed alternatives to protect the safety of the Maine electric transmission system from geomagnetic disturbances and man-made electromagnetic pulse, with report back to the Maine state legislature in year 2014. Resulted in preliminary Report of the Maine Public Utilities Commission, December 2013; Advisory Task Committee sponsored by the Maine Public Utilities Commission, meeting at Central Maine Power in years 2014-Spring 2016; and Reports submitted to the Maine Public Utilities Commission by Central Maine Power (December 2015) and Emprimus LLC (January 2016); and augmentation to the Maine Power Reliability Program (MPRP) in years 2015 and 2016, including installation of GIC monitors, synchrophasor (PMU) monitoring sites, additional reactive power system procurement, and system modeling by Ping Thing LLC. In advance of anticipated FERC rulemaking (issued in FERC Order 830 on September 22, 2016) to set criteria for cost recovery relating to regional (ISO-New England) reliability enhancements, no neutral ground blocking devices have been procured by any Maine electric utility or approved by the Maine PUC as cost-recoverable.

2013: New York: A. 3477 Rep. Jane Corwin (Assembly-Rep.) proposes New York State Electromagnetic Pulse Critical Infrastructure Protection Commission. Bill failed.

2014: Arizona: *S.B. 1476. Enacted.* Sen. David Farnsworth (Sen.-Rep.), Sen. Nancy Barto (Sen.-Rep.), et al. April 25, 2014. A measure to require the Arizona Department of Emergency and Military Affairs, Division of Emergency Management to develop recommendations for the public to mitigate electromagnetic pulse and geomagnetic disturbances. No responsive public report appears to be available on the Department's website as of September 2016.

2014: Florida: H.B. 7147 Rep. Vasilinda Rehwinkel (House-Rep.) proposes an addition to proposed legislation to "include defense against electromagnetic pulse attacks and geomagnetic storm events in [Florida's] preparedness planning"; to encourage municipal and private sector examination of infrastructure vulnerabilities; and "preparedness recommendations" to be issued to the public by the Florida Department of Agriculture and Consumer Services. Bill failed.

2014: Georgia: H.B. 1148 Karla Drenner (House-Dem.) Bill introduced March 13, 2014, to amend Art. 8, Ch. 3, titles 22 and 46, relating to evaluation of electric field levels and protection of transmission and distribution systems against damage from an electromagnetic pulse or a geomagnetic storm. Referred to House Energy, Utilities and Telecommunications Committee, March 20, 2014. Bill died.

2014: Louisiana: *S.R. 169. Approved.* Sen. Fred H. Mills (Senate-Rep.) Requests the Governor's Office of Homeland Security and Emergency Preparedness to study the "potential threats and consequences of an electromagnetic pulse (EMP)."

2014: New Jersey: A. 275 (Rep. Donna M. Simon, proposes a "New Jersey Electromagnetic Infrastructure Advisory Commission." January 16, 2014. Failed in Assembly.

2014: Oklahoma: H.B. 2623 Rep. Gus Blackwell (House-Rep.) proposes electromagnetic shield protection. Bill failed. **S.B. 2016** (Sen. Ralph Shortey, Sen.-Rep.) proposes state ballot initiative providing for installation of EMP "shield protection technology" by January 1, 2017, with cost recovery allowed. Bill failed.

2014: Virginia: *SJR 61. Approved*. Sen. Bryce E. Reeves (Sen.-Rep.) sponsored a Senate Joint Resolution for establishment of a Joint Commission to study strategies for preventing and mitigating potential damage caused by geomagnetic disturbances and electromagnetic pulses. Directs the Joint Commission on Technology and Science (JCOTS) to examine vulnerabilities of the Commonwealth of Virginia to GMD and EMP. Resolution adopted by the Virginia legislature February 19, 2014. Required a Report to the Virginia state legislature by January 14, 2015. Report not delivered. See subsequent enactment of Virginia S.B. 1238 in 2015.

2015: Colorado: H.B. 15-1363. Rep. Joann Ginal (House-Dem), Rep. Catherine Roupe (House-Rep.), and Rep. Jonathan Singer (House-Dem.) and Sen. Owen Hill (Senate-Rep.) introduced Bill on April 16, 2015, for fortification of Colorado's lifeline infrastructures to withstand large-scale electromagnetic pulses and geomagnetic disturbances. Bill requires the Colorado Public Utilities Commission to examine and make recommendations to mitigate vulnerability of existing electric generation, transmission, and distribution facilities "and other vital infrastructure." Requires estimates of costs and effects of mitigation at the state and regional levels. Assigned to House Committee on Transportation and Energy. Postponed indefinitely, April 29, 2015. Bill Failed.

2015: Maine S.P. 496 L.D. 1363. Sen. Dave Miramant (Senate-Dem.), Rep. Roberta Beavers (House-Dem.), and other co-sponsors. Bill provides authority for the Maine Public Utilities Commission to require Maine transmission and distribution utilities take necessary action to ensure their systems are protected from or negate effects of geomagnetic disturbances and electromagnetic pulses, including installation of additional GIC monitoring sites, neutral ground blocking devices, SCADA protectors, and spare transformers. Costs that are just and reasonable are recoverable. Costs of transmission system failure from GMD or EMP may not be borne by ratepayers. Maine PUC to direct mitigation measures no later than July 1, 2016. Required follow-up report to state legislature on GMD and EMP protection of the Maine electric grid. Bill passed House with 80 to 66 votes in support on June 11, 2015, after amendment to limit liability of electric utilities; opposition led by Sen. Woodsome (Senate-Rep.), previously supportive of the Bill, following Senate Republican Caucus. Defeated by 1 vote with switch from 18 to 17 in favor to 18 to 17 favoring "Ought not to Pass" in Roll Call #192, June 10, 2015, in the Maine State Senate. Bill failed and placed in Dead File by Senate vote June 16, 2015.

2015: New York: A. 3133 Rep. Jane Corwin (Assembly-Rep.) proposes New York State Electromagnetic Pulse Critical Infrastructure Protection Commission. Bill failed.

2015: Oklahoma: S.B. 599 Ballot question relating to Electromagnetic Shield Protection as requirement for Oklahoma electric utilities. Sen. Ralph Shortey (Senate-Rep.) Filed February 2, 2015, referred to Rules Committee on February 3, 2015. Bill failed.

2015: Texas: S.B. 1398 Sen. Bob Hall (Senate-Rep.) proposes legislation to direct the Public Utilities Commission of Texas to assess threats including electromagnetic pulse preparedness, geomagnetic disturbances, terrorist and cyber-security threats, and to improve the resiliency of critical infrastructure in Texas. Bill passed the Texas Senate, but did not pass in the Texas House Calendar Committee. In parallel, Texas initiated an interim study on grid safety, including but not limited to electromagnetic pulse and solar storm hazards.

2015: Virginia: *S.B. 1238. Enacted.* Sen. Bryce E. Reeves (Sen.-Rep.) Directs the Virginia Department of Emergency Management to plan for and respond to disasters resulting from electromagnetic pulses and geomagnetic disturbances. Enacted with governor's approval on March 10, 2015, effective July 1, 2015, as Acts of Assembly Ch. 97, 2015. Title 44 Ch. 3.2 § sec.148.18.

2015: Virginia: S.B. 1239 Sen. Bryce E. Reeves (Senate-Rep.) would require the governor to designate an electromagnetic pulse attack and preparedness of the Commonwealth in an annual drill using modeling and simulation technology; document damage to existing infrastructure absent improvements; and recommend steps at state and local levels. Bill Stricken at request of sponsor on January 26, 2015.

2016: Arizona: H.B. 2335 Bill sponsored by Brenda Barton (House-Rep.) introduced on May 5, 2016, to address Electromagnetic Pulse Preparedness. It would develop recommendations for supplies of food, water, medical supplies that each person in the state should possess as part of EMP preparedness. Held in the Rules Committee as of September 2016.

2016: Florida: House Memorial H.M. 1419 Vasilinda Rehwinkel (House-Rep.) A House Memorial to urge the U.S. Congress to enact legislation supporting the reconstituted Commission on Electromagnetic Pulse, and directing the Department of Homeland Security to provide funds for state plans to protect against Electromagnetic Pulse, Cyber-attacks, and Geomagnetic Storms. Died in House Committee on March 11, 2016.

2016: New Jersey: **A. 3525** is a Bill sponsored by Assembly Rep. Gail Phoebus (Assembly-Rep.), Rep. Brian E. Rumpf (Assembly-Rep.), et al. Introduced on April 4, 2016, to establish a 21-member New Jersey Electromagnetic Infrastructure Advisory Commission, "encompassing EMP attack or geomagnetic storm hazards." Staffing to be provided by the New Jersey Board of Public Utilities. Scope includes both EMP and GMD hazards. Held in Assembly Telecomm. and Utilities Committee as of September 2016.

APPENDIX 9: Reference Material and Organizational Contacts

2015 National Space Weather Strategy
White House National Science & Technology Council
October 2015
The National Space Weather Strategy (Strategy) and the accompanying National Space
Weather Action Plan (Action Plan) together seek to enhance the integration of existing
national efforts and to add important capabilities to help meet growing demands for space-
weather information.
https://www.gpo.gov/fdsys/pkg/FR-2015-04-30/pdf/2015-10113.pdf

**2015 Data Breach Investigations Report, ENERGY AND UTILITIES: CRITICAL
INFRASTRUCTURE**
Verizon Industry Report
http://www.verizonenterprise.com/resources/reports/rp_dbir-energy-critical-
infrastructure-2015_en_xg.pdf

1,000 km—First Public Photovoltaic Road Announced in France
ECOURBANLAB
By Paul Münzner
February 2016
Photovoltaic road surface withstands cars, bikes, and trucks
http://ecourbanlab.com/photovoltaic-road-surface-1000-world

"Accelerating Society-wide EMP Protection of Critical Infrastructure and Microgrids"
Press Release by DTRA, Department of Defense
June 24, 2016
The Defense Threat Reduction Agency (DTRA)/SCC announced the beginning of a Small
Business Innovation Research (SBIR) contract with Instant Access Networks, LLC (IAN) and
its subcontractors.
http://highfrontier.org/wp-content/uploads/2016/07/DTRA-IAN-Press-Release-June-24-
2016.pdf

Agricultural Disaster Assistance
Congressional Research Service (CRS)
Megan Stubbs, Specialist in Agricultural Conservation and Natural Resources Policy
April 2016   The federal crop insurance program offers subsidized policies designed to
protect crop producers from unavoidable risks associated with adverse weather and
weather-related plant diseases and insect infestations.
https://www.fas.org/sgp/crs/misc/RS21212.pdf

Alternate Funding for Disaster Recovery: A Guide to Available Federal Programs and Funding Resources
Witt O'Brien's
February 2013
The purpose of this guide is to provide basic information about programs of assistance available to individuals, businesses, and public entities after a disaster. These programs help individuals cope with their losses, and affected businesses and public entities restore their structures and operations.
http://www.wittobriens.com/external/content/document/2000/1883986/1/Witt-O'Brien's-Alternate-Disaster-Funding_Feb2013.pdf

Antifragile: Things That Gain from Disorder
Nassim Nicholas Taleb
January 2012
Random House
Antifragile is a stand-alone book in Nassim Nicholas Taleb's landmark Incerto series, an investigation of opacity, luck, uncertainty, probability, human error, risk, and decision-making in a world we don't understand.
http://cpor.org/af/Taleb_Antifragile.pdf

Apocalypse Unknown: The Struggle to Protect America from an Electromagnetic Pulse Catastrophe
Dr. Peter Vincent Pry
February 2013
A handful of political leaders, scientists, strategists, and grassroots activists struggled against gargantuan bureaucracies in government and industry to protect the nation from an EMP catastrophe. This book tells where EMP protection advocates are winning, and why they may lose.
http://michaelmabee.info/apocalypse-unknown-peter-vincent-pry

Blackout Wars: State Initiatives to Achieve Preparedness against an Electromagnetic Pulse (EMP) Catastrophe
Dr. Peter Vincent Pry
November 2015
Blackout Wars is about the historically unprecedented threat to our electronic civilization from its dependence on the electric power grid.
http://www.kurzweilai.net/blackout-wars-state-initiatives-to-achieve-preparedness-against-an-electromagnetic-pulse-emp-catastrophe

Budgeting for Disasters: Focusing on the Good Times
OECD Journal on Budgeting, Volume 2010/1
Marvin Phaup, Charlotte Kirschner
2010
This paper describes the potential for gain from alternative budgetary treatments of policies aimed at reducing the effects on consumption of random shocks to income and wealth. It identifies a critical difference between alternatives: budgetary recognition of expected costs of relief and recovery before the loss event.
https://www.oecd.org/gov/budgeting/48168599.pdf

Budgeting for Disasters
OECD
Barry Anderson, based on a paper by Marvin Phaup
June 4-5, 2009
https://www.oecd.org/gov/budgeting/42407562.pdf

Business Blackout: The Insurance implications of a cyber attack on the US power grid
Center for Risk Studies, University of Cambridge, and Lloyds
2015
The scenario in this report describes the actions of sophisticated attackers who are able to penetrate security as a result of detailed planning, technical skill and imagination. A relatively small team is able to achieve widespread impact, revealing one of the key exposure management challenges for insurers. However, the report also describes the constraints faced by the attackers, and shows that insurers should not believe this type of threat to be unlimited in its potential scope.
https://www.lloyds.com/~/media/files/news%20and%20insight/risk%20insight/2015/business%20blackout/business%20blackout20150708.pdf

Catastrophic Planning
Website CA.gov California Governor's Office of Emergency Services provides links to various emergency services sites.
2008
http://www.caloes.ca.gov/cal-oes-divisions/planning-preparedness/catastrophic-planning

City Resilience Index 2014
Rockefeller Foundation
April 2014
Risk assessments and measures to reduce specific foreseeable risks will continue to play an important role in urban planning. In addition, cities need to ensure that their development strategies and investment decisions enhance, rather than undermine the city's resilience.
https://www.rockefellerfoundation.org/app/uploads/City-Resilience-Framework1.pdf

City Resilience Index 2015
Rockefeller Foundation
December 2015
This report provides a holistic articulation of city resilience, structured around four dimensions and 12 goals that are critical for the resilience of our cities.
https://assets.rockefellerfoundation.org/app/uploads/20140410162455/City-Resilience-Framework-2015.pdf

Cloud Computing Strategy
Department of Defense, Chief Information Officer
July 2012
http://dodcio.defense.gov/Portals/0/Documents/Cloud/DoD%20Cloud%20Computing%20Strategy%20Final%20with%20Memo%20-%20July%205%202012.pdf

Common Cybersecurity Vulnerabilities in Industrial Control Systems
Industrial Control Systems Cyber Emergency Response Team
Trent Nelson, Project Manager; May Chaffin, Cyber Researcher, Idaho National Laboratory
May 2011
Correlated and compiled in this report are vulnerabilities from general knowledge gained from DHS CSSP assessments and Industrial Control Systems Cyber Emergency Response Team (ICS-CERT) activities describing the most common types of cybersecurity vulnerabilities as they relate to ICS.
https://ics-cert.us-cert.gov/sites/default/files/recommended_practices/DHS_Common_Cybersecurity_Vulnerabilities_ICS_2010.pdf

Competition and Efficiency in the International Food Supply Chains: Improving Food Security
Routledge, Earthscan Food and Agriculture Series
John Williams, Executive Director, Australian Commodity Research Institute, Managing Director, Food and Fibre Supply Chain Institute, Melbourne, Australia
2012
This book examines an array of different issues and distortions that are causing food supply chain dysfunction in many countries, particularly for staple non-perishable foods such as grains, oilseeds, pulses and sugar. It outlines the underlying changes that are currently occurring, which will have an influence on the direction of future food supply chains, and provides some solutions to current food security problems.
https://www.researchgate.net/publication/281764339_Competition_and_efficiency_in_international_food_supply_chains_Improving_food_security

Consequences to Seaport Operations from Malicious Cyber Activity
Operational Analysis Division, National Protection and Programs Directorate,
Department of Homeland Security
March 2016
This note examines the potential for malicious actors to use cyber capabilities to disrupt operations at U.S. commercial seaports and the impact major disruptions would have on other critical infrastructure sectors. The networks examined include those used at seaports and aboard vessels.
http://www.maritimedelriv.com/Port_Security/DHS/DHS_Files/OCIA_Consequences_to_Seaport_Operations_from_Malicious_Cyber_Activity.pdf

Critical Infrastructure Protection
United States General Accountability Office GAO-16-243
March 2016
Federal Agencies Have Taken Actions to Address Electromagnetic Risks, but Opportunities Exist to Further Assess Risks and Strengthen Collaboration.
United States General Accountability Office (GAO)
http://www.gao.gov/products/GAO-16-243

Cross-sector Emergency Planning for Water Providers and Healthcare Facilities
American Water Works Association
Gregory Welter, Steven Bieber, Heidi Bonnaffon, Nicholas Deguida, Myra Socher
January 2010
The twofold purpose of this article is to outline the critical nature of the water supply in sustaining the operations of healthcare facilities (particularly during periods of community emergencies) and to advocate for enhanced cross-sector support from water utilities in meeting this need. The intent of this discussion is to suggest avenues for enhanced coordinated planning for emergency water supply
http://www.academia.edu/25491893/Cross-sector_emergency_planning_for_water_providers_and_healthcare_facilities
http://www.awwa.org/publications/journal-awwa/abstract/articleid/23327.aspx

Cyber Security at Civil Nuclear Facilities: Understanding the Risks
Chatham House Report
Caroline Baylon with Roger Brunt and David Livingstone
September 2015
Across societies, the wider critical infrastructure—including power grids, transport networks, maritime shipping and space-based communications assets—is similarly vulnerable to cyber attack, with different but potentially equally dire consequences.

https://www.chathamhouse.org/sites/files/chathamhouse/field/field_document/201510
05CyberSecurityNuclearBaylonBruntLivingstone.pdf

Dark Territory: The Secret History of Cyber War
Fred Kaplan, Simon & Schuster
2016
Describes the history of and key players in the development of cyber war strategies, from
the ultra-top-secret cyber units in the Pentagon, to "information warfare" squads in the
armed services.
http://www.npr.org/books/titles/471441828/dark-territory-the-secret-history-of-cyber-war

Defense Support of Civil Authorities
Joint Publication 3-28
July 2013
This publication provides overarching guidelines and principles to assist commanders
and their staffs in planning, conducting, and assessing defense support of civil authorities
http://www.dtic.mil/doctrine/new_pubs/jp3_27.pdf

Designing Intelligent Food, Energy & Water Systems (DIFEWS): A Whitepaper
A whitepaper funded by National Science Foundation Award CBET-1541880
Kate J. Helmstedt, Kripa A. Jagannathan, Ashley E. Larsen, et al.
December 2015
In semi-arid regions, like the Western United States, the intertwined stressors of climate
variability, persistent waste, continued pollution and shifting demographics are creating
trilemmas in linked food, energy, and water (FEW) systems. The effects of these trilemmas
are environmental, economic, and social.
https://nature.berkeley.edu/pottslabwp/wp-
content/uploads/2016/01/DIFEWSUCBerkeleyWhitepaper.pdf

DoD Cloud Computing Strategy
Department of Defense, Chief Information Officer
July 2012
http://dodcio.defense.gov/Portals/0/Documents/Cloud/DoD%20Cloud%20Computing%2
0Strategy%20Final%20with%20Memo%20-%20July%205%202012.pdf

Dynamic Recovery of Critical Infrastructures: Real-Time Temporal Coordination
Int. J. Critical Infrastructures, Vol. 4, Nos. 1/2
Inderscience Enterprises Ltd.
José R. Martí and Jorge A. Hollman, Carlos Ventura, Juri Jatskevich

2008

This paper applies a systems engineering approach to the operations coordination among multiple infrastructures to minimize the impact of large disasters on human lives.
https://www.ece.ubc.ca/~jorgeh/Publications/Marti-Hollman-Ventura-Jatskevitch-IJICS2008.pdf

EIS (Electric Infrastructure Protection Council) Electric Infrastructure Protection (EPRO®) Handbook, 1st Edition
Paul Stockton, Editor in Chief; Chris Beck and Avi Schnurr, Co-Editors
December 2014
http://www.eiscouncil.com/App_Data/Upload/3dadf58f-7457-46bf-92a4-551c6608d925.pdf
Addresses man-made hazards, including terrorism, physical attacks, electromagnetic pulse weapons, cyber terrorism, and combined armed and cross-sector attacks. Considers power grid protection and restoration, and whole community preparedness. Accessible via the internet since year 2016.

EIS (Electric Infrastructure Protection Council) Electric Infrastructure Protection (EPRO®) Handbook II Volume 1—Resilient Fuel Resources for Power Generation in Black Sky Events—Infrastructure Protection
July 18, 2016
This two-volume work, EPRO provides options to strengthen the resilience of two especially vital infrastructure components against Black Sky power outages: the water sector, with its uniquely essential services, and the natural gas infrastructure on which power generation increasingly depends. EPRO II provides a detailed range of preparedness options that infrastructure owners and operators can consider and adapt to their system specific needs. The Handbook also offers a methodology to develop Black Sky playbooks to help these sectors guide emergency operational planning and resilience initiatives.
http://www.eiscouncil.com/App_Data/Upload/149e7a61-5d8e-4af3-bdbf-68dce1b832b0.pdf

EIS (Electric Infrastructure Protection Council) Electric Infrastructure Protection (EPRO®) Handbook II Volume 2—Water: Water Sector Resilience for Black Sky Events"
July 18, 2016
This second volume, EPRO Handbook II, Volume 2 provides options to strengthen the resilience of the water sector, both water supply and waste water services. EPRO II provides a detailed range of preparedness options that infrastructure owners and operators can consider and adapt to help meet their own system specific needs. The

Handbook also offers a methodology for developing Black Sky playbooks to help these sectors guide emergency operational planning and resilience initiatives.
http://eiscouncil.org/App_Data/Upload/7f41c325-654e-4c67-be3d-6941645f4485.pdf

Electric Armageddon: Civil-Military Preparedness for an Electromagnetic Pulse Catastrophe
Dr. Peter Vincent Pry
February 2013
This book tells the story of the EMP threat and of the struggle to protect our nation from this little known, but most perilous and most imminent of all national security nightmares. However, the greatest value of this book may be a bold new vision for a way to rapidly protect America from EMP.
https://www.createspace.com/4086819

Electric Vehicles support for intentional islanding: A prediction for 2030
IEEE Xplore Conference: North American Power Symposium (NAPS)
November 2009
Environmental benefits of a future micro-grid are described through a comparison of the maximum and minimum EV and micro-generation penetration predictions.
https://www.researchgate.net/publication/224145319_Electric_Vehicles_support_for_intentional_islanding_A_prediction_for_2030

Electromagnetic Pulse and the U.S. Food Security Paradigm: Assumptions, Risks, and Recommendations
University of California, Los Angeles
Maximilian Leeds
August 2011
This paper analyzes the systemic dangers posed to the U.S. economy by an electromagnetic pulse (EMP), either naturally occurring or maliciously generated, from a food security perspective.
https://works.bepress.com/maximilian_leeds/2

Electromagnetic Pulse (EMP) Attack: A PREVENTABLE Homeland Security Catastrophe
The Heritage Foundation
By Jena Baker McNeill and Richard Weitz, Ph.D.
2008
http://www.heritage.org/Research/Reports/2008/10/Electromagnetic-Pulse-EMP-Attack-A-Preventable-Homeland-Security-Catastrophe

Electromagnetic Pulses (EMPs): Myths vs. Facts
Edison Electric Institute
February 2015
This document provides claimed factual responses to allegedly unsupported or inaccurate assertions about the electric sector's preparedness to deal with electromagnetic pulses (EMPs) that may impact the electric power grid.
http://www.eei.org/issuesandpolicy/cybersecurity/Documents/Electromagnetic%20Puls es%20(EMPs)%20-%20Myths%20vs.%20Facts.pdf

Electromagnetic Pulses—Six Common Misconceptions
George H. Baker, *Domestic Preparedness*,
November 2014
This article addresses six misconceptions about EMP: 1. EMP will caused every exposed electronic system to cease functioning; 2. EMP effects will have limited, easily recoverable "nuisance" effects on critical infrastructure; 3. Megaton-nuclear weapons are required to cause serious EM effects; 4. Protecting the critical national infrastructure would be cost prohibitive; 5. Only late-time EMP (E3) will damage electric power-grid transformers; and 6. Fiber-optic networks are not susceptible to EMP effects.
https://www.domesticpreparedness.com/commentary/electromagnetic-pulses-six-common-misconceptions

Electromagnetic Pulse Threats to U.S. Military and Civilian Infrastructure
[H.A.S.C. No. 106–31]: Testimony to the House Committee on Homeland Security
Hearing before the Military Research and Development Subcommittee of the Committee on Armed Services House of Representatives
One Hundred Sixth Congress
1999
http://commdocs.house.gov/committees/security/has280010.000/has280010_0f.htm

Emergency Management Professional Associations:

American Academy of Emergency Physicians:	https://www.acep.org
American Chemical Society:	https://www.acs.org
American Gas Association:	https://www.aga.org
American Petroleum Institute:	http://www.api.org
American Public Health Association:	http://www.apha.org
American Security Officers Association:	http://www.americansog.com
American Society for Industrial Security:	https://www.asisonline.org
American Society of Civil Engineers:	http://www.asce.org
American Society of Safety Engineers:	http://www.asse.org
American Water Works Association:	http://www.awwa.org
Business Executives for National Security:	http://www.bens.org
Fraternal Order of Police:	http://www.fop.net
International Association of Emergency Managers:	http://www.iaem.com

International Association of Firefighters: http://client.prod.iaff.org
National Association of Broadcasters: https://www.nab.org
National Association of City/County Health Organizations: http://www.naccho.org
National Emergency Management Association: https://www.nemaweb.org
Nuclear Energy Institute: http://www.nei.org
Society for Risk Analysis: http://www.sra.org
Society of Nuclear Medicine & Molecular Imaging: http://www.snm.org

EMP: America's Achilles Heel

Hillsdale College, Imprimis, Volume 34, Number 6

Frank J. Gaffney, President, Center for Security Policy

June 2005

Article adapted from a speech delivered on May 24, 2005, in Dallas, Texas, at a Hillsdale College National Leadership Seminar on the topic, "America's War Against Islamic Terrorism."

http://imprimis.hillsdale.edu/emp-americas-achilles-heel

Energy Sector-Specific Plan (SSP)

U.S. Department of Homeland Security

2015

The 2015 Energy SSP is closely aligned with the National Infrastructure Protection Plan 2013: "Partnering for Critical Infrastructure Security and Resilience" (NIPP 2013) and the joint national priorities, which were developed in collaboration by representatives from all critical infrastructure sectors, including Energy.

https://www.dhs.gov/sites/default/files/publications/nipp-ssp-energy-2015-508.pdf

Estimated Value of Service Reliability for Electric Utility Customers in the United States

Ernest Orlando Lawrence Berkeley National Laboratory Report LBNL-213E

Michael J. Sullivan, Matthew Mercurio, Josh Schellenberg,

June 2009

This paper describes work to assemble a meta-database on electricity customer interruption costs for the US and analyze the resulting data to develop customer damage functions useful for evaluating the economic benefits of electric system reliability reinforcements.

https://emp.lbl.gov/sites/all/files/REPORT%20lbnl-2132e.pdf

Executive Order 13636, Improving Critical Infrastructure Cybersecurity

The White House Executive Order

February 2, 2013

https://www.gpo.gov/fdsys/pkg/DCPD-201300091/pdf/DCPD-201300091.pdf

Executive Order 13744, Coordinating Efforts to Prepare the Nation for Space Weather Events

The White House

October 13, 2016

https://www.gpo.gov/fdsys/pkg/DCPD-201600692/pdf/DCPD-201600692.pdf

Framework for Modelling High-Impact, Low-Frequency Power Grid Events to Support Risk-Informed Decisions

Pacific Northwest National Laboratory, for the U.S. Department of Energy

Office of Electricity Delivery and Energy Reliability, performed under

Report PNNL-24673

A. Veeramany, S.D. Unwin, G.A. Coles, J.E. Dagle, W.D. Millard, J. Yao, C.S. Glantz, S.N.G. Gourisetti

December 2015

Natural and man-made hazardous events resulting in the simultaneous loss of multiple grid infrastructure assets challenge the electric power grid's security and resilience. However, the planning and allocation of appropriate contingency resources for such events requires an understanding of their likelihood and the extent of their potential impact.

http://www.pnnl.gov/main/publications/external/technical_reports/PNNL-24673.pdf

The Fukushima Daiichi Accident: Report by the Director General

International Atomic Energy Agency, Publication 1710

July 2011

This report presents an assessment of the causes and consequences of the accident at the Fukushima Daiichi nuclear power plant in Japan, which began on 11 March 2011. Caused by a huge tsunami that followed a massive earthquake, it was the worst accident at a nuclear power plant since the Chernobyl disaster in 1986. The report considers human, organizational and technical factors, and aims to provide an understanding of what happened, and why, so that the necessary lessons learned can be acted upon by governments, regulators and nuclear power plant operators throughout the world. Measures taken in response to the accident, both in Japan and internationally, are also examined

http://www-pub.iaea.org/MTCD/Publications/PDF/Pub1710-ReportByTheDG-Web.pdf

The Fukushima Nuclear Accident Independent Investigation Commission: Official Report, Executive Summary

Kiyoshi Kurokawa, et al. for the National Diet of Japan

July 2012

[This] report catalogues a multitude of errors and willful negligence that left the Fukushima plant unprepared for the events of March 11 [2011]. And it examines serious deficiencies in the response to the accident by TEPCO, regulators and the government. http://reliefweb.int/report/japan/official-report-fukushima-nuclear-accident-independent-investigation-commission

The Global Risks Report 2016, 11th Edition
World Economic Forum with Marsh & McLennan, Zurich Insurance Group, National University of Singapore, Oxford Martin School at the University of Oxford, Wharton Risk Management and Decision Processes Center, University of Pennsylvania
January 2016
The Report calls for action to build resilience—the "resilience imperative" —and identifies practical examples of how it could be
http://www3.weforum.org/docs/Media/TheGlobalRisksReport2016.pdf

The Great Campout
National Wildlife Foundation
http://www.nwf.org/Great-American-Campout.aspx

Grid Assurance
2011
Strategic Resiliency Solutions Company
http://www.gridassurance.com

The Growing Threat From an EMP Attack: A Nuclear Device Detonated Above the U.S. Could Kill Millions, and We've Done Almost Nothing to Prepare
By R. James Woolsey, Peter Vincent Pry
A Wall Street Journal Commentary
Aug. 12, 2014
http://www.wsj.com/articles/james-woolsey-and-peter-vincent-pry-the-growing-threat-from-an-emp-attack-1407885281

Guest Editorial: Emerging Technologies
IEEE Journal on Selected Areas in Communications, Vol. 34, No. 3, 457
Shuguang Cui, Fellow, IEEE, John S. Thompson, Fellow, IEEE, Tomohiko Taniguchi, Fellow, IEEE, Latif Ladid, Member, IEEE, Jie Li, Senior Member, IEEE, Andrew Eckford, Senior Member, IEEE, and Vincent W.S. Wong, Fellow, IEEE
March 2016
http://ieeexplore.ieee.org/stamp/stamp.jsp?arnumber=7430394

Guidance on Diagnosis and Treatment for Healthcare Providers
Radiation Emergency Medical Management (REMM)
US Department of Health and Human Services
http://www.remm.nlm.gov

Guide to Industrial Control Systems (ICS) Security
National Institute of Standards and Technology
U.S. Department of Homeland Security
May 2011
U.S. Department of Homeland Security
http://nvlpubs.nist.gov/nistpubs/SpecialPublications/NIST.SP.800-82r2.pdf

Guidelines for Resilience Systems Analysis: How to Analyze and Build a Roadmap to Resilience
Organization for Economic Cooperation and Development (OECD)
Rachel Scott, et al.
2014
Guidance is aimed at professionals who are grappling with what resilience actually means, and how to get key stakeholders to develop a shared vision of both the risks that exist in their particular context, and what to do about them; both now, and in the longer term. We have called the outcome of the analysis a roadmap to resilience because it is just that—a shared view of the way forward towards a more resilient future.
https://www.oecd.org/dac/Resilience%20Systems%20Analysis%20FINAL.pdf

Handbook of SCADA/Control Systems Security
Robert Radvanovsky and Jacob Brodsky, editors
CRC Press
2013

Healthcare and Public Health Sector-Specific Plan
U.S. Department of Homeland Security
May 2016
The Sector's integrated approach to managing all-hazards risks to HPH (Healthcare/Public Health) critical infrastructure and the HPH workforce includes several key components: Identifying and preparing for a range of potential threats and hazards; reducing the vulnerabilities of identified critical assets, systems, and networks, including those associated with critical internal and out-of-sector dependencies and interdependencies; Mitigating the potential impacts to and enabling the timely restoration of critical infrastructure as a result of emergencies that do occur; and adapting to changing

conditions to withstand and rapidly recover from disruptions due to emergencies, irrespective of the causal factors.
http://www.phe.gov/Preparedness/planning/cip/Documents/2016-hph-ssp.pdf

Health Physics Society Website
General guidance for radiation emergency response.
http://www.hps.org

High Altitude Electromagnetic Pulse (HEMP) and High Power Microwave (HPM) Devices: Threat Assessments
Congressional Report Services
Clay Wilson, Specialist in Technology and National Security
Foreign Affairs, Defense, and Trade Division
2004—Updated August 2008
https://www.fas.org/sgp/crs/natsec/RL32544.pdf

High-Impact Threats to Critical Infrastructure: Emerging Policy and Technology: Conference Proceedings of the InfraGard National EMP SIG Sessions at the DuPont Summit 2012
Charles L. Manto, Editor
August 2013
This volume comprises the conference proceedings of the second in a series of annual DuPont Summit InfraGard conferences in Washington, D.C.   This conference occurred in December 2012, which was the second EMP SIG conference. Participants facilitated design of an earlier exercise at the National Defense University which instigated the first comprehensive DoD evaluation of a nationwide collapse of infrastructure due to space weather harm to long-replacement time equipment within the electric grid and related critical infrastructure. Participants included representatives from the White House, DoD, DOE, DHS, National Governors Association, counties, cities, FERC, NOAA, FBI, InfraGard, and others from the private sector. This conference included first-hand discussion of the Fukushima disaster (March 2011) from Mr. Karakawa of Japan. This volume is out-of-print, but limited numbers of used books and a Kindle version remain available for purchase.
https://www.amazon.com/High-Impact-Threats-Critical-Infrastructure-ebook/dp/B00G3IL9MG/ref=dp_kinw_strp_1

How to Protect Your Computer: Scams and Safety on the Internet
Federal Bureau of Investigation (FBI)
D. Harp, B. Gregory-Brown
June 2015
https://www.fbi.gov/scams-and-safety/on-the-internet

How to Stay Safe and Help Others After a Nuclear Explosion
Citizen web page, Ventura County, California.
http://vchca.org/nuclear-educational-campaign/information-for-community-members

HSPD-8 Presidential Policy Directive PPD-8: National Preparedness
Department of Homeland Security
December 17, 2003
This directive establishes policies to strengthen the preparedness of the United States to prevent and respond to threatened or actual domestic terrorist attacks, major disasters, and other emergencies by requiring a national domestic all-hazards preparedness goal, establishing mechanisms for improved delivery of Federal preparedness assistance to State and local governments, and outlining actions to strengthen preparedness capabilities of Federal, State, and local entities.
https://www.gpo.gov/fdsys/pkg/PPP-2003-book2/pdf/PPP-2003-book2-doc-pg1745.pdf

Implementation of Resilient Production Systems by Production Control
Robust Manufacturing Conference (RoMaC 2014)
Elsevier B.V. Procedia CIRP 19 (2014) 105-110
Institute of Ergonomics, Manufacturing Systems and Automation, Otto von Guericke University, Magdeburg, Germany
Matthias Heinicke   2014
Selection and peer-review under responsibility of the International Scientific Committee of "RoMaC 2014"
http://www.sciencedirect.com/science/article/pii/S2212827114006295

In the Dark: Military Planning for a Catastrophic Critical Infrastructure Event
Center for Strategic Leadership, U.S. Army War College, March 2011, CLS Study 2-11.
Kevin Cogan
May 2011
Reports on a U.S. Army War College Workshop held on September 28-30, 2010, with coordination of Prof. Cynthia Ayers, Kenneth Chrosniak, and Wendy LeBlanc. One breakout group considered preparedness for both solar and nuclear EMP hazards, including a "backup power day" exercise, and an EMP national planning scenario. A second group assessing post-event response encouraged DoD communications capabilities to be deployed at all levels to assist recovery. A third group considered recovery emphasizing the individual, and called for a renaissance of "civil defense" organization. The third group supported development of an "Integrated National Recovery Priority Plan" for EMP, to be exercised regularly with emphasis upon "resiliency" not "preparedness."
http://www.csl.army.mil/usacsl/publications/InTheDark.pdf

Insurance as a Risk Management Instrument for Energy Infrastructure Security and Resilience
Office of Electricity Delivery and Energy Reliability, U.S. Department of Energy
March 2013
Assesses insurance instruments to mitigate financial risks in the energy sector, primarily related to weather-related losses. The report considers insurance industry reluctance to underwrite intentional man-made hazards; lack of adequate reinsurance; and the federal government as an insurer of last resort.
http://energy.gov/sites/prod/files/2013/03/f0/03282013_Final_Insurance_EnergyInfrastructure.pdf

LDS Preparedness Manual
The contents of this booklet are intended to assist individuals and families in coping with emergency preparations.
January 2011
http://thesurvivalmom.com/wp-content/uploads/2010/08/LDS-Preparedness-Manual.pdf

Lessons Learned Information Sharing Program
FEMA, US Department of Homeland Security
The Lessons Learned Information Sharing (LLIS) program promotes preparedness by identifying lessons learned and innovative practices, analyzing recurring trends, and sharing knowledge with the whole community.
https://www.fema.gov/lessons-learned-information-sharing-program

Lighthouse Prime
Lighthouse Prime acts as the primary communication command disseminating radio communication and resources to other Lighthouses. All communications are two-way. Training and support for neighbors interested in sustaining good communications and resilient communities in times of trouble.
www.LightHousePrime.com

Lights Out
David Crawford
2010
Post-EMP event fiction book. Detailed description of the event and post-event society.
http://www.lightsoutsaga.com/saga.html

Lights Out: A Cyberattack, A Nation Unprepared, Surviving the Aftermath
Ted Koppel, Host of ABC's Nightline, Crown Books

October 2015

A best-selling book that addresses the consequences of an extended electric grid blackout in the United States. The author, long-time anchor of ABC *Nightline*, interviewed senior policy officials and senior retired officials, as well as experts on the vulnerabilities of the electric grid, including cyber experts. Some interviewees recommended evacuation of large urban regions during an extended grid blackout, but the Director of FEMA favored shelter-in-place as a preferred modality to expedite recovery. The author concludes there is no comprehensive federal plan to enable recovery from a widespread, long-term grid blackout in the United States.

http://tedkoppellightsout.com

Lloyd's City Risk Index 2015-2025: Executive Summary
This unique Index can stimulate discussion—and, where appropriate, prompt innovation—among insurers, governments and businesses to help improve resilience, mitigate risk and protect infrastructure.
http://www.lloyds.com/cityriskindex/files/8771-city-risk-executive-summary-aw.pdf

Lloyd's City Risk Index 2015-2025: Part I: Overview and results
September 2015
http://cambridgeriskframework.com/wcr

Lloyd's World City Risk 2015-2025: Part II: Methodological Documentation
Centre for Risk Studies, University of Cambridge
September 2015
Cambridgeriskframework.com/getdocument/25

Making Development Sustainable: The Future of Disaster Risk Management
Global Assessment Report (GAR)
United Nations Office of Disaster Risk Reduction
2015
http://www.preventionweb.net/english/hyogo/gar/2015/en/gar-pdf/GAR2015_EN.pdf

Making U.S. Ports Resilient as Part of Extended Intermodal Supply Chains
National Cooperative Freight Research Program Report No. 30
2014
Transportation Research Board, for the National Academy of Sciences
Frank Southworth, Jolene Hayes, Shannon McLeod, and Anne Strauss-Wieder
https://www.nap.edu/catalog/23428/making-us-ports-resilient-as-part-of-extended-intermodal-supply-chains

Making the World Safer (Video)
Defense Threat Reduction Agency

ARA created the Improvised Nuclear Device (IND) video for the U.S. Defense Threat Reduction Agency (DTRA) Consequence Management Division, Strategic Engagement Branch (J3BPCS).
https://www.youtube.com/watch?v=gxb9rg4MQgk

Mitigating High-Impact Threats to Critical Infrastructure: Emerging Policy and Technology Conference Proceedings of the 2013 InfraGard National EMP SIG Sessions at the DuPont Summit
Charles L. Manto, Editor in Chief; Alexandra A. Kaewert, Editor
November 2014
These conference proceedings from the December 2013 DuPont Summit include presentations on solar geomagnetic storm hazards and address the super storm near-miss of planet earth on July 22-23, 2012, presented by Bill Murtagh of NOAA's Space Weather Prediction Center. It features presentations by Dr. Chris Beck, EIS Council; Dr. Peter Vincent Pry, National Task Force on Homeland Security; Richard Waggel, FERC; R. James Woolsey; experts on cybersecurity threats to critical infrastructure; Scott McBride of Idaho National Laboratory reporting on field tests of equipment to protect power grid transformers from voltage surges on a 138 kV transmission system simulating a severe solar storm; experts on electromagnetic pulse protection options; and Rep. Andrea Boland reporting on enacted legislation in Maine to protect that state's grid from both GMD and EMP. The bibliography included 80 links to rare materials on EMP, including the economic impacts of EMP recovery, with and without prior protection of critical equipment.
https://www.amazon.com/Mitigating-High-Impact-Threats-Critical-Infrastructure/dp/1633911330

Model Act for the Facilitation and Regulation of International Disaster Relief and Initial Recovery Assistance
International Federation of Red Cross and Red Crescent Societies, United Nations Office for the Coordination of Humanitarian Affairs and the Inter-Parliamentary Union
March 2013
This Report is intended as a reference tool for voluntary use by disaster management officials and/or legislators who wish to develop domestic legislation, regulation, and/or procedures in their countries for managing potential future international disaster assistance.
http://www.ipu.org/PDF/publications/act-en.pdf

More Protection Needed to Guard Grid From Electromagnetic Storm Threat
Network World
Michael Cooney, Online News Editor
April 26, 2016

Article discusses electromagnetic risks and needs to protect electric grids.
http://www.networkworld.com/article/3061853/security/more-protection-needed-to-guard-grid-from-electromagnetic-storm-threat.html

Mother Earth News
For local sustainability
motherearthnews.com

NARUC Regional Mutual Assistance Groups: A Primer
Created under the National Council on Electricity Assurance program, a project of
the National Association of Regulatory Utility Co
Miles Keogh, Sharon Thomas, NARUC Grants & Research
November 2015
Electric utilities across the country have been providing mutual aid to each other during emergencies for years. One strategy for communicating and coordinating information as well as tangible resources needed on a wider scale is to use regional mutual assistance groups (RMAGs). This paper explains what an RMAG is, identifies some of the reasons why they are a central mechanism for assuring electric grid reliability and resilience of the power system, and offers suggestions for how we can take a great idea and make it even stronger and better.
https://pubs.naruc.org/pub/536E475E-2354-D714-5130-C13478337428

National Alliance for Radiation Readiness
NARR seeks to address the problems of limited visibility for radiation preparedness, confusion about roles and responsibilities in a radiological incident among partners, and the need for robust tools for practitioners in the field on this website.
http://www.radiationready.org

National Space Weather Action Plan
White House National Science and Technology Council
October 2015
The National Space Weather Strategy, released concurrently with this National Space Weather Action Plan details national goals for leveraging existing policies and ongoing research and development efforts. The Action Plan sets out specific actions promoting enhanced domestic and international coordination and cooperation across public and private sectors.
http://www.swpc.noaa.gov/news/national-space-weather-strategy-and-action-plan-released

National Strategy for Global Supply Chain Security Implementation Update
US Government
January 2013
United States Government's policy to strengthen the global supply chain to protect the welfare and interests of the American people and to enhance our Nation's economic prosperity.
https://www.dhs.gov/national-strategy-global-supply-chain-security

NATO's Role in Disaster Assistance Website
http://www.nato.int/eadrcc/mcda-e.pdf

Natural catastrophes and man-made disasters in 2015: Asia suffers substantial losses
Swiss Re, Sigma No. 1/2016
http://media.swissre.com/documents/sigma1_2016_en.pdf

NCFRP, REPORT 30: Making U.S. Ports Resilient as Part of Extended Intermodal Supply Chains
Transportation Research Board of the National Academies
Frank Southworth, Jolene Hays, Shannon McLeod, Anne Strauss-Wieder
2014
The report focuses on identifying and elaborating on the steps needed to coordinate freight movements through ports in times of severe stress on existing operating infrastructures and services whether being stressed because of damage to port facilities, to the highway, rail, and waterway routes leading into and out of the port, or because of the need to handle additional cargo volumes due to port disruptions elsewhere.
https://www.nap.edu/read/23428/chapter/1

National Infrastructure Protection Plan (NIPP)
Second edition, published by DHS
NIPP 2013: Partnering for Critical Infrastructure Security and Resilience
December 2013
In February 2013, the President issued Presidential Policy Directive 21 (PPD-21), "Critical Infrastructure Security and Resilience", which explicitly calls for an update to the National Infrastructure Protection Plan (NIPP). This update is informed by significant evolution in the critical infrastructure risk, policy, and operating environments, as well as experience gained and lessons learned since the NIPP was last issued in 2009.
https://www.dhs.gov/sites/default/files/publications/NIPP%202013_Partnering%20for%20Critical%20Infrastructure%20Security%20and%20Resilience_508_0.pdf

National Planning System

U.S. Department of Homeland Security

February 2016

This document contains an overview of the National Planning System and includes:

- The Planning Architecture, which describes the strategic, operational, and tactical levels of planning and planning integration; and
- The Planning Process, which describes the steps necessary to develop a comprehensive plan, from forming a team to implementing the plan.

http://www.dhsem.state.co.us/sites/default/files/National_Planning_System_20151029.pdf

The National Preparedness Goal

FEMA, US Department of Homeland Security

September 2015

Presidential Policy Directive 8: National Preparedness (PPD-8) describes the Nation's approach to preparing for the threats and hazards that pose the greatest risk to the security of the United States. National preparedness is the shared responsibility of our whole community.

https://www.fema.gov/media-library/assets/documents/25959

National Strategy for Global Supply Chain Security
Implementation Update

US Government

January 2013

United States Government's policy to strengthen the global supply chain to protect the welfare and interests of the American people and to enhance our Nation's economic prosperity.

https://www.dhs.gov/national-strategy-global-supply-chain-security

Neighborhood Preparedness Consortium (NPC)

Directory of Resources, George Washington University

The Neighborhood Preparedness Consortium (NPC) is a private-public emergency management partnership in the greater Foggy Bottom neighborhood in Washington, DC comprised of local, regional, federal, international, corporate and non-profit partners.

https://campusadvisories.gwu.edu/neighborhood-preparedness-consortium

https://campusadvisories.gwu.edu/partnerships

NERC State of Reliability 2016

May 2016

This is the annual report on the state of North American electric grid reliability by NERC, the designated Electric Reliability Organization (ERO). Based on conventional weather hazards, NERC demonstrates a high level of grid reliability in year 2015. But emplacement of foreign malware within the North American grid is not reportable as cyber incidents and at least 55,000 customers must suffer concurrent outages to trigger a reportable cyber incident. In fact, NERC reported no cyber incidents for calendar year 2015. Other commentators filed analyses for a Federal Energy Regulatory Commission Technical Conference held on June 1, 2016, showing that NERC reliability statistics do not account for low probability high consequence grid outage risks. Critiques of the NERC reliability metrics are available in documents retrievable online via FERC Docket AD16-15-000. http://www.nerc.com/pa/RAPA/PA/Performance%20Analysis%20DL/2016_SOR_Report_Final_v1.pdf

The NIPP Security and Resilience Challenge
The Department of Homeland Security (DHS)
DHS has the responsibility to lead a unified national effort to manage risks to critical infrastructure through robust collaboration with critical infrastructure partners. This program is designed to address the NIHS need for "rapidly deployable, low cost structural support that can be engineered into a facility or deployed by first responders to prevent catastrophic structural failure."
February 2016
http://www.thenihs.org/nipp/nipp.pdf

NIST Draft Cyber-Physical Systems Framework Available for Public Comment
The draft framework is intended to describe foundational concepts and provide a methodology for understanding, designing, and building CPS that can work with one another. As such, it is hoped that the framework will provide a basis upon which tools, standards, and applications can be based.
October 8, 2015
https://pages.nist.gov/cpspwg/
https://www.ansi.org/news_publications/news_story.aspx?menuid=7&articleid=d00342ab-e834-4062-8e8e-3beb4f102db5

North Korea's Arsenal Raises the Stakes for US Grid Security: Experts
CNBC
Javier E. David
February 20, 2016
http://www.cnbc.com/2016/02/20/north-koreas-arsenal-raises-the-stakes-for-us-grid-security-experts.html

Nuclear Risks and Preparedness: Unabridged, Revised First Edition

Kevin G. Briggs, USDPI LLC

August 2014

Nuclear Risks and Preparedness provides detailed information on how you can protect yourself and your loved ones against the risks associated with nuclear terrorism and war, electromagnetic pulse (EMP) attacks, and nuclear power plant disasters.

https://www.amazon.com/Nuclear-Risks-Preparedness-Unabridged-Revised/dp/0990485633

Nuclear Risks and Preparedness: Abridged, Revised First Edition

Kevin G. Briggs, USDPI LLC

June 2014

It is intended to provide the best UNCLASSIFIED, publicly available information about nuclear risks to America and how to survive these risks. It explains the growing threats we face from nuclear weapons and EMP, as well as the continuing risks we face from nuclear power plants. It explains nuclear dangers from both a technical and historical perspective.

https://www.amazon.com/Nuclear-Risks-Preparedness-Abridged-First/dp/1500235148

Nuclear Terrorism: Countering the Threat

Routledge Press

Brecht Volders and Tom Sauer (eds.)

This volume aims to improve understanding of nuclear security and the prevention of nuclear terrorism.

2016

https://www.amazon.com/Nuclear-Terrorism-Countering-Routledge-Security/dp/113893139X

Nuclear Terrorism: The Ultimate Preventable Catastrophe

Defence Against Terrorism Review, Vol.3, No. 1, ISSN: 1307-9190

Henry Holt & Co.

Graham Allison, Director, Belfer Center for Science and International Affairs, Harvard University

Spring 2010

http://www.coedat.nato.int/publication/datr/volume5/06-Nuclear_Terrorism_The_Ultimate_Preventable_Catastrophe.pdf

NWPP: Northwest Power Pool

Publicly available web-based reports, assessments, postings, and procedures

Mutual assistance between companies during emergencies takes several forms. During more routine emergencies (e.g., high loads due to extreme weather or loss of a large unit),

neighboring NERC Balancing Authorities (BAs) have emergency assistance provisions (are required in NERC Reliability Standards) for capacity and energy.
http://www.nwpp.org/our-resources/NWPP-Reserve-Sharing-Group

Official Missouri Website: Safety
http://www.mo.gov/safety/disasters

One Second After
William R. Forstchen
2009
Historical Fiction on a worst-case EMP scenario
http://www.onesecondafter.com

One Year After: A John Matherson Novel
William R. Forstchen
Forge Books
2015
Historical Fiction on a worst-case EMP scenario, one year later.
https://www.amazon.com/One-Year-After-Matherson-Novel/dp/0765376717

Optimal Recovery Sequencing for Critical Infrastructure Resilience Assessment
SANDIA Report SAND2010-6237
Eric D. Vugrin, Mark A. Turnquist, and Nathan J. K. Brown
September 2010
The federal government has started a coordinated set of government resilience initiatives to begin the process of understanding what features create resilience in critical infrastructure systems. The DHS National Infrastructure Protection Plan (NIPP), in particular, contains explicit language calling for increasing the resilience of the nation's critical infrastructure.
http://prod.sandia.gov/techlib/access-control.cgi/2010/106237.pdf

Planning Guidance for Response to a Nuclear Detonation, 2nd Edition
National Security Staff, Interagency Policy Coordination Subcommittee for Preparedness & Response to Radiological and Nuclear Threats
June 2010
This guidance was developed by a Federal interagency committee led by the Executive Office of the President (National Security Staff and Office of Science and Technology Policy) with representatives from the Departments of Defense, Energy, Health and Human Services, Homeland Security (DHS), Labor, Transportation, Veteran's Affairs, the Environmental Protection Agency, the National Aeronautics and Space Administration, and

the Nuclear Regulatory Commission. Updates focused on 1st Edition's topics relevant to emergency planning within the first few days of a nuclear detonation including: 1) shelter and evacuation, 2) medical care, and 3) population monitoring and decontamination.
http://www.remm.nlm.gov/PlanningGuidanceNuclearDetonation.pdf

Planning Resilience for High-Impact Threats to Critical Infrastructure: Conference Proceedings InfraGard National EMP SIG Sessions at the 2014 DuPont Summit
Charles L. Manto, Stephanie A. Lokmer, editors
November 10, 2015
The InfraGard National Electromagnetic Pulse Special Interest Group (EMP SIG) organized in July 2011 to share information about catastrophic threats to our nation's critical infrastructures, including extreme space weather, man-made EMP, cyber-attacks, coordinated physical attacks and pandemics. The December 2014 conference proceedings provide verbatim transcripts including speakers with hyperlinks to the recorded video presentations. Includes Sen. Ron Johnson, Congressman Roscoe Bartlett, and other federal, state, and local officials and leaders from the private sector. It also includes publications and official documents between the Dec. 2014 DuPont summit and September 2015. Key documents include the National Space Weather Strategy, the DTRA request for proposals (RFP) for EMP-protected microgrids, and the formation documents of the International Council on Systems Engineering (INCOSE) Critical Infrastructure Protection and Recovery Working Group. A hyperlinked bibliography is available at:
https://www.amazon.com/Planning-Resilience-High-Impact-Critical-Infrastructure/dp/1633912612/ref=sr_1_1?s=books&ie=UTF8&qid=1472007279&sr=1-1&keywords=Planning+Resilience+for+High+Impact

Power Blackout Risks: Risk Management Options; Emerging Risk Initiative—Position Paper.
Michael Bruch, Volker Munch, Markus Aichinger (Allianz); Michael Kuhn, Martin Weymann (Swiss Re); Gerhard Schmid (Munich re), and Markus Aichinger (Allianz), Editor
November 2011
Insured persons and organizations should be aware that they may face huge uninsured losses. This might trigger an increasing demand for new risk transfer solutions related to power blackout risks in the future. The insurance industry can offer well contained event covers which fulfill the principles of insurance: randomness, assessability, mutuality and economic viability whereas utilities and governments have to increase their efforts to make our power infrastructure resilient against such events.
https://www.allianz.com/v_1339677769000/media/responsibility/documents/position_paper_power_blackout_risks.pdf

The Power of Resilience: How the Best Companies Manage the Unexpected
Yossi Sheffi, M.I.T. Press
2015
This book focuses on deep-tier risks as well as corporate responsibility, cybersecurity, long-term disruptions, business continuity planning, emergency operations centers, detection, and systemic disruptions.
https://mitpress.mit.edu/books/power-resilience

The Predator's View: The Imperative for Critical Infrastructure Resilience
The Executive Journal of InfraGard San Diego, Vol.1 Issue 3
By Jeff Gaynor, Colonel, U.S. Army (Ret.)
Director, Board of Directors, InfraGard National Members Alliance
The absence of understanding and appreciation of the predator's view has been evident throughout history. America is the most Internet-reliant nation on Earth and for whatever reason is creating the instrument of its demise, its own Achilles Heel—a single point of national failure.
http://www.ecocommerceexchange.com/uploads/3/9/5/1/3951308/the_predators_view_-_jeff_gaynor_1.pdf

Presidential Policy Directive (PPD) 8 entitled "National Preparedness"
March 30, 2011
PPD-8 is aimed at strengthening the security and resilience of the United States through systematic preparation for the threats that pose the greatest risk to the security of the nation, including acts of terrorism, cyber-attacks, pandemics, and catastrophic natural disasters.2011
https://www.dhs.gov/presidential-policy-directive-8-national-preparedness

Presidential Policy Directive (PPD) 21
The White House
Critical Infrastructure Security and Resilience
February 12, 2013
The Presidential Policy Directive (PPD) on Critical Infrastructure Security and Resilience advances a national unity of effort to strengthen and maintain secure, functioning, and resilient critical infrastructure.
https://www.dhs.gov/sites/default/files/publications/ISC-PPD-21-Implementation-White-Paper-2015-508.pdf
Presidential Policy Directive (PPD) 21 entitled "Critical Infrastructure Security and Resilience"
The White House
February 12, 2013

The Presidential Policy Directive (PPD) on Critical Infrastructure Security and Resilience advances a national unity of effort to strengthen and maintain secure, functioning, and resilient infrastructure

https://www.federalregister.gov/documents/2013/02/19/2013-03915/improving-critical-infrastructure-cybersecurity

Press Release by DTRA (DoD) "Accelerating Society-Wide EMP Protection of Critical Infrastructure and Microgrids"

June 24, 2016

The Defense Threat Reduction Agency (DTRA)/SCC announces the beginning of a Small Business Innovation Research (SBIR) contract with Instant Access Networks LLC (IAN) and its subcontractors.

http://highfrontier.org/wp-content/uploads/2016/07/DTRA-IAN-Press-Release-June-24-2016.pdf

Protect Your Computer From Viruses, Hackers, and Spies. Retrieved February 20, 2016

Office of the Attorney General, State of California Department of Justice

Stouffer, K., Pillitteri, V. Lightman, S., Abrams, M., & Hahn, A.

May 2015

https://oag.ca.gov/privacy/facts/online-privacy/protect-your-computer

Protecting Industrial Control Systems from Electronic Threats

Momentum Press

Joseph Weiss

2010

This book is the leading reference work on protection of industrial control systems, not only in electric grids but also linked to all other critical infrastructures, and will help the reader better understand what is industrial control system cyber security, why it is different from IT security, what has really happened to date, and what needs to be done.

http://www.momentumpress.net/books/protecting-industrial-control-systems-electronic-threats

Radiation Injury Treatment Network

The Radiation Injury Treatment Network® (RITN) provides comprehensive evaluation and treatment for victims of radiation exposure or other marrow toxic injuries.

http://ritn.net

Radiation Resilient City Initiative Website

University of Pittsburg Medical Center (UPMC) Center for Health Security

The purpose of the Rad Resilient City (RRC) Initiative is to provide cities and their neighbors with a checklist of preparedness actions that could save tens of thousands of lives following a nuclear detonation through adequate protection against radioactive fallout. The Radiation Injury Treatment Network® (RITN) provides comprehensive evaluation and treatment for victims of radiation exposure or other marrow toxic injuries.
http://www.radresilientcity.org

Real Risk Management for the Electric Grid: Critical Task Planning for Long Term Power Outages

Jim LeBlanc, Center for Security Policy
This book explores the flawed approach of big government to prevent major long-term black outs and how individual awareness is the building block for business and local emergency preparedness that will lead in helping communities understand that it is far better to prevent a long term blackout than to try and recover from one.
August 2016
http://securethegrid.com/2016/08/24/press-release-new-book-real-risk-management-for-the-electric-grid

Regional Mutual Assistance Groups: A Primer

NARUC, with support from US Department of Energy
By Miles Keogh, Sharon Thomas, NARUC Grants & Research
November 2015
For regulators who haven't had very much experience with mutual assistance, this paper may help explain why it's an important grid reliability tool; for those who have extensive exposure to RMAGs, this might help catalyze discussion on ways to address larger-scale emergencies, how to coordinate better across jurisdictions, and how mutual assistance may be used to address less-understood threats like cyberattacks or large-scale acts of terrorism.
https://pubs.naruc.org/pub/536E475E-2354-D714-5130-C13478337428

Report of the Commission to Assess the Threat to the United States From Electromagnetic Pulse (EMP) Attack

Presidential Commission
2004
http://www.empcommission.org/docs/empc_exec_rpt.pdf

Report of the Commission to Assess the Threat to the United States from Electromagnetic Pulse (EMP) Attack
Critical National Infrastructures

Presidential Commission Members:

Dr. John S. Foster, Jr., Earl Gjelde, Dr. William R. Graham (Chairman), Dr. Robert J. Hermann, Henry (Hank) M. Kluepfel, Gen Richard L. Lawson, USAF (Ret.), Dr. Gordon K. Soper, Dr. Lowell L. Wood, Jr., Dr. Joan B. Woodard

April 2008

This report presents the results of the Commission's assessment of the effects of a high altitude electromagnetic pulse (EMP) attack on our critical national infrastructures and provides recommendations for mitigation.

http://www.empcommission.org/docs/A2473-EMP_Commission-7MB.pdf

http://www.empcommission.org/docs/empc_exec_rpt.pdf

Report of the Critical Infrastructure Task Force
US Department of Homeland Security
William Webster, Acting Chair, Homeland Security Advisory Council
January 2006
The objective of this report by the Critical Infrastructure Task Force (CITF) [was] to advance national policies and strategies that fosters the development of more resilient critical infrastructures.

https://www.dhs.gov/xlibrary/assets/HSAC_CITF_Report_v2.pdf

Resilience Thinking: Sustaining Ecosystems and People in a Changing World
Brian Walker and David Salt
2006
The book arose out of appeals from colleagues in science and industry for a plainly written account of what resilience is all about and how a resilience approach differs from current practices. Rather than complicated theory, the book offers a conceptual overview along with five case studies of resilience thinking in the real world. It is an engaging and important work for anyone interested in managing risk in a complex world.

https://islandpress.org/book/resilience-thinking

The Resilience Dividend: Being Stronger in a World Where Things Go Wrong
Judith Rodin
Public Affairs Press, 2014.

https://www.rockefellerfoundation.org/blog/realizing-resilience-dividend

The Resilient Enterprise: Overcoming Vulnerability for Competitive Advantage
Yossi Sheffi, M.I.T. Press
2005.
Sheffi explores high-impact/ low-probability disruptions, focusing not only on security but on corporate resilience—the ability to bounce back from such disruptions—and how resilience investments can be turned into competitive advantage.

http://sheffi.mit.edu/resilient-enterprise

Revised Critical Infrastructure Protection Reliability Standards

156 FERC ¶ 61,050

UNITED STATES OF AMERICA FEDERAL ENERGY REGULATORY COMMISSION 18 CFR Part 40 [Docket No. RM15-14-002; Order No. 829]

Issued July 21, 2016

The Federal Energy Regulatory Commission (Commission) directs the North American Electric Reliability Corporation to develop a new or modified Reliability Standard that addresses supply chain risk management for industrial control system hardware, software, and computing and networking services associated with bulk electric system operations. The new or modified Reliability Standard is intended to mitigate the risk of a cybersecurity incident affecting the reliable operation of the Bulk-Power System.

https://www.ferc.gov/whats-new/comm-meet/2016/072116/E-8.pdf

Rebuilding for Resilience: Fortifying Infrastructure to Withstand Disaster

PwC Price Waterhouse Cooper

Richard Abadie, Yumiko Noda, and Peter Raymond September

2013

This report extends the focus of the UNISDR-PwC initiative, looking specifically at the long-term opportunity for public private sector collaboration in building or rebuilding risk-resilient infrastructure.

https://www.pwc.com/mx/es/industrias/proyectos-capital/archivo/2013-10-pwc-rebuilding.pdf

Reclaiming Food Security

Routledge, Earthscan Food and Agriculture Series

Michael S. Carolan, Professor, Colorado State University

2013

This book develops and reports on a Food and Human Security Index (FHSI) for 126 nations, and makes a clear straight-forward case for the reorientation of debates on 'food security'.

https://www.researchgate.net/publication/269723360_Michael_S_Carolan_Reclaiming_food_security

Rural and Suburban Population Surge Following Detonation of an Improvised Nuclear Device: A New Model to Estimate Impact

M. Meit, I, Redlener, T.W. Briggs, M. Kwanisai, D. Culp, D.M. Abramson

March 2011

The objective of the study was to model urban evacuation into surrounding communities after the detonation of an improvised nuclear device (IND) to assist rural and suburban planners in understanding and effectively planning to address the effects of population surges.

https://www.ncbi.nlm.nih.gov/pubmed/21402807

Securing Cyber-Physical Systems
2016
CRC Press, Taylor & Francis
Al-Sakib Khan Pathan, editor
http://www.worldcat.org/title/securing-cyber-physical-systems/oclc/933591711

Selling the Apocalypse
The Hill: Congress Blog feed
David Stuckenberg
May 10, 2016
http://thehill.com/blogs/congress-blog/homeland-security/279165-selling-the-apocalypse

Significant Natural Catastrophes 1980-2012 Website
Munich Re
Website links to PDF publications on costliest natural disasters; the ten deadliest natural disasters; costliest earthquakes; the 10 deadliest earthquakes; Costliest storm events; Costliest Winter Storms in Europe; Costliest winter storms/winter damage in the U.S.; costliest hurricanes; Costliest typhoons; Costliest floods.
https://www.munichre.com/touch/naturalhazards/en/natcatservice/significant-natural-catastrophes/index.html

Social Capital: A Missing Link to Disaster Recovery
International Journal of Mass Emergencies and Disasters, Vol. 22, No. 1
Yuko Nakagawa, Rajib Shaw
March 2004
This paper examines the role of social capital in the post-earthquake rehabilitation and reconstruction programs in two cases: Kobe, Japan and Gujarat, India.
http://ijmed.org/articles/235/download

Social Contract 3.0: Implementing a Market-Based Model for Cybersecurity
Internet Security Alliance Releases Cybersecurity Framework for Government and Industry
Business Wire
September 28, 2016
Utilidata CEO authors recommendations for protecting the power utility sector. The book seeks to provide a systemic framework for collaborative action on cybersecurity, integrating public policy and economics.
http://www.businesswire.com/news/home/20160928005931/en/Internet-Security-Alliance-Releases-Cybersecurity-Framework-Government

Southeastern Electric Exchange

SEE is a non-profit, non-political trade association of investor-owned electric utility companies

For storm restoration efforts (primarily distribution-related, but can also include transmission and generation if impacted), mutual assistance organizations (most notable the Southeastern Electric Exchange, or SEE) have been in place for decades. Started in the 1930's, the name is a bit misleading today in that participants range from New Mexico to New York and Florida to parts of Michigan and Illinois.

http://www.theexchange.org/aboutus.html

The State of Security in Control Systems Today

SANS Institute

Office of the Attorney General

ICS professionals will gain insight into the challenges facing peers, as well the approaches being employed to reduce the risk of cyberattack.

June 2015

https://www.sans.org/reading-room/whitepapers/analyst/state-security-control-systems-today-36042

Strategies, Protections, and Mitigations for the Electric Grid from Electromagnetic Pulse Effects

Idaho National Laboratory, U.S. Department of Energy

January 2016

This report identifies known grid impacts from EMP threats, effectiveness, and potential costs of known mitigations, areas for government and private partnerships in better protecting the electric grid, and gaps in knowledge and protection strategy.

https://inldigitallibrary.inl.gov/STI/INL-EXT-15-35582.pdf

Strengthen Your Financial Preparedness for Disasters and Emergencies

FEMA: Emergency Financial First Aid Kit (EFFAK)

September 2015

Includes a checklist of important documents and forms to compile your relevant information:

Household Identification, Financial and Legal Documentation, Medical Information, Household Contacts

https://www.fema.gov/media-library-data/1441313659987-38b0760a58131b871d494ddacbf52b6e/EFFAK_2015_508.pdf

Strengthening Disaster Risk Governance: UNDP Support during the HFA Implementation Period, 2005-2015

February 2015

This report presents detailed findings from a selection of 17 countries in Africa, Arab States, Asia and the Pacific (Asia/Pacific), Europe and Commonwealth of Independent States (ECIS), and Latin America and the Caribbean (LAC), where UNDP worked on DRG. It also provides an overview of UNDP's portfolio of country level DRG projects. This report examines the strategies and methodologies employed by UNDP over the last decade to promote an enabling governance environment for DRR.

http://www.undp.org/content/dam/undp/library/crisis%20prevention/disaster/Strengthening%20Disaster%20Risk%20Governance-Full-Report.pdf

Supervisory Practices Regarding Banking Organizations and their Borrowers and Other Customers Affected by a Major Disaster or Emergency

Board of Governors of the Federal Reserve System, Washington, D.C.

Division of Banking, Supervisor and Regulation, Div. of Consumer and Community Affairs

March 29, 2013

This document is a highlight of the supervisory practices that the Federal Reserve can employ when banking organizations and their borrowers and other customers are affected by a major disaster or emergency. Major disasters include hurricanes, tornadoes, floods, earthquakes, blizzards, and other natural catastrophes, as well as fires and explosions

https://www.federalreserve.gov/bankinforeg/srletters/sr1306.pdf

Supply Chain Resilience: Diversity + Self-organization = Adaptation

Homeland Security Affairs, Vol. 9

Philip J. Palin

August 2013

In the last three decades a collection of linear supply chains has become a complex adaptive network of demand creating supply. The benefits are obvious. The risks tend to be insidious. With the 2012 National Strategy for Global Supply Chain Security and the 2013 Implementation Update on the strategy, a public-private process has been engaged for considering risks and cultivating resilience. Complex adaptive systems are not well suited to traditional security mindsets. In the natural environment resilience emerges from diversity, self-organization, and innovation.

http://web.a.ebscohost.com/abstract?direct=true&profile=ehost&scope=site&authtype=crawler&jrnl=1558643X&AN=90461780&h=oQvks%2fviWFRy1waDxvghN6iPVId9O%2bTA3HMMDR8vcMPN3srhadr0QRcFvMTKIlaFwcGBvA9AXoYQQQDTbihsVg%3d%3d&crl=c&resultNs=AdminWebAuth&resultLocal=ErrCrlNotAuth&crlhashurl=login.aspx%3fdirect%3dtrue%26profile%3dehost%26scope%3dsite%26authtype%3dcrawler%26jrnl%3d1558643X%26AN%3d90461780

Superstorm SANDY: Implications for Designing a Post-Cyber Attack Power Restoration System
Paul Stockton, Johns Hopkins Applied Physics Laboratory
March 2016
This study discusses opportunities to accelerate power restoration after a sophisticated cyber attack on the US grid.
http://www.jhuapl.edu/ourwork/nsa/papers/PostCyberAttack.pdf

Taking the High Road to More and Better Infrastructure in the United States
NRDC, Natural Resources Defense Council
Douglass Sims, Center for Market Innovations; Catherine Cox Blair, Urban Solutions; Sarah Dougherty, Center for Market Innovation; David Wood, Initiative for responsible Investments, Harvard Kennedy School of Government; Maria Zimmerman, MZ Strategies, and Michael Matichich, CH2M
July 20, 2016
This is the first in a series of papers examining the concept of High Road Infrastructure. Following papers will cover the necessary steps for defining and creating High Road projects, the role of intermediaries in building community capacity, how to implement innovative forms of financing and investment, and the federal role in enabling public and private investors and local governments to achieve these goals.
https://www.nrdc.org/sites/default/files/taking-high-road-more-and-better-infrastructure-ip.pdf

The Transition Handbook: From Oil Dependency to Local Resiliency
Rob Hopkins
April 2014
[This book] shows how the inevitable and profound changes ahead can have a positive effect. They can lead to the rebirth of local communities, which will generate their own fuel, food and housing. They can encourage the development of local currencies, to keep money in the local area. They can unleash a local 'skilling-up', so that people have more control over their lives.
https://www.amazon.com/Transition-Handbook-Dependency-Local-Resilience/dp/0857842153

Transferability of Self-Healing Principles to the Recovery of Supply Network Disruptions—The Case of Renesas Electronics
Robust Manufacturing Conference (RoMaC 2014)
Science Direct, Procedia CIRP 19
Marie Brüninga, J. Henning Buchholz, Julia Bendul

In this paper, the topic is approached in an interdisciplinary bio-inspired way. The transferability of biological self-healing principles to the recovery of supply network disruptions is analyzed and first propositions are derived.
http://ac.els-cdn.com/S2212827114006398/1-s2.0-S2212827114006398-main.pdf?_tid=e358b642-a3cb-11e6-b8f2-00000aacb35f&acdnat=1478400856_b6d7b405cbb572ba0d4fb9000c94695c

Triple Threat Power Grid Exercise: High-Impact Threats Workshop and Tabletop Exercises Examining Extreme Space Weather, EMP and Cyber Attacks
Dr. George Baker III, Terry Donat MD, David Hunt, Bill Kaewert, Mary Lasky, Dana C. Reynolds, Cedrick Leighton, Chuck Manto, and Bob Rutledge,
October 30, 2015
This InfraGard National Electromagnetic Pulse Special Interest Group (EMP SIG) exercise package facilitates discussions, planning, and preparation for catastrophic events involving the electrical grid and the cascading impacts to other critical infrastructure and the community. Includes a companion Power Point Presentation and a facilitator's guide via controlled circulation. The back cover provides a quick overview of the key issue regarding space weather and the link to "other high-impact threats." Proceedings focus on the concept that the federal government may not always be able to rescue at risk communities by day 4 after a disaster. In the case of high-impact events, it may be day 40 or day 400. The introduction provides an overview to the history of the space weather issue and the related EMP issues raised via the DoD DTRA RFP asking for a systematic approach to providing EMP protected microgrids for military bases and the entities they need off base. The book also has a section for "read ahead" material for an exercise that also provides an overview of the threats. Both the read-ahead material and the day of the event material include bibliographies for further reading
https://www.amazon.com/Triple-Threat-Power-Grid-Exercise/dp/1633912493

Understand A Major National Security Threat—Improvised Nuclear Device (Video)
Defense Threat Reduction Agency
National Security Staff, Interagency Policy Coordination Subcommittee for Preparedness & Response to Radiological and Nuclear Threats
June 2010
http://www.youtube.com/watch?v=gxb9rg4MQgk

Understanding and Mitigating Catastrophic Disruption and Attack
Telecommunications and Cybersecurity, a Noblis publication
Denise M.B. Masi, Eric E. Smith, Martin J. Fischer

Analysts have amassed much data that points to vulnerabilities in telecommunications and cybersecurity. Examining past natural disasters and major attacks can provide valuable insight into mitigating new ones.
https://blackboard.angelo.edu/bbcswebdav/institution/LFA/CSS/Course%20Material/BOR4301/Readings/UnderstandingAndMitigating.pdf

Unified Command and Control: Keeping "Pollution Catastrophe" off Katrina's resume' of tragic consequences.
NIMS ICS
CDR Roger Laferriere, U.S. Coastguard Deputy Sector Commander, Honolulu, Hawaii
Mr. Tracy Long, Security/Emergency Response Advisor, Chevron Pipe Line Company
Mr. Greg Guerriero, Incident Commander, Shell Oil Products U.S.
http://uscgproceedings.epubxp.com/i/85793-win-2006-07/27

Updated Value of Service Reliability Estimates for Electric Utility Customers in the United States
Ernest Orlando Lawrence Berkeley National Laboratory Report
Michael J. Sullivan, Josh Schellenberg, and Marshall Blundell
January 2015
This report provides updated value of service reliability estimates and details the revised econometric model, which is based on a meta-analysis that includes two new interruption cost studies.
https://emp.lbl.gov/sites/all/files/value-of-service-reliability-final.pdf.pdf

U.S. Department of Homeland Security
Official website of the Department of Homeland Security.
http://www.ready.gov

Water Sector Resilience Final Report and Recommendations
The National Infrastructure Advisory Council (NIAC)
June 2016
NIAC provides the President of the United States with advice on the security and resilience of the critical infrastructure sectors and their functional systems, physical assets, and cyber networks. NIAC was asked to 1) assess security and resilience in the Water Sector, 2) uncover key water resilience issues, and 3) identify potential opportunities to address these issues.
https://www.dhs.gov/sites/default/files/publications/niac-water-resilience-final-report-508.pdf

What If the Biggest Solar Storm on Record Happened Today? Repeat of 1859 Carrington Event would devastate modern world, experts say

National Geographic

Richard A. Lovett, for National Geographic News

March 4, 2011

http://news.nationalgeographic.com/news/2011/03/110302-solar-flares-sun-storms-earth-danger-carrington-event-science

When the Lights Went Out: A Comprehensive Review of the 2015 Attacks on Ukrainian Critical Infrastructure

Booz Allen Hamilton

Jake Styczynski, Nate Beach-Westmoreland, and Scott Stables

September 2016

This Booz Allen report, released in November 2016, expands on previous incident analysis published in spring 2016, going beyond by including additional detail about the attack chain based on malware execution, a more detailed mapping of targeted and affected infrastructure, and a much wider view on similar and potentially related Black Energy (BE) campaigns against Ukrainian infrastructure.

https://drive.google.com/file/d/0B7jDDYzLDGCWNlcxRlRFSnBlelE/view

World Cities Risk 2015-2025

Cambridge Centre for Risk Studies

September 2015

This study of world city risks assesses some 23 threats in five broad threat classes: Natural Catastrophe & Climate, including earthquakes and windstorms; Financial, Trade & Business, including market crashes and commodity price shocks; Politics, Crime & Security, including political conflict and terrorism; Technology & Space, including cyber catastrophe, and solar storms; and Health & Environment, including pandemics and famines. Provides risk rankings for 300 world cities.

https://www.google.com/#q=Cambridge+Centre+for+Risk+Studies+World+Cities+Risk

Publications of Federal Highways Administration, U.S. Department of Transportation

Publication	Publication Number	EDL Number	Contact
Highway Evacuations in Selected Metropolitan Areas: Assessment of Impediments (HTML, PDF 3.7MB)	FHWA-HOP-10-059	N/A	Kimberly.Vasconez@dot.gov
FHWA's Emergency Transportation Operations	FHWA-HOP-10-053	N/A	Kimberly.Vasconez@dot.gov

Publications Series Presents:
The Best of Traffic Incident
Management, Traffic Planning
for Special Events and
Evacuation & Disaster Planning
(CD)

Good Practices in Transportation Evacuation Preparedness and Response: Results of the FHWA Workshop Series (HTML, PDF 748KB)	FHWA-HOP-09-040	N/A	Kimberly.Vasconez@dot.gov
Evacuating Populations With Special Needs—Routes to Effective Evacuation Planning Primer Series (HTML, PDF 21MB)	FHWA-HOP-09-022	N/A	Kimberly.Vasconez@dot.gov
Information Sharing Guidebook for Transportation Management Centers, Emergency Operations Centers, and Fusion Centers (HTML, PDF 3MB)	FHWA-HOP-09-003	N/A	Kimberly.Vasconez@dot.gov
Operational Concept—Assessment of the State of the Practice and State of the Art in Evacuation Transportation Management (HTML, PDF 923KB)	FHWA-HOP-08-020	N/A	Kimberly.Vasconez@dot.gov
Interview and Survey Results: Assessment of the State of the Practice and State of the Art in Evacuation Transportation Management (HTML, PDF 660KB)	FHWA-HOP-08-016	N/A	Kimberly.Vasconez@dot.gov
Literature Search for Federal Highway Administration—Assessment of the State of the	FHWA-HOP-08-015	N/A	Kimberly.Vasconez@dot.gov

Practice and State of the Art in Evacuation Transportation Management (HTML, PDF 2.4MB)

Technical Memorandum for Federal Highway Administration on Case Studies—Assessment of the State of the Practice and State of the Art in Evacuation Transportation Management (HTML, PDF 1.4MB)	FHWA-HOP-08-014	N/A	Kimberly.Vasconez@dot.gov
Using Highways For No-Notice Evacuations—Routes to Effective Evacuation Planning Primer Series (HTML, PDF 20.9MB)	FHWA-HOP-08-003	N/A	Kimberly.Vasconez@dot.gov
Best of Public Safety and Emergency Transportation Operations CD	FHWA-JPO-08-037	14417	Kimberly.Vasconez@dot.gov
Common Issues in Emergency Transportation Operations Preparedness and Response: Results of the FHWA Workshop Series (HTML, PDF 1.1MB)	FHWA-HOP-07-090	N/A	Kimberly.Vasconez@dot.gov
Best Practices in Emergency Transportation Operations Preparedness and Response: Results of the FHWA Workshop Series (HTML, PDF 567KB)	FHWA-HOP-07-076	N/A	Kimberly.Vasconez@dot.gov
Communicating With the Public Using ATIS During Disasters: A Guide for Practitioners (HTML, PDF 2.3MB)	FHWA-HOP-07-068	14339	Kimberly.Vasconez@dot.gov
Managing Pedestrians During Evacuation of Metropolitan	FHWA-HOP-07-066	N/A	Kimberly.Vasconez@dot.gov

Areas (<u>HTML</u>, <u>PDF</u> 396KB)

<u>Routes to Effective Evacuation</u> <u>Planning Primer Series: Using</u> <u>Highways During Evacuation</u> <u>Operations for Events With</u> <u>Advance Notice</u> (<u>HTML</u>, <u>PDF</u> 2.8MB)	FHWA-HOP-06-109	N/A	<u>Kimberly.Vasconez@dot.gov</u>
<u>Transportation Evacuation</u> <u>Planning and Operations</u> <u>Workshop</u>	FHWA-HOP-06-076	14184	<u>Laurel.Radow@dot.gov</u>
Coordinating Military Deployments on Roads and Highways: A Guide for State and Local Agencies (<u>HTML</u>, <u>PDF</u> 1.6MB)	FHWA-HOP-05-029	N/A	<u>Kimberly.Vasconez@dot.gov</u>
<u>What Have We Learned About</u> <u>Intelligent Transportation</u> <u>Systems? Chapter 2: What Have</u> <u>We Learned About Freeway,</u> <u>Incident and Emergency</u> <u>Management and Electronic</u> <u>Toll Collection?</u> (PDF 116KB)	FHWA-OP-01-006	13318	<u>Kimberly.Vasconez@dot.gov</u>
<u>Intelligent Transportation</u> <u>Systems Field Operational Test</u> <u>Cross-Cutting Study:</u> <u>Emergency Notification and</u> <u>Response</u> (PDF 273KB)	FHWA-JPO-99-033	6326	<u>ITSPUBS@dot.gov</u>
<u>Faster Response Time, Effective</u> <u>Use of Resources—Integrating</u> <u>Transportation and Emergency</u> <u>Management Systems</u> (PDF 929KB)	FHWA-JPO-99-004	6874	<u>ITSPUBS@dot.gov</u>
<u>Speeding Response, Saving</u> <u>Lives—Automatic Vehicle</u> <u>Location Capabilities for</u> <u>Emergency Vehicles</u> (PDF	FHWA-JPO-99-003	6866	<u>ITSPUBS@dot.gov</u>

823KB)

Enhancing Public Safety, Saving Lives—Emergency Vehicle Preemption (PDF 1.12MB)	FHWA-JPO-99-002	6871	ITSPUBS@dot.gov
Effects of Catastrophic Events on Transportation Systems Management and Operations: Howard Street Tunnel Fire Baltimore City	Web publication only	13754	Kimberly.Vasconez@dot.gov
Effects of Catastrophic Events on Transportation Systems Management and Operations: Northridge Earthquake January 17, 1994	Web publication only	13775	Kimberly.Vasconez@dot.gov
Effects of Catastrophic Events on Transportation Systems Management and Operations: Cross-Cutting Study	Web publication only	13780	Kimberly.Vasconez@dot.gov

Organizational Contacts

InfraGard https://www.infragard.org/

National Governors Association (NGA) http://www.nga.org/cms/home.html

National Association of Counties (NACO) http://www.naco.org/

National Emergency Management Association (NEMA) http://www.emacweb.org/

Department of Homeland Security Protective Security Advisor Program (PSA)

https://www.dhs.gov/protective-security-advisors

Voluntary Organizations Active in Disasters (VOAD) http://www.nvoad.org/ (see the following table of those organizations who are members of VOAD)

American Red Cross http://www.redcross.org/mo2s

American Logistic Aid Network (ALAN) http://alanaid.org/

FEMA Region I http://www.fema.gov/region-i-ct-me-ma-nh-ri-vt

FEMA Region II https://www.fema.gov/region-ii-nj-ny-pr-vi-0

FEMA Region III http://www.fema.gov/region-iii-dc-de-md-pa-va-wv

FEMA Region IV https://www.fema.gov/region-iv-al-fl-ga-ky-ms-nc-sc-tn

FEMA Region V https://www.fema.gov/region-v-il-mi-mn-oh-wi

FEMA Region VI https://www.fema.gov/region-vi-arkansas-louisiana-new-mexico-oklahoma-texas

FEMA Region VII http://www.fema.gov/region-vii-ia-ks-mo-ne

FEMA Region VIII https://www.fema.gov/region-viii-co-mt-nd-sd-ut-wy

FEMA Region IX https://www.fema.gov/fema-region-ix-arizona-california-hawaii-nevada-pacific-islands

FEMA Region X https://www.fema.gov/region-x-ak-id-or-wa

National Members: 62		State/Territory Members: 56	
Adventist Community Services	International Medical Corp		
All Hands Volunteers	International Orthodox		
Alliance of Information and	Christian Charities		
Referral Systems	Islamic Relief USA	Alabama VOAD	Missouri VOAD
Amateur Radio Relay League	Latter-Day Saint Charities	Alaska VOAD	Nebraska VOAD
American Bible Society	Link2Health Solutions (Disaster	American Samoa VOAD	Nevada VOAD
American Red Cross	Distress Helpline	Arizona VOAD	New Hampshire VOAD
Americares	Luther Disaster Response	Arkansas VOAD	New Jersey VOAD
Billy Graham Rapid Response	Mennonite Disaster Service	California VOAD	New Mexico VOAD
Team	Mission to North America	Colorado VOAD	New York VOAD
Brethren Disaster Ministries	NESHAMA Association of Jewish	Connecticut VOAD	North Carolina VOAD
Buddhist Tzu Chi Foundation	Chaplains	Delaware VOAD	North Dakota VOAD
Catholic Charities	National Baptist Convention	District of Columbia VOAD	Northern Mariana Islands VOAD
Churches of Scientology	USA	Florida VOAD	Ohio VOAD
Disaster Response	Nazarene Disaster Response	Georgia VOAD	Oklahoma VOAD
Church World Service	Disaster	Guam VOAD	Oregon VOAD
Convoy of Hope	Operation Blessing	Hawaii VOAD	Pennsylvania VOAD
Cooperative Baptist Fellowship	Points of Light	Idaho VOAD	Puerto Rico VOAD
Direct Relief	Partnerships with Native	Illinois VOAD	Rhode Island VOAD
Disciples of Christ	Americans	Indiana VOAD	South Carolina VOAD
Episcopal Relief and	Presbyterian Disaster Assistance	Iowa VOAD	South Dakota VOAD
Development	Rebuilding Together	Kansas VOAD	Tennessee VOAD
Feeding Americas	Samaritans Purse	Kentucky VOAD	Texas VOAD
Feed the Children	Save the Children	Louisiana VOAD	United States Virgin Islands
Habitat for Humanity	Southern Baptist Convention	Maine VOAD	VOAD
International	St. Bernard Project	Maryland VOAD	Utah VOAD
Headwater Disaster Relief	Team Rubicon	Massachusetts VOAD	Vermont VOAD
Heart to Heart International	The Jewish Federation of North	Michigan VOAD	Virginia VOAD
HOPE AACR	America	Minnesota VOAD	Washington VOAD
Hope Coalition America	The Salvation Army	Mississippi VOAD	West Virginia VOAD
Hope Force International	Society of St Vincent De Paul	Montana VOAD	Wisconsin VOAD
HOPE Worldwide	ToolBank		Wyoming VOAD
Humane Society of the U.S	United Church of Christ		
ICNA Relief USA	United Methodist Committee		
Institute for Congregational	on Relief		
Growth and Trauma	United Way Worldwide		
	World Renew		

Table 9: National Volunteers Active in Disasters.

APPENDIX 10: Contributor Biographic Information

George Baker is emeritus professor of applied science at James Madison University. In addition to teaching graduate and undergraduate S&T courses at JMU, Baker directed the start-up and served as Technical Director of the university's Institute for Infrastructure and Information Assurance (IIIA). For much of his career he served at the Defense Nuclear Agency (DNA) and the Defense Threat Reduction Agency (DTRA) directing national programs to protect strategic systems against EMP and RFWs, including developing EMP protection standards, guidelines and test technology. A primary research interest stems from his experience as the Director of DTRA's Springfield Research Facility—a national center for critical system vulnerability assessment, applying DoD lessons learned to critical infrastructure protection and community resilience. During 2002-2008 Baker served as principal staff on the Congressional EMP Commission. He presently consults in the areas of infrastructure protection, vulnerability assessment of DoD facilities, EMP and geomagnetic disturbance (GMD) protection, and nuclear and electromagnetic weapon effects. He presently serves on the Board of Directors of the nonprofit Foundation for Resilient Societies, the Board of Advisors for the EMP Task Force on National and Homeland Security, the JMU Research and Public Service Advisory Board, the North American Electric Reliability Corporation GMD Task Force, the EMP Coalition, the National Defense Industrial Association (NDIA) Homeland Security Executive Board and the InfraGard Richmond Chapter. Baker holds a Ph.D. in engineering physics from the U.S. Air Force Institute of Technology and an M.S. in physics from the University of Virginia.

Steven E. Bieber is the Chief, Urban Watershed Programs and Homeland Security Department of Environmental Programs Metropolitan Washington Council of Governments. Mr. Bieber has over 25 years of experience in water quality management, environmental regulation, critical infrastructure protection, and public policy. Presently, he is responsible for managing COG's regional Anacostia Restoration Partnership, water security programs, energy security programs, critical infrastructure protection, drought management and response, urban stream restoration, green infrastructure, and other related environmental programs for local governments and utilities in the Washington, DC area. Previously, Mr. Bieber was Chief of Watershed Planning and Outreach for the Maryland Department of the Environment. Mr. Bieber also has extensive experience working with international groups on watershed management and water security issues. Mr. Bieber holds a B.S. degree in Zoology from Michigan State University, an M.S. degree in Oceanography from Old Dominion University, and a Master of Public Administration degree from the University of Baltimore.

John M. Contestabile is the Program Manager for Homeland Security–Emergency Preparedness and Response Systems for the Johns Hopkins University/Applied Physics Lab (JHU/APL). He joined the Lab in July of 2009, after retiring from the State of Maryland Department of Transportation (MDOT), where he was Acting Assistant Secretary for Administration as well as the former Director of the Office of Engineering & Emergency Services. In that capacity, he had been responsible for Emergency Planning/Response/Recovery activities for the MDOT since 1996. In addition to working at MDOT, Mr. Contestabile was named by Governor O'Malley as the Director of the Maryland Statewide Communications Interoperability Program, reporting to the Superintendent of the Maryland State Police. Previously, Mr. Contestabile served on assignment with the Governor's

Office during the Ehrlich administration as the Acting Deputy Director of the Office of Homeland Security. Mr. Contestabile participates on a number of committees including: a member of the National Infrastructure Advisory Committee (NIAC) Transportation Resilience work group, the Chair of the Committee on Critical Infrastructure Protection for the Transportation Research Board (TRB), Chair of the National Public Safety Telecommunications Council (NPSTC) Video Technology Advisory Committee, and Chair of the Department of Homeland Security Science and Technology Directorate Video Quality in Public Safety (VQiPS) working group. He was appointed in 2013 to a three-year term on the District of Columbia Homeland Security Commission. Mr. Contestabile was also a former board member of the Public Safety Spectrum Trust (PSST), who held the national license for the proposed 700 MHz National Public Safety Broadband system. He is a former Vice Chair of the American Association of State Highway and Transportation Officials (AASHTO) Security and Emergency Management Committee, and a former member of the Department of Homeland Security's "Safecom" Interoperable Communications Advisory Committee. He belongs to several organizations including: the All Hazards Consortium, the American Society of Civil Engineers, the International Association of Emergency Managers, the Maryland Emergency Management Association and the National Domestic Preparedness Coalition. Mr. Contestabile received his Bachelor of Science Degree in Engineering from Worcester Polytechnic Institute in Massachusetts and holds a Master of Business Administration Degree from the University of Baltimore.

Torry Crass is an information security expert with over 7 years in the information security field and more than 20 in information technology. In addition to owning an internet services and private consulting company, he is currently employed with SPX Corporation, a global manufacturing company, as Senior Lead of Information Security overseeing a team of individuals responsible for computer systems security, policy, and governance tasks within the global organization. He holds ITIL and GIAC Certified Enterprise Defender certifications and membership in OWASP and ISSA security organizations. He is also an advisory board member for the South Piedmont Community College Cyber Crime Degree Program and has participated in the 2016 SANS GCED standards setting workshops and has been invited to the SANS mentor program. Mr. Crass also serves in the South Carolina State Guard, G2 Cyber Security and Intel unit, working closely with the South Carolina Army National Guard on matters of varied aspects of cyber-security. In addition to his unit mission, the State Guard works with state emergency management to provide disaster relief and recovery in times of crisis when activated by the state. Adding to his information security activities, Mr. Crass is a member of the InfraGard National EMP-SIG, serves as a board member of the Charlotte InfraGard Chapter with a focus on SIG and Cyber Camp programs, and as the Director, InfraGard Southeast Region EMP-SIG, which participated in the 2015-2016 North Carolina State Emergency Management EMP response planning sessions.

William R. Harris serves on the Board of Directors, and is the Secretary of the Foundation for Resilient Societies, a New Hampshire-based non-profit engaged in research and education on critical infrastructure protection. He is an international lawyer (Harvard, J.D., 1966) and former energy, nuclear non-proliferation, environmental, and national security project manager at the RAND Corporation. Working with physicists and engineers, he supports electric and other critical infrastructure "reliability standard" development for international, federal, and state institutions.

Dave Hunt has 30 years of progressive experience in all phases of emergency management—from the development of comprehensive plans to the direction of emergency response. His response experience includes law enforcement, terrorism response, explosives investigation, fire and arson investigation, hazardous materials response, and emergency medical response. He has conducted technical planning projects for FEMA and its predecessor agencies with all 56 States and U.S. Territories. Over the past 18 years, his work has addressed all phases of disaster response, and he has led multiple large-scale programs to develop national guidance for strategic planning, as well as many of FEMA's Comprehensive Preparedness Guide (CPG) annexes. In addition, he has developed intelligence fusion center guidance, and mitigation, response, continuity of operations planning and recovery planning on behalf of FEMA. Mr. Hunt led the development and facilitation of the Congressional Caucus Severe Space Weather Threats to the Electrical Grid exercise in October 2011, in conjunction with the National Defense University. He also worked with Johns Hopkins Applied Physics Lab and the Maryland Emergency Management Agency on an Electromagnetic Pulse and Severe Space Weather Seminar. He also worked with the National Weather Service Space Weather Prediction Center in Boulder, CO in the development of space weather event planning guidance and training materials for first responders. Mr. Hunt managed Improvised Nuclear Device response planning for FEMA's National Preparedness Directorate, leading a large team including Lawrence Livermore National Laboratory and Virginia Tech's Center for Technology Security and Policy.

John Jackson, FBCI (hon.), CORE, Executive Vice President, Fusion Risk Management, brings to Fusion over 30 years of industry leadership and is widely regarded as an early and current visionary in enterprise Business Continuity, Crisis Management and Disaster Recovery. John was awarded the Business Continuity Institute's first ever North American Lifetime Achievement Award and has been awarded an honorary FBCI (Fellow designation) certification from the BCI based on his experience and contributions to the industry. In 1984, John joined Comdisco Disaster Recovery Services and was instrumental in launching and leading their recovery center and consulting businesses. In his 18 years with the company, John ran Comdisco's Operations and Consulting businesses, Comdisco's European continuity operations from 1994 thru 1996, established several Asia-Pacific recovery businesses during the early 1990s, and was named president of Comdisco Continuity Services in 1999. In his capacity leading Comdisco's worldwide services organization, John managed through the division's sale to SunGard in 2001, after which he moved on to general management positions with Hewlett-Packard and IBM, running their U.S. continuity services organizations. John joined Fusion in the fall of 2005 to drive yet another industry transformation. Today, John is very active in leading innovative consulting engagements for large enterprise organizations, and also contributing to the industry by serving on the Executive Advisory Board of Disaster Recovery Journal and the Editorial Advisory Boards for Continuity Insights and the Disaster Resource Guide. Currently, John serves as Vice Chair of Enterprise Risk Management for the InfraGard National Members Alliance and was previously Vice president and a National Board Member as well as a founding board member of the Northern Illinois ACP Chapter. In addition, he has served as the InfraGard Chicago Chapter President is currently the U.S. Chapter Vice President for the Business Continuity Institute.

John Juhasz is CEO and President of Telepath Systems Inc., a scientific non-profit entity advancing the adoption of systems engineering and MBSE methods in complex systems. He is a practicing systems engineer and entrepreneur with 40 years' experience in various industry sectors, including automotive, aerospace, telecommunications and energy. He is an INCOSE CSEP (Certified Systems Engineering Professional), and has been involved with INCOSE since its inception in 1991. He was a founder and first president of the Cleveland/Northern Ohio chapter of INCOSE, co-founded the Power & Energy Systems Working Group and the Critical Infrastructure Protection and Recovery Working Group, and chair of regional conferences focused on systems methods and energy. He is a member of InfraGard and currently serves on the Midwest Regional Board for InfraGard EMP-SIG. Mr. Juhasz has engaged in systems engineering activities in various programs in aerospace, including NASA's International Space Station and the Constellation System space exploration program, among others, developing and applying early model-based engineering methods. In automotive systems, he led OnStar system development efforts at Opel/GM Europe. He holds ten patents dealing with innovation on vehicle information systems and adaptive braking systems. He was awarded the prestigious Rockwell "Engineer of the Year" award for his innovative work on vehicle information systems. Mr. Juhasz holds a Bachelor and Master's degree in Electrical Engineering from Cleveland State University, and a Master of Business Administration from University of Detroit. He served as Adjunct Professor at Baldwin Wallace College in the MBA program, teaching Management Decision Models and Information Systems.

William Kaewert is founder of two power protection companies and has over 30 years of experience applying technology-based solutions that assure continuity of electrical power to critical applications. He is currently president and chief technology officer of Colorado-based Stored Energy Systems LLC (SENS), an industry leading supplier of nonstop DC power systems essential to electric power generation and other critical infrastructures. The company also produces COTS-based power converters used in EMP-hardened military systems including ground power for Minuteman III ICBM and THAAD ballistic missile interceptor. He received his AB in history from Dartmouth College and MBA from Boston University. He serves on the board of directors of the Electrical Generation Systems Association (EGSA) and on the management team of the Federal Bureau of Investigation's InfraGard Electromagnetic Pulse Special Interest Group (EMP SIG).

Frank J. Koza is the Executive Director, Infrastructure Planning PJM Interconnection LLC. He is a registered Professional Engineer in PA. He has worked at PJM over 14 years, previously in charge of system operations. Presently, he is the Executive Director of Infrastructure Planning and in charge of the technical staff associated with generator interconnection and implementation of transmission enhancements. He is the Chair of the NERC Geomagnetic Disturbance Standard Drafting Team and former Chair of the NERC Operating Reliability Subcommittee. Previously, he worked for 29 years at Exelon/PECO Energy in a variety of assignments including construction of fossil and nuclear generation facilities, construction and maintenance of transmission, system planning, and system operations.

Mary D. Lasky is a Certified Business Continuity Professional (CBCP). She has been the Program Manager for Business Continuity Planning for the Johns Hopkins University Applied Physics Laboratory (JHU/APL), and coordinated the APL Incident Command System Team. She is the immediate Past President of the Community Emergency Response Network Inc. (CERN) in Howard County, Maryland as well as the immediate Past President of the Central Maryland Chapter of the

Association of Contingency Planners (ACP). She is a member of InfraGard and the vice chair of InfraGard EMP-SIG. She is a member of the FEMA Nuclear–Radiation Communications Working Group. She has held a variety of supervisory positions in Information Technology and in business services. For many years, she has been on the adjunct faculty of the Johns Hopkins University Whiting School of Engineering, teaching in the graduate degree program in Technical Management. Ms. Lasky is the President of the Board of Directors of Grassroots Crisis Intervention Center in Howard County, MD. She served on the Finance Committee for Leadership Howard County and is co-chair of the Steering Committee for the Leadership Premier Program. Her consulting work has included helping non-profit organizations create and implement their business continuity plans.

Stephanie A. Lokmer is a senior executive and entrepreneur in international and federal government business/projects, driving strategic initiatives in commercialization and deployments of technologies for Critical ICT Infrastructure (Telecommunications, IoT, Cybersecurity, Cloud, Big Data, Satellite, Fiber Optics, Sea Cable, Broadcast Cable), Engineering, Energy (Biofuels, Mining). Based in Washington, DC, Ms. Lokmer is an active member of InfraGard's EMP SIG, OSAC (DoS Overseas Security Advisory Council), ASIS and other technology and security Boards and associations, including NIST's Cloud, Cyber, and IoT Working Groups. She was selected into the National Security Program at the U.S. Army War College; has a BA from Bethany College and Tübingen Universität (Germany), an MGC in Negotiations and Influence from Georgetown University, with post-graduate work in National Security in Telecommunications at George Washington University.

Chuck Manto is chairman of the InfraGard EMP SIG. He is the CEO of the Maryland-based company Instant Access Networks LLC (IAN). Mr. Manto won six patents in information, telecommunications, and EMP shielding with others pending on microgrids and EMP shielding. He founded the InfraGard National EMP special interest group (SIG) and serves as its volunteer national manager. His company was awarded a Small Business Innovation Research contract by the Defense Threat Reduction Agency to propose approaches for EMP-protected microgrids for critical infrastructure. Mr. Manto's education includes a BA and MA from the University of Illinois at Urbana/Champaign. He is a Senior Member of the IEEE.

Curry W. Mayer is an emergency management and homeland security professional with over 25 years of experience in California and Washington, D.C. Between June 2014 and October 2016 she was an Emergency Management and Homeland Security Advisor to the Undersecretary of California's Department of Food and Agriculture, focusing on threats and hazards to California's food supply and agriculture. She has managed and directed the development and implementation of comprehensive emergency management programs for the private sector and all levels of government. Ms. Mayer's career includes 17 years with the Governor's Office of Emergency Services primarily in Training and Exercises, with part of that tenure as Director of the California Specialized Training Institute (CSTI). She is the author of state and federal level emergency management curriculum, including scenario development and exercise design. Ms. Mayer was a senior member of the project/training staff for the White House Military Office's Executive Support Contingency Operations and Readiness Training course; a weapons of mass destruction (WMD) protection of the Chief Executive program. In addition, she developed and implemented training for a number of federal departments and agencies, including the Department of the Army, and the National Guard Bureau. She developed and presented a decision support tool for the United Nations and taught Incident Command System planning to members of Congress. Ms. Mayer has earned her Master's Degree in Education, focusing on curriculum development and instruction, a Bachelor's degree in Communications, and maintains Homeland Security certifications in Exercise Design and Practice (Homeland Security Exercise and Evaluation Program, HSEEP), and Master Exercise Practitioner and Instructor (MEP).

Robert McCreight After serving the United States government at the State Department and other federal agencies over a 35-year career, Dr. McCreight retired from civil service in 2004 and served as a consultant for major homeland security and national defense contractors. His professional career includes work as an intelligence analyst, treaty negotiator, arms control delegate to the UN, counter-terrorism advisor, political-military affairs analyst and Deputy Director of Global Scientific Exchanges at State Department. During his service at the State Department, he was a senior Soviet military analyst with INR specializing in the assessment of nuclear, chemical and biological weapons programs. He was involved in the design and coordination of White House nuclear readiness command crisis exercises during the Reagan administration possessing extensive experience in geopolitical wargame design and strategic simulations. He spent 27 years of combined active and reserve military service concurrently with his civilian work in U.S. Army Special Operations and has devoted 12 years to teaching graduate school as an adjunct at Georgetown, Virginia Tech, Penn State, George Mason, and George Washington Universities in subjects as diverse as disaster and emergency management, strategic intelligence, nonproliferation policy, homeland security policies, terrorism analysis, intelligence analysis, and assessing WMD threats. He has written and published three books on emergency exercise design, homeland defense, and neuroscience issues in national security along with over 35 articles on chemical weapons use, disaster management, disaster recovery, post-strike attribution, and WMD biological weapons threats to homeland security. He is a Senior Fellow at GMU in infrastructure protection and he lectures and assists periodically at National Defense University and the Naval War College.

Major General Robert B. Newman, Jr., USAF (retired), has over thirty years of business, military, and homeland security expertise in both government and private sectors in the fields of infrastructure protection, financial services, energy, and information security. As Senior Vice President and Director of Strategic Partnerships for Sera-Brynn, Mr. Newman assists the CEO with the company's strategic planning effort and is responsible for the strategic marketing and industry awareness programs. Following graduation from VMI, Mr. Newman attended U.S. Air Force pilot training at Reese AFB, TX. Following the attacks on September 11, 2001, Mr. Newman was mobilized and assigned to the National Guard Bureau in Washington and was later promoted to brigadier general serving as the deputy J3/4 for operations and logistics at US Joint Forces Command. In 2006, Governor Tim Kaine selected Newman to be the Adjutant General of Virginia commanding 10,000 Virginia Army and Air Guardsmen and promoting him to the rank of major general. Newman served on many national committees while serving as adjutant general including the Reserve Forces Policy Board and, drawing on his business experience, as a member of the Board of Directors of the Army and Air Force Exchange Services. Mr. Newman continues to be active in the community having served on many local and national boards to include the Board of Advisors for Linxx Global Solutions, the Board of Advisors of the Center for American Studies at Christopher Newport University, the Board of Directors of the Virginia War Memorial Educational Foundation, and the Board of Directors of the Congressional Award.

Philip J. Palin currently serves as the principal investigator and staff consultant on supply chain resilience for the National Academy of Sciences; he consults with the City of Los Angeles and Federal Emergency Management Agency on disaster logistics, he serves as a Senior Fellow in Homeland Security with the Graduate School of Rutgers University and he is affiliated with the Institute for Public Research at CNA Corporation. Mr. Palin is the principal author for the *Catastrophe Preparation and Prevention* series from McGraw-Hill. Other publications include *Threat, Vulnerability, Consequence, Risk* and *Consequence Management*. The Homeland Security Affairs Journal has published several pieces by Mr. Palin including *Resilience: The Grand Strategy*. In June 2008 Mr. Palin retired after ten years as Chief Executive Officer of Teleologic Learning Company. While with Teleologic he advised clients including the Department of Homeland Security, Department of Defense, and several private corporations. Prior to Teleologic, Mr. Palin served as the CEO of an international education not-for-profit and as President of a liberal arts college in Japan. Over his career, Mr. Palin has been involved in several start-ups and early stage ventures.

Steve Pappas has over 30 years of experience on active duty in the U.S. Army, higher education at Indiana University and in system safety and security positions in the public and private sectors. Steve Pappas is a partner with 4 Star a homeland security consulting firm based in Indianapolis, Indiana. He served as the G-3 Operations, Training, and Plans officer and the G-4 Logistics Officer for the Indiana Guard Reserve, Indiana's State Defense Force from 2008 to 2012, retiring as a Colonel (O-6). He has written a variety of USEPA, FEMA, and OSHA regulatory compliant programs and has lectured on security and safety related topics at the state and national level. In a DHS funded grant program, he revised several Indiana county level Comprehensive Emergency Management Plans and their state agency emergency support function annexes. During this same period, he developed and facilitated a number of Homeland Security Exercise Evaluation Programs (HSEEP) from workshops to full-scale exercises. From 2009 through 2012, he designed and implemented HSEEP compliant exercises for Indiana's State Defense Force. In 2008, he was awarded grant funding from the United States Department of Homeland Security and the FBI to conduct security related workshops for several InfraGard chapters. For the past six years, Steve Pappas has conducted NIMS workshops, HSEEP tabletop scenario-based exercises and functional exercises for the public and private sectors. Steve Pappas has extensive experience with local government emergency management agencies. He served both as a Deputy Director for the Johnson County, Indiana Emergency Management Agency and concurrently the Local Emergency Planning Committee chair for over eight years.

Thomas Popik is Chairman of the Foundation for Resilient Societies, a nonprofit group dedicated to the protection of critical infrastructure against infrequently occurring natural and manmade disasters. He is principal author of a Petition for Rulemaking submitted to the Nuclear Regulatory Commission that would require backup power sources for spent fuel pools at nuclear power plants. Previously, as a U.S. Air Force officer, Mr. Popik investigated unattended power systems for remote military installations. Mr. Popik graduated from MIT with a B.S. in mechanical engineering and from Harvard Business School with an M.B.A.

Fred M. Rosa Jr. is Senior Advisor for Homeland Security at the Johns Hopkins University Applied Physics Laboratory (APL) in Laurel, Maryland. He is also a Senior Fellow with the Center for Cyber and Homeland Security at George Washington University in Washington, DC. A U.S. Armed Forces veteran with extensive operational, emergency response, and national security policy experience, Rear Admiral Rosa's military career culminated as Commander of the Fifth Coast Guard District headquartered in Portsmouth, Virginia. In this capacity, he led an integrated team of military, civilian, and auxiliary personnel in carrying out the full range of Coast Guard maritime safety, law enforcement, and security operations throughout America's Mid-Atlantic Region, extending across six states from central New Jersey down through North Carolina and including the National Capital Region. Prior to the Fifth District assignment, he also served at The White House on the National Security Council staff during two successive Administrations in several different capacities, including Director of the International Crime Group and Special Assistant to the President for Border and Transportation Security. Additional military assignments included: Deputy Director for Coast Guard Intelligence and Criminal Investigations in Washington, DC; Deputy Commander, Seventh Coast Guard District, headquartered in Miami, Florida; Commander, Coast Guard Group St. Petersburg, Florida; Deputy Commander, Coast Guard Group Detroit, Michigan; Legal Advisor, Coast Guard Enforcement of Laws and Treaties Program, Washington, DC; Deputy U.S. Representative, Legal Committee, International Maritime Organization, London, England; and Instructor, then Assistant Professor of Humanities, U.S. Coast Guard Academy, New London, Connecticut.

John Rosica is founder of NVIS Communications/Barrett Communications Consulting. He is a subject matter expert in the area of HF Communications for Resiliency and Fallback from normal infrastructure dependent means/methods. John has been active in this Industry for over 30 years, he founded NVIS Communications over 14 years ago and today it serves federal, state, and local government entities as well as many private industries within the energy sectors as well as telecommunications. John personally holds multiple FCC Licenses to be able to provide this capability and he also personally serves with U.S. Army MARS which is sponsored by the DoD to be able to provide secure backup communications (voice and data) for DoD and their served agencies/customers. He founded and served as CEO of a Silicon Valley Management Consulting firm for over 20 years in parallel with his other interests but as of 2009 fully divested of that role to dedicate 100% of his time and energy to the NVIS Communications Mission. He also serves on several industries specific boards. He has been a member of FBI/InfraGard Silicon Valley and Southern California Chapters and is on board of the InfraGard EMP SIG (very involved in protecting the U.S. Electric Power Grid).

Dr. James Terbush was the physician to U.S. personnel in more than 80 countries in more than 30 years of Government service. He is published in scientific journals on; Influenza and Air Travel, Mass Fatalities Management and Public Health Consequences of a Cyber Attack. Dr. Terbush currently serves on multiple boards of directors; Public Health for El Paso County Colorado, Peak Military Care Network (veterans affairs), graduate medical education (Univ. of Colorado), and disaster medicine. He is also an advisor to the National Academy of Sciences Institute of Medicine

Forum on Disaster and Public Health and is the Past President of the American Academy of Disaster Medicine. Dr. Terbush received his MD degree from the University of Colorado and a Master's in Public Health from the University of California, Los Angeles. From 2006 to 2009, Captain Terbush USN, served as Command Surgeon to North American Aerospace Defense Command (NORAD) and U.S. Northern Command (USNORTHCOM). In this role, he served as the Medical Advisor to the Commander and was responsible for the integration of Department of Defense medical assets internally and with other agencies in support of military response to civilian disasters combating terrorism and protecting Americans. From 2009-2011, Dr. Terbush served as the Fleet Surgeon for Commander, U.S. Naval Forces Southern Command. He was deployed forward to Port au Prince in response to the devastating earthquake disaster in Haiti, integrating DOD medical capabilities into the overall International response. Dr. Terbush's final assignment before retiring from military service was with the Science and Technology Directorate at NORAD and USNORTHCOM where he served as the lead for medical innovations.

Janet R. Thomas, Supervisory Special Agent is a 20-year veteran of the Federal Bureau of Investigation, and has a Masters of International Business from the Monterey Institute of International Studies. She has a broad range of experience and accomplishments; from conducting cyber, terrorism, intelligence, criminal and internal investigations to managing national investigative programs. She was the FBI representative to the Proliferation Security Initiative on Nuclear Non-Proliferation. She possesses extensive experience evaluating threat intelligence, identifying vulnerabilities, and developing mitigation strategies in international and domestic settings. She has evaluated and updated emergency response plans related to natural disasters, kidnappings, extortions, and terrorism based on evolving threats. She designed and conducted training to local, state, federal, and foreign officers for 20+ years.

Stephen Volandt is Vice President of Auroros Inc., a contracting and management-consulting firm based in Raleigh, NC. He specializes in successfully connecting strategic purpose, risk management, decision-making, enterprise project portfolio management, operational user requirements, and the technology that supports them. He has been instrumental in the establishment of governance structures for global and nationwide organizations. Mr. Volandt co-authored the DoD CIO Executive board governance charter and participated in establishing enterprise-wide portfolio rationalization, harmonization, and transformation governance for the DoD technology portfolio. Mr. Volandt served as the lead architect for transforming the multi-billion-dollar United States Marine Corps business enterprise to better support combat operations and readiness cycles. He provided policy, operations modeling, IT and communications modeling, planning, and budget justification for a global U.S. Army weapon of mass destruction response capability; and was a principal operations planner and architect for joint U.S. Army and National Guard response to smuggled nuclear weapon ground burst terrorism in the homeland. Mr. Volandt has also supported the Joint Requirements and Integration Office (JR&IO), NRO, and served as the governance team leader for the FBI's CJIS Division. Other areas of expertise include cyber business-risk assessments, technology portfolio transformation management, disaster recovery planning and operations, and military operations. Prior to transitioning to management and technology consulting, Mr. Volandt performed or managed thousands of environmental assessments and remediation projects, to include radioactive and complexly contaminated industrial and military SUPERFUND sites, and supported state government and FEMA during several hurricane recoveries. He is a former U.S. Marine Corps reserve officer who served at the infantry battalion, brigade, expeditionary force, and headquarters levels; specializing in readiness, decision support, exercise management, logistics, sustainment, and global operations in austere remote environments. He graduated from The Citadel with a Bachelor of Arts in Mathematics. He currently volunteers as the 2nd Vice President for the Eastern North Carolina InfraGard Chapter, as the Deputy Director, InfraGard SE Region EMP-SIG, and as the National InfraGard EMP-SIG Administrative Officer. Mr. Volandt authored the exercise scenario, exercise process, provided the maturity model for the 2015 EMP SIG annual workshop and conference. His current passion is the design, funding, and creation of resilient communities.

Loren Mark Walker was the BCT VP, Systems Engineering Programs (retired). He is a co-lead for the INCOSE Critical Infrastructure Protection and Recovery (CIPR) WG. His degrees include a BS Electrical Engineering (Bucknell) and MS Systems Management (USC) and is an INCOSE Certified Expert Systems Engineering Professional (ESEP). Mr. Walker has over 49 years of systems engineering and leadership positions in the USAF, DoD Agencies and Contractor communities (BCT LLC, Lockheed, BAH and TASC). He helped develop and has taught Systems Engineer Courses and led SE working group since 2000. His experience includes several systems design, development, integration/testing, and deployments and has been a lead systems engineer and architect on several multiyear System of Systems programs for over 30+ years. He has held leadership positions on many high-priority/high-visibility programs and organizations. He is a leader in SE development concepts, Model Based Systems Engineering (MBSE) processes/methods, DoD architecture/design and their implementation on many customer RF and IT systems developments. He has published numerous articles on systems engineering and architecture, and presented papers at INCOSE and other Symposia, Conferences, Chapter meetings and customer conferences. He also helped found and was President twice (1994 and 2000) of the INCOSE Chesapeake Chapter and the INCOSE Object Oriented Systems Engineering Method (OOSEM) WG since 2000.